For your health

Stratford General Hospital 1891-2002

Dean Robinson

with Carolynn Bart-Riedstra

The writing of this book is dedicated to M. B. Robinson

Copyright © 2003
All rights reserved, Dean Robinson 2003
ISBN 0-9682148-3-5

Published by Stratford General Hospital, Stratford, Ontario

Production and art by Peter Schlemmer

Cover design by Peter Schlemmer and Dean Robinson

Cover photos: Colour, 2002, Dean Robinson
              B & W, front, SGH 1950, Stratford-Perth Archives;
              back, the first SGH early in the 1900s, Stratford-Perth Archives

Printed in Canada by Stratford Printing & Graphics, Stratford, Ontario

Contents

Blindness was imminent

About halfway between his fourth and fifth birthdays, he was a lot like other kids his age growing up in Mitchell, Ont. At least that's what his mother and father had hoped.

But by September 1950 there were indications that something was wrong, and getting worse. At first, they noticed the boy having trouble keeping his tricycle on the sidewalk. He noticed too, and became frustrated. As well, he began to walk into door jams as he went from one room to another. No longer could he align a glass under a tap for a drink of water. On the ceiling he saw circles and images. The leaves that fell outside looked more like snow. As the family drove by the Mitchell fall fair, the boy couldn't pick out the Ferris wheel that towered above the midway.

The family doctor, William Elvey Pridham, was mystified, and referred his young patient to George H. Ingham, an ear, eye, nose and throat specialist in Stratford. To take a candy offered by Ingham, the lad had to first grasp the doctor's arm and then feel his way down to the hand that was holding the treat.

Dr. W. E. Pridham, 1946

NURSING SCHOOL ARCHIVES

While the boy was unable to see objects that were passed before his eyes, Ingham found the movement of those eyes to be normal. Externally, they appeared OK, though they reacted sluggishly to the presence of light. The liquid in each eye was so cloudy the doctor was unable to see the back of the retina. The boy's ears, nose, throat, heart, lungs, abdomen and extremities checked out fine. Ingham, too, was mystified. He told the boy's parents he thought blindness was imminent.

On Sept. 26, 1950, the child was admitted to the spanking new Stratford General Hospital. By this time his vision was hazy, and he was unable to see anything clearly, from any distance. He groped for the knobs on doors, and felt his way up and down stairs. He grumbled about well-lit rooms being dark. His mother had noticed his eyes had become bloodshot. Everyone had noticed his irritability and fretfulness.

In hospital there was a spinal test for meningitis, which proved negative. X-rays of the boy's skull and sinuses also proved negative. And, apart from the white cell count being a bit high, his blood was normal. Ingham wondered about a link to tonsils, though there was no sign of tonsillitis. There was wonder, too, about a brain tumour, and talk of a transfer to the Hospital for Sick Children in Toronto.

The doctors said the boy was suffering from acute bilateral iritis – inflammation extending into the iris – but they had no idea what had caused it, nor did they know how to correct it. By his third day in hospital the boy's condition was unchanged. He was the lone patient in a semi-private room. His mother visited daily, in time to feed him supper. When she was late, he whined.

In addition to his practice in Mitchell, Elvey Pridham was the medical officer of health for Fullarton Township. It was in that capacity, at about the time his young patient was going blind, that Pridham attended a conference in Toronto. There, he recalled in later years, he heard someone – possibly the medical director – from Armour Laboratories in Chicago talking about cortisone. Cortisone had originally been known as compound E, after it was isolated by workers at the Mayo Clinic in Rochester, Minn., in 1936. Mostly because of difficulties in obtaining adequate amounts, little interest was shown in the drug until 1949, when it appeared to have dramatic, if transitory, effects on rheumatoid arthritis.

What Pridham heard that day prompted him to approach the speaker and, in turn, obtain some cortisone. He said he was told by Armour that the drug had not been released for general use, but that he could have some if he agreed to monitor its use and results, and forward his findings to the company, known today as Armour Pharmaceutical Co.

Pridham had the drug, adrenocortico-tropin (ACTH), administered to the Mitchell boy as soon as it arrived in Stratford. Five days later, the doctors noticed some improvement in the condition of the boy's eyes. Too, there came a general improvement in the temperament of the child. When the only side effect appeared to be puffiness in the face, the dosage was increased to four times a day.

A week later there was significant improvement in the eyes; the backs of the retinas could be seen. The child could distinguish objects, and his appetite had improved. By now he was making regular trips up to the sixth floor, to the hospital's lab, to hear, and increasingly see, the guinea pigs and rabbits that were kept there for testing purposes. Those excursions became a highlight of his hospital stay. In his room, he was visited daily by Ingham and Pridham. On some of the earliest of those days the boy told them the crayon marks in his colouring book were orange. On others he told them they were black. It was clear to them he could no longer distinguish colours.

At some point, as the boy's eyes improved, Pridham suggested skipping the ACTH for a day. But by nightfall the patient was again seeing orange circles. The drug was reordered in twice-daily doses.

After 17 days on ACTH, and 20 days in rooms 409, 413 and 416 at SGH, the boy had improved enough to be discharged. At home, however, the cortisone injections continued, at 9 a.m. and 9 p.m., administered by Mildred Scott, Pridham's office nurse. Eventually, the daily medication was reduced to one shot and drops in the eyes. Finally, recovery was sufficient enough that all treatment was stopped.

In exchange for the cortisone, for which there was no charge, Pridham forwarded his findings to Armour. Reflecting on the case more than 30 years later, the doctor said that, for whatever reason, blood was hemorrhaging into the fluid in the boy's eyes. "But I can't tell you what caused it," he added. For whatever reason, the ACTH stopped the oozing of that blood.

After he left SGH in October 1950, the boy went for more than 40 years before his eyes again required the attention of a doctor, namely Stratford eye specialist John Pyper. On that occasion a racquetball had been driven far enough through protective eyewear that it had hit his left eyeball, and his vision had gone blurry. At SGH, Pyper noticed what he called scar tissue on the surface of the eyes. He then covered both eyes with patches and required the patient to remain in hospital, as immobile as possible, for all of that Thanksgiving Day weekend. By the time the patches were removed, the man's sight had returned. For a second time, he walked from SGH with renewed sight.

Today, apart from needing reading glasses – a need he claims has more to do with age than with disability, his sight is fine.

Fine enough, at least, to write this book.

Acknowledgements

Without interested people there would not be a Stratford General Hospital. Without interested people there would not be this book about Stratford General Hospital. The author is indebted to many people, most of whom, it is hoped, are listed here.

I am also thankful for the efforts of those who, through the years, recorded the history of the hospital as it unfolded. Some of those people are or were affiliated with the hospital, others with organizations connected to the hospital, and still others with the likes of the *Stratford Beacon Herald*, the *London Free Press*, weekly newspapers in Stratford and Perth County, and assorted other publications.

There was willing help, too, from the Stratford-Perth Archives (Brandi Borman, Cindy Farmer, Lynda Greve and Kate Jacob, in particular); from the staff at the Stratford Public Library; and from Mary Smith and her colleagues at the St. Marys Museum.

The best collection of material relating to SGH's school of nursing is in two rooms on the second floor of Avon Crest. By extension, those rooms also hold a wealth of hospital history. The collection's primary promoter and protector is Joan MacDermid, a former nurse at SGH, and she was most accommodating and generous in her support of this project.

Mostly, I am grateful for the research assistance provided by Carolynn Bart-Riedstra, who spent many hours tracking down names, dates and places. A sincere *thank you* to all.

While a sincere effort has been made to present this story of SGH accurately and fairly, it remains a history based on records and recollection, both of which fail us on occasion.

Dean Robinson
January 2003

Barb Barrett
Marion Burr
Irene Burt
John Callan
Robert Cameron
Laurie Clark
Barb Cull
Richard Ferguson
Ellen Fangrad
Oliver Gaffney
M. Elizabeth (Betsy) Gilmore
W. Arthur Gingras
Larry Gordon
Mary Groothuis
Gary Harloff
Peggy [Hoy] Heinbuch
Nahnda Hill
John Howard
Norah Huggins
W. W. (Bob) Hughes
Jim Houze
Jane Jackson
Bill Jeffrey

Henry Kalbfleisch
Rose Anne Kreps
Alistair MacLeod
Brian Le Souder
Dr. A. Jeffrey Macdonald
Melanie Mackenzie
Sharon Malec
Danny Martin
Fiona McCulloch
Marion McNaught
Kathy Micks
Bob Miller
Dr. John B. Moore
Lois Mountain
Margaret Murr
Andrea Page
Thelma Pelley
Dr. John E. Pyper
Olive Pyper
Betty Reid
Catherine (Cae) Roberts
Dr. Robert B. Salter
Carol [Stanley] Schlemmer

Bernie D. Schmidt
Sandra Schuett
Ruth Scratch
Dave Sherwood
Brenda Smellie
Melissa Steinbach
Margaret [Sebben] Stoskopf
Suzanne Strahan
Dr. Susan Tamblyn
Marvin Thomas
Pearl Thomas
Charles Trethewey
Tina Tschanz
Grace Untucht
Dr. Arthur vanWalraven
Nelda [Yantzie] Wagler
Dr. Robin Waite
Andy Werner
Andrew Williams
Dr. Dave Williams
Dr. Angus M. (Gus) Wilson
Hazel Wivell
Cheryl Yost

The publication of this book has been made possible in part
by a donation from the Edwards Charitable Foundation

A noble and imposing beginning

As the 19th century drew to a close, Perth had been a county for almost 50 years and Stratford an incorporated municipality for about 40. After some harsh pioneer times the perseverance and toughness of their founders had started to pay off.

Locomotive repair shops were established in Stratford in 1871, and they gave the community an industrial backbone. A dozen years later there were telephones and, by the late 1880s, the beginning of a long and prosperous association with the manufacture of furniture. Something called electricity was just around the corner.

Around that same corner was a new general hospital, which drew mention in Mayor Charles J. Macgregor's inaugural address in January 1887. In fact, the mayor talked of the necessity of a hospital *and* a poorhouse. Stratford had become a city in 1885 and found itself struggling with matters pertaining to the sick and the poor. Said the mayor: "In a city with large manufacturing establishments in which machinery is in constant motion – in the working of the railways and in other similar operations, accidents are liable to occur, and do occur very frequently. There is always a number of persons who have no houses of their own – clerks, mechanics and labourers. Where can these go when sickness and disease overtake them to get the necessary care and nursing if there is no hospital prepared for their relief? At present they have to be taken care of at their boarding houses, or at the homes of some kind friends who, per chance, have neither the experience nor the skills requisite for their restoration to health. And how many there are even amongst those who have houses, who would gladly avail themselves, when overtaken by serious illness, of the medical skill and scientific nursing found in a well-appointed hospital? I think the subject only requires to be mentioned to awaken a responsive sob in the breast of every citizen of Stratford, and I trust that means will be taken to bring the question in all its hearings before the ratepayers."

At about the time the mayor made that

plea, the odds of anyone in Ontario living beyond his or her fifth birthday were 50-50. For those who did make it past five, life expectancy was 36 years. But the matter of health care was getting more attention by the day. By 1880 there were just 15 hospitals in the province, but by the turn of the century that number would be 43. In 1881 a medical school was founded at the University of Western Ontario in London, the third in Ontario, after Toronto and Kingston. A year later, the first Canadian school of nursing was established, at St. Catharines General and Marine Hospital. In 1883, two medical schools for women were opened. There were more than 2,000 doctors practising in Ontario, but many were so isolated they were unaware of the medical discoveries that were being made almost daily. To increase awareness among doctors, the Ontario Medical Association was founded in 1880.

Stratford had always been well-served by doctors who had their own infirmaries, and a few small private hospitals had come and gone. But there had been no central hospital, except a short-lived structure built in 1847 during an outbreak of cholera. It was in the bush, on land later occupied by Stratford Collegiate.

To support his contention about a caring public, the mayor held up as examples the cities of Guelph and Brantford, where "philanthropic and benevolent citizens" contributed significantly to the building of a hospital in each centre. The city of Stratford, said Mayor Macgregor, had residents who were just as benevolent and philanthropic. And he suggested they celebrate Queen Victoria's 50th year of rule by building a hospital and naming it after her.

Macgregor's suggestion about a poorhouse – to provide food and lodging for the destitute – was referred to the city's health and relief committee and that body recommended no action be taken. The jail, it was decided, would continue to offer what

help it could to such people. The jail also provided a bed for the sick. The roster of its inhabitants two weeks after the mayor's speech contained the names of "seven paupers," in addition to those in attendance for criminal matters. A man from Hamilton was "supposed to be dying but recovered." Another, from Goderich, was not so lucky; he was brought in after an assault at the Ellice ditch and did die. Two others, one from Scotland and another from the city, were suffering from delirium tremens.

The mayor's talk of a hospital struck a more positive chord. He and Ald. John Gibson went to Guelph to tour the $14,000 facility there, and they came back more convinced of the need for a like institution in their city. Locally, there was encouragement from several sources, among them the railway employees. At a public meeting to discuss the Queen's jubilee celebrations in Stratford, the notion of a Victoria Hospital generated more than passing comment. Several speakers favoured a county hospital and that prompted questions about location.

The meeting resulted in the appointment of a committee to assess the possibilities of raising $12,000 through public and private solicitation. The group consisted of Mayor Macgregor, headmaster at the high school; John Idington, a lawyer; William Buckingham, editor of the *Beacon*; A. J. McPherson, a furrier; John H. Schmidt, editor of the *Kolonist*; Dr. D. B. Fraser and eight members of the clergy, namely Revs. Kilroy, Deacon, Wright, McEwen, Panton, Gordon-Smith, Cunningham and Patterson.

The hospital proposal stirred mixed reaction in the city, and letters to the weekly Stratford *Beacon* suggested the issue was more complicated than it first appeared. Indeed, the assessment committee concluded there was not enough support to build the hospital as a Queen's jubilee project. It recommended finding another way to honour the queen and proceeding with the hospital at a later date. That was in April 1887.

In January 1888, Henry T. Butler began a two-year term as mayor, and he made no mention of a hospital in his inaugural address. Nor did he bring up the matter of a poorhouse. But in September of that year city council appointed a special committee to again investigate the possibilities of erecting a public hospital. The committee included the mayor, and aldermen William Mowat, A. J. MacPherson, John Payne, William Gordon and T. J. Douglas. Two weeks later they reported that, because it was late in the year, the idea be put back on the shelf. And there it stayed until late in November 1888 when Rev. Robert Ker of St. James' Episcopal Church appeared before council on behalf of a group of women who were concerned about the city's treatment of the poor. They sought to work with the council's health and relief committee to improve the situation. They also wanted the city to look more seriously at the matter of a hospital.

At the end of Rev. Ker's presentation, council instructed the board of health and finance to meet with the women and discuss with them the distribution of relief money in the city, and also to hear their ideas about building a hospital. Within a week, on Nov. 22, there was another public meeting about the hospital proposal. It was chaired by Judge James P. Woods, who asked the large turnout to consider the establishment of a hospital *and* a poorhouse. He also recommended a co-operative effort – involving city and county – in both ventures.

There were several speakers at the meeting and in the end they resolved to have a committee of provisional directors attempt to raise, in cash or pledges – $5,000, an amount they agreed would be enough to get the hospital project off the ground. The committee members included the mayor, Alexander McLaren (Perth County warden), John Hossie (county sheriff), Samuel S. Fuller (Stratford postmaster), Ald. William Davidson (county clerk), James O'Loane (Stratford police magistrate), James Corcoran (listed in the 1891 census as a `gentleman'), Edmond T. Dufton (manufacturer of woollen goods), Thomas Ballantyne (South Perth member of the provincial parliament), John McIntyre (merchant), John Idington (Crown attorney), W. R. Tiffin (Grand Trunk Railway superintendent) and Charles Fell Neild (roundhouse foreman with the GTR). For the money, they were to look to the private sector and to various levels of government.

Within 24 hours of that meeting, the City of Stratford General Hospital Trust was established and Mayor Butler was named its chairman. But he stepped down after only a few meetings because of workload, and was replaced by Sheriff Hossie. William Buckingham, manager of the British Mortgage Loan Company – who was added when Fuller said he was unable to serve on the committee – was appointed honorary secretary and James Corcoran honorary treasurer. When Corocoran moved to British Columbia, Thomas Ballantyne assumed that role. Soon after the trust was announced, there was talk of location for the proposed hospital, and the members generally favoured some city-owned land along the western portion of the Avon River. There was, however, some discussion about using the old county buildings at the corner of William and Hamilton streets, or the old secondary school on Norman Street.

By Dec. 14, 1888, the committee had rounded up more than $2,000 in pledges. A week later the total was at $3,000. As the year came to a close, the committee reported $5,600 in pledges and asked for time to gather more. The trustees said they thought they could raise $10,000.

In January 1889 the trustees made a presentation to county council, but it was not until June of that year that the council authorized a grant of $2,000 towards the hospital fund. Also in January, lists of subscribers and the amounts of their pledges began to appear in the paper. The donations ranged from $5 to $200. Thomas Ballantyne, John Idington and James Trow were the $200 donors. By Jan. 25 the committee had collected $7,500.

In March the hospital delegation made its pitch to city council. The aldermen deferred the request for money to a later meeting but they did grant five acres (two hectares) of land in an area known as Avondale Park – south of Cambria Street. Later that month, at the first annual general meeting of the subscribers to the City of Stratford General Hospital Trust Fund, the site was approved. The land was valued at about $1,000. The city also came up with $2,000 in cash.

The women who earlier had enlisted the representation of Rev. Ker demonstrated their concern for Stratford's sick and poor by canvassing the city's five wards. The role they played in making the fund-raising drive successful was significant. As well, money was generated by groups that entertained with song, dance and theatre.

Trust fund members were dispatched to study the hospitals in Kingston, Brockville, Guelph and Brantford, and they came back favouring Brantford's, though on a smaller scale. They also reported that in Brantford only one patient was treated at the hospital in its first four months of operation; apparently, residents were reluctant to use the new institution, fearful of what it might entail. However, in the next 12 months, 240 patients received treatment at the new facility, they were told.

The hospitals in Brantford and Guelph kept about six dairy cows on their property, and officials advised the Stratford delegation to do the same. They said it was an economical and healthy investment.

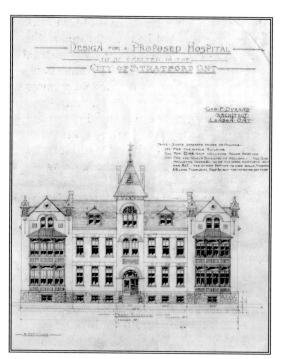
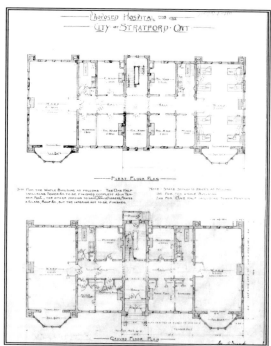

George Durand's design sketches for the original SGH.

In April 1889 the committee settled on a young architect from London, Ont., George F. Durand, to draw up plans for their hospital. Four years earlier he had been hired to design the Perth County courthouse at the west end of Ontario Street. He had also designed the city's jail and pumping station, now Gallery Stratford. Durand came to Stratford and met with trustees and the city's park and cemetery committee. They assembled at the Avondale Park site, and Durand said he was pleased with the location. He promised preliminary sketches within a week. The hospital was to be built on high ground, well back on the west side of John Street, south of the John and Cambria streets intersection. William Buckingham was given the honour of placing a stake to mark the building's northeast corner. A colourful Englishman, he was owner of the Stratford *Beacon* and had used his editorial pages to campaign long and hard for a hospital. The stake he held on this day was driven in by Ald. William Davidson.

Committee members were looking at a budget of about $13,500 to build the hospital as designed, but just $8,000 if they wanted to complete only part of it. They opted for the works, and in the end they had money to spare – $15,500 before a shovel was turned. The city and county each came up with $2,000. Another $9,500 came from public subscription. The remaining $2,000 was a bequest from the late William Byers, a Downie Township pioneer who had moved into the city upon retirement. In June 1889 the trustees called for tenders.

But not everyone in Stratford was excited about the prospects of a hospital – at least not everyone approved of how it was being funded. Ald. Alexander Smith wanted city council's offer of Avondale Park land and the $2,000 to be decided by the electorate. He caused lengthy debate on the matter but could gain no support; not even Ald. Robert Daly, who was the seconder, voted for Smith's motion. In defeat, Smith said, "I give notice that I will serve an injunction to restrain the city from granting the five acres in Avondale Park to the hospital trust."

Threat of injunction or not, the hospital committee let two contracts in July. E. A. Causey of St. Marys was to complete the excavation, stone and brickwork by Oct. 5 for $6,014. The brickwork was to be white. Scrimgeour Bros. was given the carpentry work – including that which needed to be done in the separate, but attached, fever ward – for its bid of $4,560. That work was to be finished by Dec. 1. Later that month, architect George Durand died; Stratford's turn-of-the-century hospital was one of his last designs.

Construction was completed in May 1891, and by that time the building fund had reached more than $17,600. Costs had been $13,361 (excluding a heating system, outhouses, drainage, furnishings and some other services), so the citizens of Stratford had acquired a debt-free institution. In the High Victorian, Queen Anne style, it stood three storeys in height (above a basement) with 102 feet (31 metres) of frontage and a depth of 36.5 feet (11 metres). Elizabethan and Romanesque features highlighted the exterior. In addition to Causey and Scrimgeour Bros., work had been done by Cash and Penny (painting and glazing, $812); Boyd, London (galvanized iron work, $425), James Greenaway, London (plumbing and gas fitting, $850), Thomas Henderson (plastering, $700). The heating contract went to an Oshawa company for $1,779.50 and included the installation of Gurney furnaces. John Chenoweth put in a system of electric bells. Gas mains had to be extended from the street to provide light and to fuel the cook stove in the kitchen. Gas was also used for various apparatus throughout the building. In a five-year deal, the Water Supply Co. agreed to provide water for the hospital for $50 a year. It also

A horse-drawn conveyance in front of the newly built original SGH.

guaranteed a fee of no more than $150 a year for laying and servicing the necessary pipes, and it installed two hydrants nearby to ensure some protection from fire.

The building designed by Durand provided more hospital than Stratford needed at the time. But the trustees reasoned the city would soon grow into it. They also chose to finish and open only the tower and the south wing, leaving the north wing as a detached ward for fever patients. To start, they offered eight beds in each of two public wards and another eight in private or pay wards. The north wing, when needed, would provide another 16 public beds and seven more in private wards. Furnishing those wards was handled by the women who so actively campaigned to have the hospital built. They also rounded up a lot of the equipment and appliances needed for the new hospital.

The attic-like third floor was reserved for the kitchen, laundry facilities and rooms for the nurses and porter-gardener. The hospital's early bylaws required the latter to "reside in the hospital and take charge of the furnaces and heating apparatus and carry out the instructions of the lady superintendent as to the degree of heat to be maintained, attend to and store the fuel, pump water, feed and attend cows, pigs and poultry, cultivate and keep the grounds in order, act as a messenger, assist the nurses when needed and act generally under the direction of the lady superintendent." The first man to answer that call was George L. Frame, who was about 30 years old. He and his wife Lillias had a year-old son, James.

Live-in quarters for the lady superintendent were provided on the first two floors, along with all of the patient wards. The lady superintendent was responsible for the hospital's day-to-day operation, including nursing care and the training of nurses. Specifically, as dictated by the hospital bylaws, she was to "have care of all the furniture, bedding and stores including food; order all provisions and keep an account of all donations; keep under lock and key all wine, beer and spirituous liquors; have charge and supervision of nurses, with power to hire and discharge; see that all provisions are properly cooked and punctually supplied, whether as meals or medical treatment; frequently visit wards, kitchen and laundry to see that nurses and servants are properly attending to their duties; order clothing of patients admitted with infectious diseases to be purified or, if necessary, destroyed by burning; keep posted in a book a full account of the daily state of each patient, changes in diet and remedies ordered; compound and dispense all prescriptions

and medications. She shall not absent herself from the Hospital unless on business of the Hospital or her own necessary affairs and then not until she has placed one of the head nurses in charge."

With justification, the trustees were proud of their ability to give Stratford a mortgage-free hospital. But they also expected the institution to be self-sustaining. Reports on other hospitals indicated that two-thirds of the cost of maintenance fell upon the communities served by the hospitals, and the bulk of that assistance came from county and urban municipalities. The next largest source of revenue was patient fees. Then there were bequests of cash or property, and subscriptions and donations from individuals.

While the trustees were grateful for the outpouring of money they received to build the hospital, they made it clear their fund was still open. In their bylaws they said they would endow a bed in perpetuity to any person, society or corporation which donated or bequeathed to the hospital $2,500 in cash, securities or real estate, if such gift generated at least $150 a year for the hospital. The donor could nominate one patient to such bed, free of all charges. The bylaws also included provisions for those wanting to donate money as a group: "Any municipal corporation, society or individual, or any five or less number of individuals uniting for such a purpose, who contribute annually $100 to the support of the hospital will have the right to the same admission of one free patient or succession of free patients for said term in one year for every $100 so contributed, but such nomination must be of an indigent person or indigent persons, and no other. Any number of persons exceeding five, so united and contributing, have the like right but in such case they must appoint some one person to make the nominations and sign the necessary certificates."

All other patients, who had the means to

pay, were to be assessed $2.80 per week in advance. If they wanted a private ward the fee was $3 to $10 "according to the situation of the room or ward." Special accommodation and attention for any patient would result in extra charges.

Official opening of the hospital was during the evening of Thursday, May 7, 1891, but programs were planned for both afternoon and night. The weekly *Herald* called the building "noble and imposing." Its reporter estimated the afternoon crowd to be 700 to 800 and the evening gathering 1,200. Hundreds more were unable to get into the building at night. Many citizens took advantage of the free bus service provided by John and Robert Forbes, brothers who ran a city livery business. The day's guest register included the names of people from as far away as Nebraska, Idaho and England. There was a contingent from St. Thomas that included the mayor and a man named Amass Wood, a philanthropist who was funding the construction of a hospital in that city.

It was a kind of daylong open house, but from 2 to 5 in the afternoon there was musical entertainment in a large room known as the William Byers ward. William J. Freeland's juvenile select choir opened and closed the program with several selections. Between, there were piano duets by Salla (Mrs. Robert M.) Ballantyne and Miss Kate M. Harding, and by Harriet F. (Mrs. James) O'Loane and her daughter Mary. Mrs. Ballantyne also performed a piano solo, as did Miss Nora Macklin and Amelia (Mrs. Fred J.) Scarff. Vocal solos were rendered by Mrs. James Gordon, Kate Carlin, John Kennedy and Frank Moore.

The secretary of the province, John Morison Gibson, arrived in Stratford by train in the afternoon and immediately visited the new hospital. But he reserved his official opening of the facility until around 8 p.m., in a ceremony in the Byers ward. Sheriff Hossie, chairman of the hospital

trust, emceed the program, during which William Buckingham read letters and telegrams of congratulations from dignitaries unable to attend.

In declaring the hospital open for the reception of the wounded, sick and distressed, Gibson was generous in his praise of the building and of all the people responsible for it. He directed special commendation to the women involved. He also said the hospital would come under the public institutions he had in his charge, and it would be entitled to public aid - to the tune of 37 cents per patient per day. There were shorter speeches by Perth County Warden John Schaefer, Stratford Mayor John Brown, ex-mayor Charles MacGregor and others. And there was a choral offering by the Apollo Club, under the direction of William Freeland. (A drinking fountain at the east end of upper Queens Park was dedicated to Freeland, the first full-time public school music teacher in Stratford schools. It was refurbished and in September 2002 unveiled at its new location, in Memorial Park, in Stratford's city centre.) More musical entertainment was planned for the hospital opening but the performers were scattered throughout the building and could not make their way into the Byers ward because of the throngs.

Admission fees were charged during opening day and resulted in almost $230. An additional $111.07 was raised through the sale of refreshments. So popular was the new hospital that another three-hour open house was scheduled for the following Saturday – but it was free.

Of concern to some of those in attendance was the width of the Cambria Street sidewalk that led to the hospital. It was just three planks abreast, and many felt that what was destined to be a popular summer promenade should be more accommodating. Three-plank sidewalk notwithstanding, Stratford and area had its long-awaited new hospital.

Growing pains

Stratford's new hospital drew citizens by the thousands on and about the day it was declared officially open. But they came out of curiosity not necessity. In fact, in its first few months of operation, the hospital attracted only a few in need of medical attention. But that was no surprise; many people were suspicious of the huge new institution. They thought the care it offered would be expensive, and they continued to set up sick rooms in their homes. The hospital, many thought, was a place in which to die.

It took more than a little missionary work on the part of city and area physicians to sell the hospital as a place for treatment, recovery and recuperation. After a decade, the number of persons treated was up to 271. In 1903 they cracked the 300 plateau for the first time and in 1907 went over 400 for the first time. They surpassed 500 in 1910, 1,000 in 1921, 2,000 in 1926, 3,000 (admissions 1,914) in 1935, 4,000 (admissions 2,255) in 1937, 5,000 (admissions 2,501) in 1938. Many patients in the early years were

termed "free" – that is, they were indigents and designated by the Stratford mayor, the county warden or the chair of the hospital board to receive treatment without personal cost.

The Women's Hospital Aid was formed in 1892, and a year later a training school for nurses was established.

Also in 1893, the north wing of the hospital was completed and opened, and that brought the total cost of the hospital to $21,833. By then there were nine doctors using the facility.

Taking the suggestions of other municipal hospitals, Stratford trustees had a barn built near the western limits of their property and acquired some dairy cows. In 1900 they received permission from the city to fence off part of Avondale Park and create pasture for the herd. The city's rental fee was $1 a year, and there was a stipulation that no barbed wire be used for the enclosure.

The average stay for the 271 patients admitted to the hospital in 1902 was 24.3 days. Eighty-two of those patients had

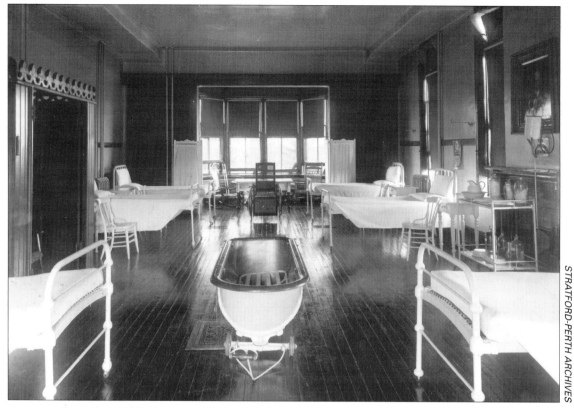

A ward in the original SGH, soon after 1900.

smallpox or diphtheria, 38 had typhoid.

There were 37 major operations and 37 of the minor variety. Some of the 63 "public" patients paid $2.80 a week for their treatment; for the others it was free. The treatment included drugs such as morphine and strychnine, dressings, and the medical attention of a doctor. Patients paid extra for special diets, fruit, wine and alcohol. There were five patients that year who paid $12 a week for private care. The hospital's budget of $8,149 included a cost of $49 for hay and straw. No doubt the overall costs would have been higher had not women in the community donated canned goods, fruits and vegetables. Indeed, the hospital received all kinds of help from a variety of sources. A number of groups and individuals donated flowers. Others, from as far away as New York, donated money.

The Women's Institute of North Easthope earmarked $10 for surgical books for the nurses. The next year, North Easthope Township came through with an unsolicited $50. Stratford and area churches initiated hospital Sundays and gave all the money collected on those days to SGH. The King's Daughters made the hospital a priority and regularly catered to the needs of patients.

As early as 1903, SGH learned what it was like to live with decreased money from the province. That was the year funding was reduced because the government decided Ontario hospitals could no longer count private patients when calculating their grant eligibility. This is how the hospital's 1904 annual report explained a deficit of more than $1,000. "The causes are not far to seek. Although the affairs of the institution continue to be conducted with a due regard to economy, having respect to efficient administration, the treatment of more patients, at an ever-increasing cost-per-patient for maintenance, requires larger expenditures, while the grants of $500 each from the city and the county remain the same and the aid from the province is less. In 1902 the province contributed $1,014, as against $411 this year. The city promised $1,000 annually and, although that sum is known to have been contributed by ratepayers for the purpose, half of it was used by the council for other purposes. It is deemed right that the financial situation should be fairly faced, and that the city and county should admit the justice of hospital claims. It is a public institution, and charitable persons who are interested in its work ought to have at their disposal an adequate annual income for its support. It is noticed that the Brantford hospital receives yearly grants of $3,000 from the city and $1,000 from the county. It is believed that ours is the poorest publicly assisted hospital

The original SGH, officially opened on May 7, 1891. Behind it is the barn built a few years later. It was used to house cows, which provided fresh milk for patients. Beyond the hospital to the left is the cottage built in 1904 for the porter-gardener and his family.

round about."

In 1904 a cottage for the porter-gardener-caretaker-herdsman was constructed on the hospital grounds. And in 1905 the laundry facilities were expanded and updated, thanks mainly to the fund-raising efforts of

The original SGH after it was enlarged in 1910. In 1948 the spacious corner verandas were enclosed and converted to wards, capable of handling 16 more patients.

the WHA. There was also talk about a new wing for the hospital, and in 1907 the board sent some of its members to look at the facilities in Niagara Falls, Woodstock and Hamilton. They came back recommending a three-storey addition measuring 40 by 60 feet (12 by 18 metres), with verandas and an elevator. By 1909, donations for the expansion had reached $15,000, among them $1,000 from the WHA for the elevator. But costs were expected to run to $25,000 without furnishings.

Nevertheless, contracts were let in February of that year, and on April 20, 1910, John Morison Gibson was back in town, this time as Ontario's lieutenant-governor, to officially open the new wing. Coming in at a cost of $25,491, it included an operating suite which was called by the provincial inspector of such facilities "the finest in Ontario." The addition also contained verandas and sunrooms, fire escapes, an elevator and proper maternity accommodations, something the hospital had been getting along without.

The lady superintendent of the hospital at that time was Anna Stabler, who was hired for $600 a year to take over from Emily Chilman, who had died. Stabler viewed expansion of the facility among her priorities. Years later she recalled, that when she arrived at SGH, "The original building was too small. The operating room and equipment were not up to date, and we lacked a maternity department. The new addition gave an opportunity also to make changes in the main building for more public and semi-private beds and for better working facilities for the nurses."

There were 19 births at Stratford General in the 1910-11 fiscal year, the first year for which the number of births was recorded in the hospital's annual report. The hospital fee for each baby was 25 cents per day. The number of births surpassed 100 by 1920, 200 by 1927 and 300 by 1937.

By 1913 the hospital's deficit was almost $3,800, and its trustees were faced with either raising rates or securing more financial support from the community. The board favoured the latter and said it was "looking to our city fathers for a very liberal

STRATFORD-PERTH ARCHIVES

Looking northwesterly at the original SGH (right) and its two major additions, in 1910 (middle) and 1923 (left). In the left of the photo is the cottage built in 1904 by the hospital for its porter-gardener and his family.

consideration of our case, and think we will not be disappointed." Eventually there were increases in funding from the city and the county, and the hospital, led by board chair Alex Faill, launched a fund-raising campaign, which included this somewhat convoluted plea: "In appealing to the public for aid each year, we do so on the ground that the hospital is a public property, held in trust for the public, and it cannot be conducted as a purely business proposition, and only by the extra money received from the public is it possible to carry the public ward patients. And it should also be remembered that on the extra amount received in this way, does to a certain extent, depend the efficiency of the hospital, and on that efficiency in apparatus and staff depend the lives of the patients and that patient may be you or yours."

Electricity was wired to the old sections of the hospital in 1915. In 1916 there were 13 doctors using the facilities. An eight-station telephone system was installed in 1917, by which time the staff included a superintendent, nine senior nurses, five intermediate nurses, six juniors and the hospital's first dietitian, Miss Beattie, who signed on in March but was replaced by Isabel Westloh on July 1. The work of the staff was eased somewhat by the introduction of large rubber-tired castors for the patients' beds. As well, two new sterilizers were installed.

Also in 1917, the hospital built a 16-by-30-foot (five-by-nine metre) poultry house and established a flock of 100 hens. For the patients that now meant fresh eggs in addition to fresh milk. A year later, a brooder house was added to the poultry operation. Much of the interior of the old portion of the hospital was repainted and many of its hardwood floors replaced in 1917. The electric lighting system was improved and expanded, electric heaters were added, and there was some new plumbing. Awnings and screens for the verandas were purchased.

In 1918-19 an influenza known as the Spanish flu swept the world and killed 21 million people, including 50,000 Canadians. More people died of influenza than had been killed in the First World War. Stratford General was not unaffected by the flu; it admitted 154 cases during that time period.

Superintendent of SGH at the time was Elizabeth McArthur and years later, as Mrs. Alex B. Manson, she reflected on the epidemic that claimed two of her student nurses: "One morning when we started to work we had only one nurse, one maid, the janitor and myself. All the other members of the staff had been stricken with the flu." The breech, she said, was filled by Grand Trunk Railway workers trained in first aid and by nurses throughout the city who volunteered their services.

McArthur resigned the position of superintendent in September 1919, but it was during her term that the hospital acquired its first motorized ambulance – to replace its horse-drawn vehicle. According to McArthur, Clayton Duff, a patient from Bluevale, was the force behind the purchase of the new ambulance. He arrived in town by train and was carted to the hospital by horses. That experience prompted him to push for a conveyance more modern. And that push resulted in the new ambulance.

In 1920 the hospital opened an X-ray department, and in 1922 a new laundry was built and equipped. A year later another wing was opened, complete with an isolation unit for up to 30 patients with communicable diseases. In 1924 Stratford General became a member of the Ontario Hospital Association.

In 1924 a specially equipped room was opened for the treatment of emergencies and minor surgery.

In 1925 a laboratory, with a microscope and urinalysis equipment, as well as pneumothorax service for lung tuberculosis, was set up in the basement, and in 1926 it

Dr. T. Russell Nichols, 1946

Mickle. As well, in 1927, Dr. Nichols put the lab in the medical limelight when he instituted basal metabolism service for goitre patients.

A central heating plant was installed in 1928, and in 1929 a new nurses residence was completed and furnished. The residence housed students for about four decades and now is the hospital's special services unit. To complement its new power plant, SGH built an incinerator and 80-foot chimney. That chimney stood until March 2000.

In 1929 medical eyes in Ontario focused on another epidemic, this time polio. More than 550 cases were reported across the province, and 46 people died.

A modern switchboard, with three incoming telephone lines, was installed in 1930, and each floor of the hospital was equipped with an electric refrigerator. A year later a cement driveway was built in front of the hospital.

When Dr. Pollock resigned his part-time radiologist's position in 1933, he was replaced by Dr. G. H. Ramsay of Rochester,

was placed under the direction of Dr. T. Russell Nichols, a general practitioner and anaesthetist, who ran it for about two decades. Also, Dr. Frederick R. Pollock was appointed radiologist on a part-time basis; the Kitchener-based doctor supervised X-ray services in Stratford two days a week.

Also in 1926, city council passed a resolution that called for the hospital to get an annual grant of three-quarters of a mill from Stratford's overall mill rate.

In 1927 the hospital received full approval from the American College of Surgeons for conforming to prescribed standards of organization. The struggle for that recognition had begun about two years earlier, sparked by the determination of the superintendent of nursing, Aillie

The nurses residence built in 1929. It is now the hospital's special services unit.

N.Y., on a full-time basis. But Ramsay stayed only four months before moving on to Regina General Hospital. His successor in Stratford, in 1934, was Dr. William McCauley (Mac) Gilmore of London. A few years later Gilmore travelled to the United States and returned with Stratford's first supply of radium for the treatment of cancer. That led to a study group in the hospital as part of a provincewide effort by the Ontario Medical Society to co-ordinate the battle against cancer. Gilmore became a fixture at the hospital until he retired in 1971.

Also in 1934, a modern gas anaesthetic machine was added to the operating room, an automatic fire alarm system – connected to the city fire hall – was installed, the dining rooms were refurnished and a ward was renovated and outfitted by the Women's Hospital Aid specifically for children. The women enlisted the financial help of service clubs and the public in general to put bright curtains on the windows and to supply over-bed tables and dishes featuring Mother Goose characters. The ward admitted 184 children in its first year and 126 in its second.

That same year, the worn-out furnace in the caretaker's cottage was replaced by heating from the hospital's central plant.

In 1935 the hospital had an oxygen tent donated and acquired the equipment necessary to offer pneumothorax treatments for tuberculosis. In the next year, the X-ray department, the fracture room, the emergency room and the lab were incorporated into one unit in what had formerly been the men's ward. New X-ray equipment, including a portable machine which could be used in patients' homes, was added. And the sterilizers in the operating room – two for water and two for instruments – were replaced.

As well, the nursery was moved from the north to the south side of the obstetric wing – to provide more sunshine for the babies.

ED DAVIES, SGH

The chimney for the Avon Crest power plant comes down in March 2000, by which time it had taken on a bit of a lean. At the same time, the old incinerator was demolished, much to the dismay of the pigeons for whom it had become a residence. The power plant was taken out of service in 1995.

By now the hospital was running chest and psychiatry clinics, and using the basement of the nurses residence for its crippled children clinics and for the examination of students attending the city's teachers college.

The first clinic for crippled children was held at the hospital on Aug. 16, 1923. Orthopedic specialists W. E. Gallie and A. M. LeMesurier, from the Hospital for Sick Children in Toronto, volunteered their time to do the examinations, assisted by local doctors and medical personnel. Extensive notes were taken and at a luncheon the

From left, the nurses residence, the first SGH, and the Ballantyne house – in the late 1930s or early 1940s.

specialists summarized their findings and recommended treatment for 56 cases. That clinic and those that followed were organized and sponsored by the Rotary Club of Stratford, whose members helped found the Ontario Society for Crippled Children (which later became the Easter Seal Society) in 1922. Club members sought out crippled kids throughout the county and, if necessary, provided transportation for them to attend the clinics.

In the clinic's early years the kids who were brought in for diagnosis were given a bag of candy by Alex Faill, who chaired the hospital board from 1915 through 1925. Faill was a successful farmer in South Easthope and Downie townships before he moved to Stratford in 1912 and involved himself in a number of community activities.

"Those (clinic days) were very busy days," recalls W. Arthur Gingras, who joined Rotary in 1936 and worked at his first clinic in 1937. "Back in those days I had an ambulance service and I remember using it to bring in some people who needed transportation. And some of us would be delegated to look after parents while their children were at the clinic. There would be sandwiches and coffee. Some of us stayed for most of the time and others for whatever time they could spare from their jobs."

Dr. David Smith, who began practising in Stratford in 1905, was a Rotarian and founding member of the OSCC. He pushed hard for Perth to become the first county in Ontario to organize crippled children's work. Then he took his message on the road and similar clinics in others areas of the province followed. Smith was an untiring champion of crippled children and years later was honoured by the society for his work in that area.

In 1937 the Women's Hospital Aid furnished a travelling library (actually, a bookcase on wheels), bought electrically heated food conveyors and Goetch-frame beds, and installed the roll-curtain systems around those beds.

During the polio epidemic in 1938, the Stratford branch of the Royal Canadian Legion donated an iron lung and oxygen tent to the hospital. A new medical wing was furnished and opened and management of the isolation hospital was transferred from the city to the hospital's board of trustees. The move was designed to save the city about $3,000 a year in operating costs. Because of the increased demand for hospitalization, the trustees remodelled and refurnished the first two floors of their new acquisition and created a 15-bed medical unit.

A medical records department was established in 1939. A full-time nursing instructor was appointed, and a call system replaced the bells which had long been used to summon nurses. Electrocardiograph equipment was added and placed under the direction of Dr. Nichols. The kitchen was modernized with a new cooker and cold storage room. And for the physical plant there was a new boiler and stoker. In 1939 and 1940 the X-ray department examined more than 1,000 military recruits destined for service in the Second World War. Some of them included Stratford doctors, among them George Ingham, Harold B. Kenner and R. Stanley Murray, as well as several hospital staff members.

The passenger elevator was updated in 1940, going electric and automatic. Washers for bed pans, and sterilizers, were donated by the WHA. A new hospital was opened in Listowel, which improved health services for the people of Perth County and took some of the load off SGH.

In 1941 a physicians' register was installed in the hall to help office staff locate doctors when called. That was the year Stratford General turned 50. And, while hundreds gathered to celebrate the building's silver jubilee and appreciate its freshly painted exterior, they could not ignore how overcrowded the place had become.

A blood donors bank was established in 1943 and was successful mostly because of donor groups - with the Canadian National Railways and Bell Telephone foremost among them. In 1944 the ambulance service was transferred from the city's jurisdiction to the hospital's trustees. When Evelyn V. McCaul came to town in 1944 she was the first female doctor connected to the hospital since Daisy Macklin in 1925. In 1945, Stratford's lab became a branch pathology laboratory for the provincial department of health, and it expanded to a larger area in the basement. Dr. Stephen J. C. Miller was appointed its first director, and subsequently a regional pathologist

NURSING SCHOOL ARCHIVES

Dr. Stephen Miller, 1946

working out of Stratford. All of this served to improve diagnostic services at Stratford's hospital and at those in smaller communities in the area.

In 1947 the hospital hired its first full-time business manager, William B. McDonald, and embarked on a program to reorganize its 160-person staff. It also revised its bylaws and rules and regulations for staff, and changed departments into units. In the next year, to help alleviate the overcrowded conditions, the board spent $16,294 to enclose the corner verandas and convert them to wards that could accommodate 16 additional patients.

In isolation

Of the hospital's 277 admissions in 1901, 110 were for communicable diseases (82 smallpox or diphtheria, 28 typhoid). For a number of years such patients were isolated in tents on grounds to the north of the hospital – in an area that would come to be known as the Old Grove. It took more than 10 years for the board of health to convince city council of the need for suitable accommodation for patients requiring isolation.

Finally, in 1910, an isolation hospital was built at a cost of $5,000, on four acres (1.6 hectares) of land at the southwest corner of St. Vincent and Easson streets. Officially opened in September 1911, the home was furnished by the Women's Hospital Aid. It was designed to accommodate only diphtheria patients; there were plans to put up two more buildings in succeeding years for the treatment of those with smallpox, typhoid and scarlet fever. But those plans never materialized and the St. Vincent Street facility handled those with a variety of diseases.

Until then, smallpox patients usually wound up in shacks, sometimes called "pest houses," in Avondale and Queen's parks. Typhoid, diphtheria and scarlet fever patients were quarantined in their homes, which often meant entire families were confined for the duration of the victim's illness. In such cases the afflicted often stayed in backyard tents.

It was in December 1900 when the board of health first proposed an isolation hospital. It asked the 1901 city council to put up one building with solid dividing walls, or separate buildings. In March 1901 the council called a meeting comprising its finance committee, board of health representatives and members of the Women's Hospital Aid. The latter had long been pushing for at least a part of the general hospital being set up as an isolation ward.

But an isolation hospital in any form was not going to be an easy sell. From the outset, council members didn't want to increase taxes to raise money for a facility "which people might not care to use." Eventually, a committee that included Dr. James A. Robertson, the county's medical officer of health; Mayor James Stamp; Ald. William Davidson; and lawyer John Idington was set up and charged with gauging the community's interest in such a hospital. Little was made of their findings.

In 1903, the King's Daughters, a church-oriented organization, offered to provide a tent that could be erected on hospital grounds and used for patients requiring isolation. But the hospital trustees rejected the offer, saying the project should be governed by the city's sanitation regulations. The Daughters then offered the $650 they had raised to go towards the construction of an isolation hospital.

Board of health members continued to lobby council, and in 1905 they thought they had found the ammunition they needed. There was a smallpox outbreak in Downie Township, and it was pointed out that one case, near Dunn's bridge, was no more than two miles (about 3.3 kilometres) from the core of the city. If council was shaken by the news, it was not enough to result in action.

In 1909 the hospital trustees decided to enlarge their facility and include in the addition an isolation unit. While roundly applauded in some circles, the proposal was quashed by Dr. R. W. Bruce Smith, the provincial inspector of prisons and public charities. He said isolation hospitals had to be separate buildings under control of the board of health. General hospitals, he said, "do not care for such patients."

The house at 290 St. Vincent St. S. in 2002. From 1911 to 1923 it was the isolation unit for Stratford General Hospital.

DEAN ROBINSON

The hospital went ahead with its addition, but deleted the isolation wing. The board of health, in turn, asked architect R. Banks Barber to prepare preliminary plans for an isolation hospital to the rear of the main hospital. He came up with drawings that called for an expenditure of $10,000. When the board balked at the price tag, Barber then prepared plans for two cottages, each to cost $2,500, exclusive of site.

The hospital board, meanwhile, did not favour isolation facilities on SGH grounds.

By August 1910 the city fathers agreed to issue debentures for $5,000 to cover the cost of a building site and a building. Eventually, four acres of land at the corner of St. Vincent and Easson were purchased from Nicholas Griffin for $1,000, and a building contract for $3,000 was let to Henry Jacobs and George Litt. The plumbing and heating job was given to Joseph Myers.

To furnish the building, the women's aid came up with $1,600, money it had accumulated by setting aside half of its general revenue for a number of years.

Sampson B. Webb was named superintendent of the facility, and his wife, Sophia, was hired as matron.

The 3½-storey white brick building was officially opened Sept. 28, 1911. With 11 rooms, two toilets, two bathrooms, and the most modern appliances, it was considered suitable accommodation for five adult patients and four children. The basement contained a furnace room, dining room, pantry, kitchen, laundry room and sterilizing room. The latter was connected to the floors above by a laundry chute, through which soiled clothes and bedclothes could travel, and be disinfected before going to the laundry.

On the first floor there was a doctors' room, nurses' quarters, the Webbs' bedroom, a sitting room, a toilet and a bathroom.

The public ward, with accommodation for two adults and three children, extended across the front of the second floor. To the rear of those rooms was the semi-private ward, which could accommodate three people, as well as a private ward with one bed and a cot. There was a medicine cabinet and dispensing table in the upstairs hall.

Initially, the attic was reserved as a children's play area, though it was felt it would eventually be needed for more nurses' quarters.

The building also had verandas on which patients could enjoy the sunshine.

The second major addition to the original SGH, in 1923, included an isolation wing, so the building at what is now 290 St. Vincent St. S. was declared redundant. In 1924 it was sold by the hospital to CNR engineer Charles W. Mace and his wife Catharine. About a dozen years later it was sold to Charles Parkins. In 1939 it was purchased by William G. Morrice, an employee with the city's board of works department. More than half a century later, it remains in the Morrice family.

Stratford General Hospital

Golden Jubilee

1891 - 1941

Enter to learn
Go forth to serve

Cover of the 20-page booklet published when SGH turned 50 in 1941.

A splendid example
of a new hospital

Almost from the day it opened in 1891, Stratford's general hospital was in need of expansion. And expand it did, with everything from minor renovations to major additions. For half a century those changes were made to suffice. But in the 1940s there were rumblings about a new facility, rumblings that gained currency when the trustees resolved on Sept. 8, 1944, to build a new hospital. They then sent that resolution to the federal department of health.

That was the same year money was spent to replace the roof on one of the wings and on the nurses residence. As well, the main office was renovated and venetian blinds were added. The sunroom was converted to a cast room, and a new X-ray machine was purchased. Recently introduced health insurance services were bumping up the requests for X-rays.

In 1945, the trustees contracted the architectural firm of Marani and Morris of Toronto to design their new hospital. They also suggested their present building be maintained as a chronic care facility. It was agreed that a new hospital, initially referred to as Stratford and Perth County General Hospital, would need endorsement from both the city and the county.

In December 1946, after two years of negotiations between the trustees and municipal councillors, citizens of Stratford approved a $1-million-dollar debenture to build and equip a new general hospital. Residents of Perth County, however, were less enthusiastic, but in 1947 the townships of Downie, Logan and Ellice committed to the amount thought to be a fair contribution from the county.

Meanwhile, Band-Aid solutions continued to get the old hospital through a year in which it admitted 3,600 patients and delivered 764 babies.

In 1947 the trustees decided to seek $150,000 in private donations to help equip and furnish their new hospital. To enhance the appeal they agreed to hold off on any large expenditures for the next 20 years. Donald B. Strudley, vice-president of Imperial Rattan Co. Ltd., was named head

Workers at the south end of the new hospital pause for a photo, Dec. 16, 1948.

A view of the west side of the new hospital from the front steps of the original hospital, May 4, 1949.

NURSING SCHOOL ARCHIVES

NURSING SCHOOL ARCHIVES

health established a division of public and private hospitals. By the end of 1951 that division would be keeping an administrative eye on 21,000 beds in 175 hospitals, which were treating about 650,000 patients annually. That represented seven million days of care.

The hospital's equipment purchases in 1947 included a specialized orthopedic table, two presses and a tumbler for the laundry, as well as two teaching aids: a female torso and a head, eye and ear model.

On June 11, 1948, construction contracts were let to Pigott Construction Co. for the main building ($1,235,790) and for a new boiler house and laundry ($107,546). Based in Hamilton, Pigott was the foremost construction company in southwestern Ontario at that time, and for it, the new SGH became job No. 4530. Five days later, a group of nurses turned the first sod for the new hospital, on a site across John Street from the original hospital, a building that was destined to become a chronic-care facility. The new hospital was going up on what had been a mostly unused city-owned field.

On occasion that field had exploded with life – when circuses came to town and were given permission to set up on the northeast

of the committee that would oversee the building of the new hospital, which by now was depicted in architectural sketches.

The provincial government's capital grant policy of 1947 specified construction monies to public hospitals in the amount of $1,000 per bed for active treatment and $2,000 per bed for chronic care. The grants resulted in the construction of hospital space for 10,000 beds in general hospitals and another 1,900 for the chronically ill. As a result, between 1945 and 1950 the hospital field in Ontario was busier than it had been during any time in the preceding half century. And to monitor all that activity the department of corner, bounded by St. Vincent Street South and Cambria Street. Pearl (Mrs. Harold) Thomas, who lived on Birmingham Street at the time, thought the last of those circus visits was in the spring or early summer of 1947. They were memorable events, she said, complete with two or more tents and a parade that came up West Gore Street. She also remembered her mother telling her about tents of a different kind, set up on undeveloped land west of Birmingham over to St. Vincent, to house overflow patients from the isolation hospital at the corner of St. Vincent and Easson streets. She remembered, too, having her appendix out as a child in 1921 in what is now referred to as the old hospital. "The poorhouse was on one side and the cemetery on the other," she said with a grin.

Construction of the new hospital began in July 1948, and in September the expected government grants for the project were confirmed publicly. The federal government came through with $239,667 – $86,667 for the main building and $153,000 to help transform the old hospital into a chronic care facility. The Ontario government chipped in $202,666, in addition to 50 per cent of the approved expenditure for renovations to the old building.

By November, the fund to raise $150,000 for furnishings and equipment for the new hospital was $30,000 beyond its goal.

Meanwhile, it was business as usual in the over-taxed old hospital. In 1948, a small X-ray machine, for chests, was added to the equipment inventory, as were a wheeled stretcher, an ice cream cabinet and a power lawn mower. Purchases the next year included night tables for nurses, chairs for the sun porches, a small oxygen tent for pediatrics, a therapeutic drainage pump, a microscope and filing cabinet for the lab and two typewriters for the office. The X-ray department expanded in size and staff.

On Oct. 26, 1948, Russell T. Kelley, the provincial health minister, laid the

NURSING SCHOOL ARCHIVES

Looking back to the original hospital from the west side of the new hospital, July 13, 1949. The tunnel that continues to link the two buildings also has an offshoot to the south, to what is now the special services unit.

cornerstone of the new building. Kelley was no stranger to Stratford. In 1922 he was a prominent advertising agent in Hamilton. He was also a Rotarian in that city, and in that capacity he had come to Stratford to represent the governor of District 27 and present the charter to 22 men who became the Rotary Club of Stratford.

By April 1949 the new laundry was completed and by November of that year the new boiler house – with its 225-horsepower boiler – was finished.

In January 1950, John F. Ward replaced McDonald as hospital administrator, and four months later, the hospital's first pharmacist, Mary Asquith, was hired.

On the afternoon of Saturday, July 22, 1950, about 200 invited guests sat around part of the circular drive in front of the main entrance for the official opening of the new hospital. David Smith, one of the city's longest-serving and best-loved doctors, was a member of the hospital board at the time, and on this day he chaired proceedings that included words from Harold W. Strudley, the chairman of that board, formally known as the Stratford General Hospital Trust. The hospital was something of a passion for Strudley, who was president of Imperial Rattan, a company that manufactured furniture. He had become a member of the SGH board in 1914 and had served as its chairman since 1939. His son had headed the building committee for the new hospital. Between them, the Strudleys were SGH board members for 60 years, a third of them as head of that board.

Dr. W. Douglas Piercey, superintendent of Ottawa Civic Hospital and president of the Ontario Hospital Association, brought best wishes from the 160-member OHA and congratulated the community on achieving a goal it had identified as far back as 1944.

Mayor Thomas E. Henry welcomed everyone to the "finest, cleanest and healthiest" city in Canada.

Introduced as special guests were Dr. Harvey Agnew, professor of hospital administration at the University of Toronto and executive secretary of the Canadian Hospital Council; Don Strudley, chairman of the building committee; R. S. Morris of Marani and Morris, architects for the building; Joseph Pigott, who represented Pigott Construction Co. Ltd., general contractors for the building; Miss E. R. Dick, Toronto, director of nursing for Ontario; Sister St. Elizabeth, superintendent of St. Joseph's Hospital, London; Dr. Howard C. Hazell, president of the medical staff at SGH; John J. Vosper of Mitchell, warden of Perth County; Helen (Mrs. Albert L.) Baker, president of the Women's Hospital Aid; Miss Minerva Snider, director of nursing at SGH; and Jack L. Bateman, newly appointed administrator of SGH.

Jack Bateman, SGH administrator 1950-1968

Also present were Mrs. Rahno M. Beamish, superintendent of Sarnia General Hospital and president of the Ontario Nursing Association, and Lewis H. Dingman, president of the Stratford *Beacon-Herald* and the St. Thomas *Times-Journal*. Dingman was the only surviving member of a group that had met Nov. 22, 1888, to discuss the provision of hospital facilities in Stratford. The new building was officially dedicated by Rev. Earl E. Hooper of Memorial Baptist Church and past president of the Stratford Ministerial Association. That was followed by Justice J. Maurice King's introduction of Paul Martin Sr., the federal minister of health and welfare. King had been mayor of Stratford in 1946-47 – when the debentures for the hospital were approved – but gave up his Ontario Street law practice to become a member of the Supreme Court of Ontario. He told the crowd he and Martin had been classmates years earlier at St. Michael's College in Toronto.

It was Martin's job to cut a ribbon stretched across the front door and declare the new hospital officially open. He did that, but not before delivering the kind of speech that is predictable when politicians

24

The second SGH, soon after it opened in July 1950.

take part in such ceremonies. "The building of the Stratford General Hospital is part of a nationwide development," said the minister. "Under the National Health Program, started two years ago, we have well and truly laid the cornerstone of a national health structure, which is firmly founded on the health achievements of municipal and provincial governments, voluntary health agencies and all of Canada's thousands of health workers.

"The building of a hospital like this is more than the expenditure of money, the drawing up of plans, the actual work of construction – it is, above all, the bringing into being of an idea. For a hospital must be more than a building; it must be a haven of good health, a place of healing, a centre of humanitarian service.

"Nurses, dietitians, social service workers, hospital administrators and technicians of many kinds depend almost entirely upon the hospital for their education and training. Medical students and interns find it necessary to supplement their academic instruction.

"The training of nurses has always been

the active concern of Stratford General Hospital, and in your new building excellent laboratory facilities have been provided not only for routine analyses but for research activities as well. In the areas of education and research lie the future hopes of medicine."

It was Martin who had approved federal grant money for the new SGH, which he now described as "a splendid example of a modern hospital." He said members of his department told him the building plans submitted were among the best they had seen.

Those plans resulted in a building with 90,000 square feet (8,361 square metres) of floor space and 1.1 million cubic feet (33,000 cubic metres) of capacity. Its construction required 4,400 cubic yards (3,344 cubic metres) of concrete, 362 tons (328 tonnes) of steel reinforcing, 52 miles (84 kilometres) of wire for telephones and the 1,105 light fixtures, and 22 miles (35 kilometres) of pipe for carrying hot water and steam. It contained 593 windows, 432 doors, and 427 rooms and closets. Outside there were 26 parking spaces for hospital staff and another 76 spaces for the public.

Initial plans called for equipping 136 beds for adults and children and 40 more for babies. Eventually those numbers were to be bumped to 170 and 54, respectively. There were eight operating rooms, including emergency and delivery. It cost $653 to furnish each private room, $1,051 for each semi-private room and $1,944 for each standard four-bed room.

In the basement of the building were the dietary department, dining rooms, pharmacy, central sterilizing, and supply and storage rooms. The ground floor contained the X-ray department, emergency room, physiotherapy department, medical unit, administration offices and chapel. On the second floor were the surgical unit and eight operating rooms. On the third there was the maternity unit, with nurseries and birth rooms. Units for the care of children and chronic patients were on the fourth floor. There were nursing stations on each of the first four floors. The fifth floor contained the pathological department and the sixth and seventh housed air conditioning equipment and elevator machinery.

The impressive but institution-like red-brick building had cost about $1.7 million, roughly $114,000 more than had been budgeted. City residents contributed $178,678 to the furnishings fund, and more than $200,000 had come from each of the provincial and federal governments.

Musical selections at the opening ceremonies were presented by the Aeolian

Building the tunnel that connects the old and new hospitals – as well as what was originally a nurses residence.

Quartet. For the open house that followed, it was the band of the Canadian National Railways that provided the music. That open house attracted more than 6,300 people.

As the new hospital was officially opened, the old hospital, though with no fanfare, was officially closed, at least for the purposes that it was originally built. However, the two would remain connected, if by no other means than the pedestrian tunnel that was carved out under John Street as part of the construction job that resulted in the new SGH.

From footings and frames to chairman of the board

by Alistair MacLeod

I emigrated to Canada in June, 1948, with my pal Jim Broadfoot, landing at Pier 21 Halifax, N.S., on June 21st. We had served our five-year apprenticeships together with the same building firm in Edinburgh, Scotland, and were fully qualified joiners or, if you like, finish carpenters.

Hamilton, Ont., was our destination. We started work finishing up new houses after the plasterers were through. A few weeks later we were offered a job with Pigott Construction, which asked us if we would travel to Stratford, where the company was starting a new hospital. Our inquiries as to the size and location of this town garnered few answers. As I recall, the superintendent of construction, a fellow Scot, said, "I've only been there twice, and there is a wee river." We accepted the job and arrived in Stratford on a hot August day.

Reinforced poured concrete buildings were really in their infancy in 1948. Most buildings were solid brick, block or stone. The original hospital is a good example.

Looking back on the construction

methods we used, by today's standards they were almost crude. No ready-mixed concrete, no climbing cranes able to reach any part of the building, no forklifts, no power trowellers, no plastic sheeting to keep out the wintry blasts, no skill saws, no steel or aluminum forms – and no hard hats. Nevertheless, it was a challenge, as we had no experience of concrete-forming whatsoever. We soon learned the hard way in blazing heat and freezing cold.

The Pigott workforce in Stratford was made up of a group of French Canadians who followed the "forming jobs" and left after the concrete skeleton was completed, eight or nine from the Maritimes and Newfoundland, and at least 10 from the United Kingdom, plus a group of local and district men. Many of the men were veterans of the Second World War, and three or four had been decorated for bravery, one of them being my mate James Proudfoot, who had won the Distinguished Service Cross while serving with the Royal Marines.

The construction superintendent was

Tommy Hamill, who was in charge of the concrete and brickwork. He left to begin another project after this part of the work was completed, and another super took over to complete the finishing of the building.

A disaster was narrowly avoided as the first major pour of the first floor began from the north end. Columns were in place and clamped. All outside and inside beams were in place on their T shores, and all reinforcing electrical conduits and plumbing sleeves had been installed. Two of us were assigned to watch the pour from below. We wore rubber boots, coats and hats as a constant drip of cement water fell on us. I heard a strange noise and looked up to see a large interior beam beginning to bulge. Shouts to stop the pour and frantic shouts for 10-ton jacks and shores rang out – screamed out, really. We managed to contain the bulge, but it was impossible to squeeze the concrete back in.

The cause of that near disaster was soon discovered; someone had forgotten to put a four-inch spike in the two-by-four kicker plate which lay on the T shore to hold in the beam side. It was a near disaster for the want of seven four-inch nails. The bulge is still there, covered by the ceiling in the basement corridor. All this excitement and no safety helmets.

By the time we reached the fourth and fifth floors, freezing winds and ice storms were creating difficult working conditions. Bundled in parkas, and with metal freezing to bare skin, it was not much fun. Time was lost trying to keep warm. However, the concrete skeleton was completed, and the

ALISTAIR MACLEOD

Smoke break for Alistair MacLeod (right) and his pal Jim Proudfoot.

bricklayers began to close in the building.

The forming carpenters moved on, and Jim and I were left. It seemed that we were the only ones that had hand planes in our tool kits. Our job then was to install the window frames and fit the sashes. A young Pigott employee from another job site, whose name was Bill McCann, arrived to act as finishing foreman. He was being groomed for a management position. We helped with his grooming.

After the windows were finished, we installed every steel door and interior window frame in the building, a tedious task at times. The bricklayers could then begin on room layouts.

Under the watchful eyes of Dr. John Penistan, we installed all the cabinets and work stations in his beloved labs. They are still there, 52 years later. A few years on, I was privileged to count Dr. John as a good friend and fellow performer in the local little theatre group.

Our final job was the finishing of the reception area and front vestibule, which was trimmed out in oak. The lock for the golden key was checked to ensure it worked for the opening ceremonies, which duly took place with the appropriate fanfare. Our work was then over.

I chose to stay in Stratford and went to work for

ALL ALISTAIR MACLEOD

Pigott Construction puts up the present SGH, 1949-50.

A view of the west side of the new hospital from the front steps of the original hospital, May 4, 1949.

Pounder Bros. for six years. During that time they won the contract to renovate the old hospital, and I worked on that job for a few months. Not long after, they won the contract to build the St. Marys hospital. Once again I was in hospital construction. My job there was to hang the room doors of solid birch. They weighed a ton, and my arms stretched by two inches.

In 1955 I left the construction trade and joined the teaching profession for the next 30 years. Six of those were at the then Stratford Collegiate, 24 at Northwestern in the technical department.

For eight immensely challenging and satisfying years I served the community on the Stratford hospital board, the last two as chairman. I would not have missed the experience at any price. The knowledge I gained and the friends I made throughout my hospital stay from the footings to the board chair will remain highlights of my life's journey.

New hospital, new growth

The old hospital was officially closed the day the new one opened – July 22, 1950. But patients in the old building, 102 of them, were not transferred to the new facility until Aug. 16. On that Wednesday, the six most seriously ill were moved by ambulance. The business of shuttling the others through the pedestrian tunnel began soon after they had finished eating breakfast. By noon half of them were settling in to their new surroundings. By 1 p.m. the switchboard in the new hospital was operational.

On hand to assist with moving day were 10 members of the Rotary Club of Stratford and seven Rotary Anns. As well, four Kroehler employees and three from Preston-Noelting helped out, as did members of the St. John Ambulance Brigade.

The movement of patients to the new building was completed in the afternoon. The last to arrive were those in the maternity ward, whose numbers jumped by one at about 5:30 that afternoon with the birth of Gordon Donald Grant (seven pounds, seven ounces), the second of four sons for Don and Peggy Grant of Lot 13, Concession 13 Downie Township. From the women's aid, which in this year changed its name to the Women's Hospital Auxiliary, the Grants received a sterling silver spoon and a bank account opened in Gordon Donald's name.

Another presentation of note in 1950 involved Isabelle McGillawee (widow of Alex McGillawee), who, upon her resignation from the board, received a sterling silver tray to mark her 21 years as secretary-treasurer of that body.

By this time the hospital had a payroll of 200, and one of the board's four stated goals was to establish a pension plan for all of its permanent employees. The three others were to establish an auxiliary cancer clinic, to have the hospital approved by the Canadian Medical Association for post graduate medical training, and to refurbish and reopen the old hospital as a chronic and long-term convalescent facility.

In its earliest days, most of the public served by the new hospital carried no health insurance. In fact, less than 22 per cent of the patients were covered. The Blue Cross health insurance numbers for that period listed 3,745 members in Stratford, 5,568 in the county. Day rates at SGH were $5 for someone in a four-bed ward, $7 for semi-private (two beds) and $8 to $10 for private accommodation. Still, in 1950, 4,749 patients were treated at SGH by 22 doctors.

High employment and increased participation in the private insurance plans was resulting in a sharp increase in the use of Ontario public hospitals. In 1952, for instance, 15 per cent of the province's population received hospital care, compared to 10 percent in 1943. Also in 1952, 71 per cent of the province's births took place in hospital. Within a decade that percentage jumped to more than 90. In the mid-'50s, all duties of the division of public and private hospitals were transferred to the newly legislated Hospital Services Commission of Ontario, the body also charged with setting up a hospital insurance plan for the province. In preparation for such a plan, the commission surveyed hospital facilities and staff, and met with representatives of the various other groups which would be affected. That led to the Hospital Services Commission Act of 1957, the cornerstone of modern medical care in Ontario.

By 1959 the Ontario Hospital Insurance Plan was in place, which meant every citizen of the province was assured of getting hospital and medical care when necessary, regardless of income and without being designated a ward of the public. In 1969 Ontario agreed to take part in a national plan under the Medical Care Act of Canada. In Ontario, on April 1, 1972, existing hospital and medical plans were combined into one insurance scheme called the Ontario Health Insurance Plan. Under OHIP, almost seven million residents were protected with family plan insurance, while another 1.3 million held individual policies. Premiums totalled $520 million. Through the Medical Care Act of Canada, the federal government contributed another $225 million. The provincial government covered the rest of the cost to run the OHIP system.

But all of that was well down the road in 1951, when the Stratford hospital board came up with a new set of bylaws. The following year it shed its designation as a trust in favour of a corporation under the companies act. The new charter replaced a declaration made by trustees back in 1888, when all they had to do was file a letter of incorporation with the county. Under the new arrangement, the board reduced its number of directors from 20 to 15.

By 1951 the hospital had a medical and surgical staff of 21. Near the end of that year it hired George Mayer as its first full-time intern. It also added Dr. Vince A. Corrigan of Kitchener, a specialist in urology, and received $3,245 from the Atkinson Charitable Foundation to help equip its first urological department. Its application as an auxiliary cancer treatment centre was denied, but it did take a step towards becoming a post graduate training facility. It managed a place in the "commended section" of the CMA list of hospitals which were seeking approval for internship training. Its application for such status was to be reviewed after a year in the commended class. Eventually, the CMA decided all intern training should take place in hospitals affiliated with medical schools. In Ontario that meant centres such as Toronto, Kingston, Hamilton, Ottawa and London.

In the late 1970s the medical clinic in Tavistock was approved to teach med students in the area of family practice. In turn, the students' affiliation with SGH was also approved. Through the years, various approval has been granted to SGH for the training of specialists. Application for such approval has often been instigated by a specialist practising at the hospital.

There was less progress to report

regarding the after-life of the old hospital, except a growing need to do something with it to relieve some of the bed-short conditions already facing its successor.

In the matter of a pension plan for permanent employees, it was hoped one could be in place by 1953. The employees, meanwhile, joined the Canadian Union of Public Employees, which resulted in a collective bargaining unit that covered dietary, housekeeping, laundry, boiler house and maintenance workers, as well as nursing orderlies and assistants and X-ray and lab assistants.

Undoubtedly, hospital administrators expected union demands to increase their cost of doing business. Their operating budget was already showing red, in part due to the amount of care for indigent patients that they had to underwrite. Still, they were able to buy a 1938 Packard ambulance (helped by $1,000 in donations), and establish a library for the medical staff. Actually, most of the cost of the library was covered by a bequest from a former member of the medical staff.

By the end of 1952, the deficit was reported to be $11,413. The care of indigents was still a big contributor to that shortfall. As well, chronic care patients continued to occupy beds in the new hospital while politicians, bureaucrats and the public debated the future of the old hospital. Government money was apparently on its way, a fact that may or may not have influenced the taxpayers when they rejected a proposal to spend $300,000 to upgrade the now-vacant original SGH. As far as the patients were concerned, this was the year selective menus were introduced and they were given some choices when it came to their meals.

In 1953, those who provided round-the-clock patient care at SGH were categorized in this way: 60 student nurses, 47 graduate nurses, 22 nursing assistants, 25 dietary-kitchen, 19 housekeeping, 11 administration, 10 lab, 10 laundry, six X-ray, six power plant and maintenance, two pharmacy. It was also in that year that Ontario hospitals were required to adopt a standard accounting system, as set out in a manual that covered Canadian hospitals.

The numbers in Stratford were still shaded in red, though in December 1953 the city debentured $150,000 to renovate the old hospital and Perth County committed to $50,000. In the donation department, the Rotary Club furnished money for two croupette humidifiers, oxygen tents and some radium for the X-ray department.

On March 16, 1954, renovations began at the old hospital. In the following July the long-promised pension plan was introduced, and the 28 workers who qualified began paying five per cent of their salary into it. Their contributions were matched by the hospital. The initial plan was later replaced by one operated by the Ontario Hospital Association. Still in force, it provides commonality among Ontario hospitals and transferable benefits for employees who move among them.

Renamed Avon Crest, the old hospital was reopened, at a cost of $525,000, as a chronic care and convalescent facility on June 15, 1955. The man who cut the ceremonial ribbon was Dr. Mackinnon Phillips, the provincial health minister. The event drew about 300 people, many of them seated on benches on the lawn in front of the building. Others stood farther back, under trees and out of the late-spring sun.

Rolph M. Trow, chairman of SGH's board of directors, presided over the formalities, which included an introduction of Dr. Phillips by the dean of the city's medical profession, David Smith. Also on hand were Stratford Mayor Wilfrid P. Gregory, Perth County Warden Willoet J. Kelterborn, Perth MPP-elect J. Fred Edwards, and chairman of the hospital board's building committee Hans Buscher.

The remodelled facility was designed to

accommodate 105 patients in seven private rooms, a dozen two-bed rooms, six three-bed rooms, 10 four-bed rooms, and two eight-bed rooms. There was also accommodation for 23 nursing students and two supervisors on the third floor, as well as a classroom, two laboratories and a recreation area for staff. The basement contained the building's main kitchen, single rooms for four male staff members, two three-bed rooms for patients requiring isolation because of infectious diseases, nurses' locker rooms and supply rooms for linen and uniforms. For fire protection the building was equipped with a sprinkler system throughout, as well as special doors to section off parts of each floor. The architectural firm of Marani and Morris, Toronto, planned the renovation, and Pounder Bros. of Stratford was the general contractor. English and Mould Ltd. of Toronto did the plumbing. After the official ceremonies, the building was open for public tours – not unlike May 7, 1891.

Only the first floor – with 45 beds and an out-patient clinic – was ready for use in June 1955. The second floor, with the other 60 beds, was scheduled to open at a later date. What visitors saw on opening day were north-facing rooms painted in warm colours and south-facing rooms in cool colours. Those colours were of mushroom tones with pastel shades of yellow, blue, green and rose. Bathrooms were tiled in colours that matched adjoining rooms. There were noiseless light switches and handrails down both sides of the corridors, whose walls were surfaced with a plastic composition to reduce the risk of injury for anyone falling against them.

The nurses' quarters comprised single and double rooms, each with beds, easy chairs, combination desk-dressing tables and large closets. The old kitchen on the third floor became the staff recreation room, and the old operating room became a sitting room, brightened with a picture window. In addition to the main kitchen, in the basement, there were supplemental units on the first and second floors, each with an automatic dishwasher. Most of the hot food for Avon Crest was to come in bulk from the kitchen of the new hospital, through the freshly painted pedestrian tunnel that still links the two buildings. At Avon Crest that food was to be readied for individual servings. Cold dishes and salads were also to be prepared in Avon Crest's three kitchens.

Across the street at the new hospital, the north wing of the fourth floor was redecorated and refurnished. There were now 220 staff members at SGH, as well as 58 student nurses. In 1955 the board suggested ways in which the county might pay for costs the hospital was incurring through its treatment of indigent patients. By year's end there had been no response from the Perth councillors.

In 1956, however, the county did respond, to the tune of $25,000 for the care of indigents. That money, along with the increased popularity of health insurance, relieved the hospital's operating woes significantly. In the capital expense department in 1956, SGH bought a new boiler and installed new laundry equipment. It also converted two rooms near the operating suite to a recovery room. As well, it began physio- and occupational therapy programs.

In 1958 the staff at SGH grew to 261 and there were 54 student nurses. Those students, and those who followed, were the recipients of a trust fund established that year by members of the medical staff to honour doctors who had died.

Also in 1958, the workweek was reduced to 40 hours from 44, a subject that probably received some play in the newly founded staff magazine, The Back Rub. As well, a liaison committee was established to improve communications between the staff and the board of directors.

Since 1954 the hospital had been setting aside some of the money it received in provincial grants. The reserve fund was used mostly for capital expenditures, which in 1958 included a standby generator for electricity and a well for all its water needs, exclusive of drinking water. The fund meant that by 1958 the hospital was able to scale down its monetary requests of city council.

But it did not mean its money problems were over. The introduction of health insurance had hospital operators worried from the beginning. Without question, they believed, insured care would result in more care, which would tax their facilities to the limit. The problem was compounded when the province said it would no longer fund the city's hospital debentures. For a further $25,000 to underwrite the health-care costs of indigents, the hospital sought combined help from Perth and Oxford counties and from St. Marys. The counties chipped in, but St. Marys was not as keen.

In the face of an uncertain and somewhat scary future – which was to become a way of life for SGH – the board hired a consulting firm to survey the needs of the area its hospital was expected to serve. It wanted a projection for active, convalescent and chronic beds, as well as recommendations for the needs in other areas. Within eight years of its opening,

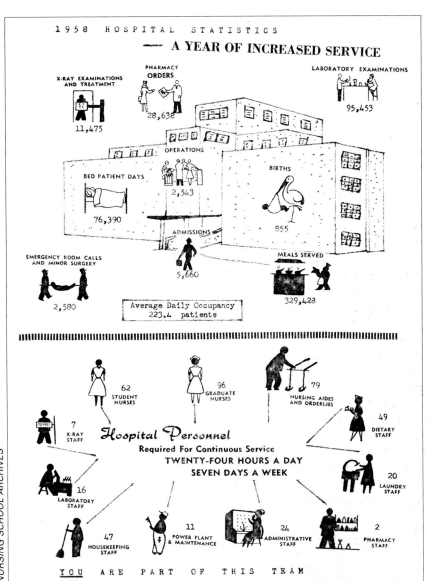

An illustrated page of statistics from the spring 1959 issue of *The Back Rub*, a magazine published for the employees of SGH.

Stratford's "splendid example of a modern hospital" was badly needing a prescription.

On a more positive note, the community in general remained supportive. In 1958, in addition to the annual contributions made by the women's auxiliary, the hospital also received two walkers and a scale for weighing babies from the Beth Israel Sisters. And five wheelchairs were donated by the Stratford Old-time Baseball Association.

Growing pains and hospital expansion remained foremost on the minds of board members in 1959. The consultants they had hired came back with a 10-year vision that called for 250 treatment beds and the facilities – among them an X-ray department, a lab, and operating rooms – to support those beds. With Avon Crest in the equation, there needed to be dietary, laundry, power plant and physical medicine facilities to serve another 100 patients, 350 in all.

SGH, then, needed to come up with an addition that could accommodate 50 more medical and surgical beds. Revamping the obstetrics department, it was reasoned, could make room for 10 of the 50. The Ontario Hospital Services Commission approved an expansion project that would cover the remaining 40 beds. The OHSC figured such expansion should cover the hospital's needs to 1966.

History would later show the population projections for Stratford and area to be overestimated. To further confound the needs-vision mix, the Health Ministry reduced the number of beds-per-thousand-people it felt was necessary to provide adequate care. The acute-care ratio went from 3.5 beds to 3.0.

Original plans called for the building to extend in three directions – north, south and west, with each addition having a basement and at least three floors. In the end, however, the west wing, which was a service wing, was widened rather than extended. Also, it was decided an extension of the south wing was not necessary. Construction began in September 1961 and, because of a short general strike and some bad weather, it didn't end until the spring of 1963.

Meanwhile, administrators and staff were dealing with the added paperwork that accompanied insured health care. Doctors were asked why patients seemed to be staying in the hospital for longer periods. There was a feeling among some board members that some beds were being occupied by patients who could complete their recovery at home. At Avon Crest, steps were taken to see that beds in that facility were used only for patients requiring chronic – not custodial – care.

To improve the environment in the emergency, operating and delivery rooms, for patients and staff, air conditioning was installed. As well, the hospital devised a set of procedures to be used in the event of a disaster. And an employee bowling league was started.

By the end of 1960, the staff at SGH had doubled over the previous decade, mostly because of the shorter workweek and the addition of 100 treatment beds in Avon Crest. There were now 303 full-time and 85 part-time employees, and 72 student nurses. The SGH pension plan was integrated with the provincial plan and a transfer of benefits became available to those leaving Stratford for jobs at other hospitals. Cost of the pension plan to SGH began an upward spiral as more employees became eligible to enrol in it.

This expansion of SGH facilities wound up costing more than $1.6 million, of which $200,000 was donated by the city and another $100,000 by the county. The rest, all but a shortfall of $14,000, came from public subscription and government grants. The price tag covered the establishment of some new departments, including physiotherapy, and the expansion or relocation of others, among them X-ray and the laboratory. A new operating suite was added, as was an intensive care unit, though the latter did not function as designed until 1967 because of a lack of qualified staff. There was a new pharmacy, a new locker room for staff, a pay cafeteria in the basement and an another elevator. Emergency services were moved to the same ground-floor level as the West Gore Street ambulance entrance and expanded. Air conditioning was extended to the X-ray department, recovery rooms, labour rooms and the ICU. The piped oxygen system was to be extended to cut down on the use of portable cylinders. And a gift shop was built for the women's auxiliary.

In 1961 the boiler system had to be upgraded to handle the enlarged facilities. To make more efficient use of those facilities the board established an admissions and discharge committee, whose role was mostly to ensure that patients stayed in hospital no longer than they had to. As well, during this year, there were rumblings about a separate building for the school of nursing – perhaps the establishment of a college of nursing.

By the end of 1963, 58 doctors were using the facilities at SGH, compared to just 35 when the new hospital opened in 1950. And some of what they used continued to come from community groups. In 1963 the Beta Sigma Phi sorority donated two oxygen tents and the Stratford Kiwanis Club a resuscitator.

On May 24, 1964, a new and larger first-floor chapel, and book of remembrance, were dedicated at the hospital. The ceremony was conducted by Leonard C. Webster, chairman of the SGH board; Rev. James Ferguson of St. Andrew's Presbyterian Church, vice-chairman of the board; and Mary (Mrs. William A.) Johnston, head of the hospital's public relations committee. The book of remembrance was designed to honour those in whose memory donations were made to SGH, and was to be on permanent display in the lobby of the hospital. It stayed there for more than two decades, until a new lobby was built as part of a major expansion program in the 1980s.

The memorial fund was established to buy "life-giving equipment" that the hospital might otherwise not be able to afford. It had already covered the purchase of a dual defibrillator unit, an electronic pacemaker unit and a breathing assister controller.

Also in 1964, visiting hours were fixed at 11:30 a.m. through 8:30 p.m. A program to identify and establish specific departments continued, in accordance with the provincial guidelines related to hospital accreditation. At the same time, the psychiatric clinic was discontinued.

In the mid-'60s, SGH was reporting a shortage of nurses and hospital workers in general. There just were not enough to go around. Simultaneously, the Ontario Health Ministry was predicting the need for twice as many nurses by the end of the decade. That pronouncement sparked more talk in Stratford of a new or expanded nursing school, perhaps a regional facility, and the residence to accommodate expected students.

Indeed, in 1965 Stratford was selected as the site for the Perth-Huron Regional School of Nursing, which meant, at the least, a detached building to house some classrooms and a residence. In the interim, the shortage of nurses continued at SGH, at a time when there was pressure to expand the medical services. It was expected 30 to 40 more beds would be required by 1970, and a fund-raising campaign was started. There was a decision to revise the 13-year-old bylaws of the hospital, which by now employed more than 500 people. That number included 72 general-duty nurses and 72 nursing assistants and orderlies. As of June it also included Nena Arelano, the hospital's new dietitian. A native of the

Philippines, Miss Arelano came to Stratford via hospitals in Ohio and Cornwall, Ont. After settling into the Ballantyne nurses residence, she said, "I feel the warmth of Canadian hospitality, and feel very much at home."

In 1966, the boiler, laundry and power facilities needed another upgrading. And renovations of the student quarters in Avon Crest were required, especially those for males, who had become part of the Stratford nursing scene in 1962. The jobs of nursing assistants and ward aides were redefined; no longer were they considered part of the housekeeping staff.

During Canada's centennial year, 1967, government money was available for a variety of capital building projects. Some of it – about $178,000 – came to SGH for the construction of a two-storey, eight-unit 20-bed staff residence on the northwest corner of John and West Gore streets, behind the nurses residence that was built in 1929. On each floor there were four fully furnished apartments, two with three bedrooms and two with two. Each unit was equipped with a sliding door that opened onto a balcony or small patio, and out back were a tennis court and swimming pool. According to Richard Brigg, assistant administrator at SGH, the residence was built because the scarcity of housing for staff was affecting the hospital's ability to hire new people. Centennial House was officially opened in June 1968, and its first tenant was Eng Stew Tan, a 22-year-old Malaya-born physiotherapist who had studied in Ireland. That fall, rent for one of the two-bedroom apartments was $95 per person per month.

In 1968 the Ontario Health Department established the emergency health service, to improve, among other things, ambulance service throughout the province. Ambulances were to be available around the clock, and training programs were started for ambulance attendants, hospital personnel and emergency medical volunteer groups. Under the Ambulance Act of 1968-1969, all ambulance services, public and private, fell within government authority and were administered by the Ontario Hospital Services Commission.

Late in August 1968, the new Perth-Huron Regional School of Nursing, to the north and east of the hospital, at the corner of St. Vincent Street South and Cambria Street, was accommodating its first 49 students – eight of them from Stratford.

Administration of the hospital fell to new hands on St. Patrick's Day, 1969, the date Robert J. Cameron, a native of Saint John, N.B., officially replaced Jack Bateman. Bateman, in Stratford since 1950, left to become administrator of the Joseph Brant Hospital in Burlington.

The 39-year-old Cameron had a bachelor's degree in business administration and a diploma in hospital administration. He came to Stratford from Kirkland Lake, where he had been the administrator at the 165-bed Kirkland and District Hospital for 10 years. Before that he had been assistant to the administrator at the Moncton Hospital in Moncton, N.B., for three years.

Two years into Cameron's reign at Stratford – which lasted until October 1990 – the title of the top job at SGH was changed from administrator to executive director. It was changed to chief executive officer with the hiring of Cameron's successor. While the CEO designation has long existed in the corporate world, it was not until the 1980s that it was adopted in the area of hospital administration. Cameron is among those who say that title accurately describes the top administrative position in hospitals.

In 1969 the hospital's laundry was expanded and further automated, as was the boiler room and water softening equipment. A new substation, to meet increased electrical needs, was built. There was a new bedside TV system that

Signs of Stratford General

Few people in Stratford don't know where Stratford General Hospital is – at least few among those who live in Stratford. But it's the city's annual influx of visitors that got SGH officials concerned about better visibility. Two instances in the early 1970s brought the matter to a head. As former executive director Bob Cameron recalls, they unfolded like this:

"A man driving his car did not feel well and drove around until he found the emergency entrance doorway. He apparently had a heart attack. He pushed down on the gas pedal and the car shot forward through the iron-pipe railing at the top of the retaining wall,

DEAN ROBINSON

where it got hung up, overhanging the 20-foot drop to the pavement below. The engine was roaring and the wheels spinning. The staff managed to get the driver out of the car and into the emergency department, but his time and chance had passed.

"Shortly thereafter, another driver who felt he might be having a heart attack drove up to the front door and

staggered into the lobby, where staff immediately recognized his stress. They summoned the necessary emergency staff who took him to the emergency department, treated him and, in due course, sent him home well. When asked why he had gone to the main door and not to emergency, his response was that he did not know where it was. He was a stranger in town and knew only the general location of the hospital. He drove west on Cambria Street, and when he saw the building he headed for the nearest door.

"Those two experiences started us thinking of the necessity of a few signs around the hospital, which up until then had been only over the main door. We put up several more signs to point the way to different units of the hospital, There were a few cries that it was a waste of money, because everyone in town knew where the hospital was and didn't need signs. And strangers could ask directions from any local person. However, by then the signs were erected.

"We never did figure how or where to erect a big blue and white H (for hospital) at a sensible place and at a sensible cost. The provincial highways ministry erected H's on all roads leading to the hospital, and we heard of no further incidents involving people unable to find the hospital when they were in urgent need."

incorporated headphones. There was also a new garage for the ambulance service that was added that year.

In 1970, in response to a request by staff, Avon Crest was renamed the Rehabilitation and Extended Care Unit (RECU). Employees in the building said there was an undeserved stigma attached to Avon Crest, that the public regarded it as a place where the elderly waited out the inevitable. In fact, they said, many patients were being rehabilitated and discharged.

As of 1970 the SGH laboratory was no longer a public health lab. Instead, it had become an inter-hospital lab, offering its services to the hospitals in Goderich, Seaforth and Clinton. The service grew in popularity and with it the list of hospitals and clinics wanting to use it. Six days a week a contract courier picked up test samples across Perth and Huron counties.

In 1970 a second generator was installed at SGH, and the heat source for the boilers was switched to natural gas. There were also some renovations in the dietary department. By now the hospital was completely departmentalized and again had full accreditation in the eyes of the provincial Health Ministry. Staff meetings were replaced by department meetings. There were 70 general practitioners and specialists on the active and courtesy staff, and in 1970 they treated 7,271 patients at SGH. By now a ward bed was being billed out at $63.50 a day. Semi-private beds were going for $67.50 and private for $72.50. Those rates were inclusive, and covered the costs of X-rays, operations, childbirth, drugs, physiotherapy, lab tests, intensive care, and the like.

In May 1970, the Toronto firm of Agnew, Peckham and Associates was hired to do a

A westerly view of SGH, from St. Vincent Street, after construction of the Perth-Huron Regional School of Nursing, out of the photo to the right.

role study, to update SGH's master program and master plan – something required by the ministry before there could be any redevelopment. By now the existing facilities were again deemed to be inadequate.

In 1971 the SGH school of nursing held its last graduation exercises, and the Perth-Huron regional school held its first.

In 1972 the board reduced its consecutive annual terms from five years to two for the offices of president, vice-president and committee chairs. It also approved expenditures for new equipment in the X-ray department, a new special procedures room, a new incubator in the pathology department, and a new elevator in the RECU.

Financial constraints forced the closure of 23 beds in the south wing of the third floor in 1973. That was a year in which the X-ray department was renovated. It was also the year in a which a psychiatric services department was opened. Its offerings included a day-care centre under the direction of Dr. William Tobin.

On Sept. 1, 1973, the Ontario Ministry of Colleges and Universities announced the transfer of all diploma nursing programs from hospitals to community colleges. For the Perth-Huron regional school that college was Conestoga, whose main campus was at Doon (Kitchener). Conestoga rented classroom space from SGH, and its students continued to gain clinical experience in the hospital. The college struck similar deals at five other hospitals, in Kitchener-Waterloo, Guelph and Cambridge.

There were a number of developments at SGH in 1974, but in terms of publicity they all paled against the labour unrest that dominated the summer months. About 10,000 graduate nurses across the province were upset with what they felt was minimal differential between their pay scale and that of registered nursing assistants. In late June – about a month before a July strike date –

nurses from 39 hospitals, including Stratford, set up an information picket line in Toronto. As of September 1974, RNAs were to be earning $9,276 a year. Graduate nurses had been offered $10,680, effective September 1975. "Why go to school and take all the extra training and take all the extra responsibility an RN must take when you could take on no responsibility after 10 months of training?" asked Jean Aitcheson, president of the Stratford local of the Ontario Nurses Association. "They (RNAs) must actually work under the supervision of an RN, and it's the RN who takes responsibility for the patient."

On June 27, Aitcheson and her colleagues voted unanimously to join a provincewide strike on July 22 if no wage settlement was reached. "Strike talk is really premature," said Bob Cameron, executive director at SGH. "Negotiations are still open, and I doubt that it will go that far." Under the Ontario Hospital Arbitration Act it was illegal for nurses to strike. At the same time, Health Minister Frank Miller was saying his government's restraints on the budgets of Ontario hospitals would not adversely affect the dispute. Miller told the legislature that imposed spending limits "will not interfere with bargaining, nor will I." He said he was optimistic about the chances of a settlement.

In mid-July the dispute became a little more public as RNs set up picket lines at members' hospitals across the province. Locally, about 30 off-duty association members marched in front of SGH carrying signs to support their negotiators in Toronto. Some of the signs read "Dedication won't feed my children." The ONA was seeking salaries and benefits to match an arbitration award made to 1,000 nurses at Ottawa Civic Hospital in June. The vice-president of the ONA local in Stratford, Nancy Kennedy, said the marchers were part of "a peaceful demonstration to show our support."

With the strike date less than a week away, a tentative agreement was reached – similar to the Ottawa arbitration award – and members of the Stratford local voted their acceptance on July 22. Wayne Keddy, assistant director at SGH, said the deal affected about 130 full-time nurses and another 98 working part time, and that it would increase hospital costs by about $600,000. After settling their differences on two items within the contract, the agreement was signed by nurses and hospital representatives on Aug. 26.

Nurses were not the only disgruntled SGH employees in the summer of '74. Late in June about 260 members of the Canadian Union of Public Employees (CUPE), Local 424, turned down the board's wage offer of $1.50-an-hour increase, for a two-year contract that would have been retroactive to January 1974. By September 1975 they would have been earning $4.33 an hour. The workers were after an increase of $1.67 an hour, which would have given them parity with similar employees in Toronto. SGH board chairman B. J. (Bo) Sibold said, "I think the 17 cents represents a fair difference in living costs between here and Toronto. I was rather disappointed that CUPE turned it down. It's difficult for me to understand. I think the offer was very, very fair, and that's the only amount the minister (of health) is prepared to back us on. There is no money in the kitty to increase it." That was the amount, too, that the board approved for its 100-or-so non-union workers – therapists, some clerical staff, lab and X-ray technologists and supervisory staff. In addition to wage parity with Toronto workers, CUPE members were seeking a job security clause so, as Patrick O'Donovan, head of local 424, put it, "union members will not lose jobs through the hospital contracting out services done by the employees."

The CUPE local, representing kitchen workers, nursing aids, registered nursing assistants, cleaners, maids, ambulance operators and other non-professional staff, voted to go on strike July 22, the same date chosen by the nurses.

At about the time of the nurses' tentative agreement, the CUPE workers postponed their strike date until locals at 18 other hospitals could hold strike votes. "We are going to co-ordinate our efforts with the other hospitals," said O'Donovan. "They are holding strike votes now, and until they're completed no definite date can be set." By the end of July a strike date was set – Sept. 2, and CUPE said more than 5,000 workers at 13 Ontario hospitals were prepared to take part. A few weeks later workers at five other hospitals had voted to join the walkout. Workers at 16 of the 18 hospitals were prepared to accept the $1.50-an-hour increase authorized by the Ministry of Health, but those at SGH and at the New Liskeard unit of Timiskaming General balked because, they said, it wasn't enough to give them parity with colleagues at the other hospitals. They said they were behind the others because of previous contracts that had been negotiated locally.

On Aug. 30, Justice Allan Goodman granted SGH a four-day injunction to prevent its CUPE workers from striking. The ruling followed a presentation of arguments prepared for the hospital by Keddy and a team of lawyers who worked through the night. Bob Cameron says, "Keddy was incensed over the prospect of a strike in a general hospital." He told the court that a strike by the non-medical workers would shut down the hospital. Cameron also says it was the first time such an injunction had been issued to delay or ward off an illegal strike in an essential public service.

Also on Aug. 31, the Friday before the Labour Day weekend, Cameron and O'Donovan met but they could come to no agreement. With the injunction in place, on Sunday O'Donovan appealed to union members to report to work as scheduled, which they did. But because no settlement was reached, the injunction was renewed, and renewed, and renewed. Trevor Smith, a mediator with the Ontario Labour Relations Board, joined the talks, which continued on an on-again-off-again basis. On Sept. 13 the hospital tabled what it called its final offer. On Sept. 19 the workers voted to accept that offer. It gave 40-hour-a-week workers an increase of $1.50 an hour and 37.5-hour-a-week workers an increase of $1.60 in a contract that ran to Dec. 31. 1975. It contained no job security clause.

By 1974, wages and salaries represented more than 71 per cent of SGH's $5.5 million in expenditures. After a deficit of $14,000 in 1972, the hospital reported a surplus of $43,000 in its 1973 fiscal year. But board members were forced to wait for that information because financial statements were not prepared in time for their 1974 annual meeting on April 10. The meeting was suspended until June 27, and when it resumed, auditors Monteith and Monteith and Co. were reappointed as long as they could ensure the 1974 report would be ready by March 31, 1975.

The elevator for the RECU, approved in 1972, was completed in 1974. In May of that year the average length of stay for patients at SGH was 6.9 days, the lowest ever, and the first time it had ever gone below seven days. Still, activity at the hospital was about 20 per cent above the predicted level, and the operating budget was stretched by a corresponding amount. On June 3 the hospital started a day-surgery program and was treating about five patients a day for things such as tooth extraction and nail (finger and toe) removal. It was the year, too, when the hospital had to replace 18 of its 42 electric kettles because they were declared lead hazards in tests done to federal government standards. Also in 1974, Nancy Wilson was named director of psychological services, and a speech pathology department was established under the direction of Joan Szymberski.

Still in 1974, some rooms on the top floor of the RECU were allocated for the establishment of a speech therapy clinic, which began part-time operation in June. A first-of-its-kind in Ontario, the experimental-type satellite clinic became full time Sept. 1, 1974, by which time it had treated 81 people (up to the age of 19), and another 15 were on a waiting list. The clinic was under the direction of therapist Margaret Ellis, who transferred from the London Crippled Children's Centre in London, which was in charge of the Stratford operation. It was Bob Miller who had pushed for the clinic. Since the mid-1960s, he and fellow Stratford Rotarians had long been driving Perth County children to the LCCC, as well as to Kitchener, for treatment. Through what Miller now calls "that underground taxi," he learned that most of the passengers were seeking speech therapy. So, in the early '70s, he began lobbying health and education officials, and politicians, to set up a speech clinic in Stratford. It was a lengthy process, fully supported by the London centre. There was hope the service could be extended into Perth County with a specially equipped van. Indeed, the Rotarians expressed an interest in funding the cost of such a vehicle, which in the end was not a practical idea.

On July 1, 1976, the hospital assumed full control of the speech therapy clinic and its caseload of about 100. Also at this time, Ellis left the clinic for a job in Winnipeg, and she was replaced by Szymberski.

The south wing of the third floor was reopened in 1975 for obstetrics and gynecology. However, the south wing on the fourth floor was closed, and orthopedic patients were moved to the north wing of the third floor. The ministry turned down SGH's application to reopen 23 beds as an orthopedic unit.

Approval was received for an inpatient psychiatric unit in 1975, when the psychiatric hospital in Goderich was closed. A diabetic teaching program was also initiated at SGH. As well, it was the inaugural year for the Volunteen Program, for which teenagers were recruited to help in various wards – with meals, Sundae Mondays, pet therapy, the strawberry social, summer barbecues, shopping trips, nature walks and one-to-one visits. Some were also involved with the physiotherapy and occupational therapy programs in what is now called the chronic care and rehabilitation unit. But, as the hospital's number of extended-care beds declined, so did the number of teen volunteers and the variety of their duties. The program is now called Teen Volunteers, and, mostly, its members still assist with meals and visit patients in the rehabilitation unit. In the summer, two or three occasionally help in the leisure recreation program.

In 1975-76 the former nurses residence was renovated to house the psychiatric day-care centre, other psychiatric and psychology services, social workers, speech pathologists and the home care program. It became known as the Special Services Unit.

There were more labour problems in 1976. The Ontario Public Service Employees Union applied to the Ontario Labour Relations Board for certification to represent the lab and X-ray technologists at SGH. It wanted all college and university graduates in its bargaining unit. Some employees, on the other hand, expressed an interest in joining the Allied Health Services Union. When SGH made it known it was not interested in dealing with that many bargaining units, the LRB called a hearing – which lasted almost two years. In the end, the number of units was restricted, and most of the bargaining continued to be done on a provincewide basis.

Also in 1976, SGH applied to have the word "corporation" dropped from its

Dr. W. M. (Mac) Gilmore, 1946

official name, a request that was approved in 1977. As well, an 18-bed psychiatric unit was approved for an area of the south wing of the second floor that had been closed. Renovations began April 1, 1977, and the unit was opened Dec. 5, 1977.

As discussions about collective bargaining for the various hospital unions continued in 1977, so did talks with the Health Ministry about budget cuts. There was a recommendation to update the emergency department, and moves to establish summer internships in a number of departments.

Queen's Jubilee medals were presented in 1977 and four well-known SGH employees received them: Dr. William Macauley (Mac)

Dr. Bob Bissonnette, 1968

Gilmore, Dr. Robert N. (Bob) Bissonnette, Helen (Mrs. Luxton B.) Thuell and Miss Margaret Murr.

Gilmore had practically built the hospital's radiology department from scratch, and was also in charge of the urology and cancer treatment units.

The son of a well-known educator, Bob Bissonnette was just as well known as a general practitioner, pilot and boating enthusiast. For many years, he also served as physician for the Stratford jail.

Margaret Murr, 1940

Lux Thuell, 1968

Helen Thuell's husband Lux ran the hospital's laundry department for many years. He retired after 48 years of service – an employment record at SGH. Indeed, as a widow in 1977, Helen accepted the jubilee medal reluctantly; she said it should have gone to her husband. But her service in the laundry department was just as impressive, though not recorded as such because for many years she was a part-time employee.

Murr enrolled in the SGH nursing school in 1938 and, after a few years in private duty as a graduate nurse, she returned to the hospital, where she stayed until retirement in January 1984. In a SGH career of just less than four decades, she was a nurse, an administrator, a teacher and, for the last 11 years, the employees' health services nurse.

In 1978 the hospital changed its fiscal year to run from April 1 to March 31 to coincide with those of the provincial and federal governments. It also managed to reach labour agreements with all its unions except the Ontario Nursing Association. With the ONA it was waiting for settlements in Toronto and Kingston, for something that might establish a precedent.

The study by Agnew, Peckham and Associates was completed and presented to SGH officials in 1978. It outlined programs and reconstruction plans that would carry the hospital 10 to 15 years down the health-care road.

For the immediate future, however, those officials hired a management firm to look at the administrative side of the SGH operation and to come up with some suggestions that would make it more cost effective. They also endorsed expansion of outpatient and emergency facilities and renovation of the nursing facilities in the acute care unit. And they determined that the RECU was no longer suitable for rehab and extended care and that facilities required to care for patients needing those services be built adjacent to the acute care unit.

SGH's engagement of a management firm was music to the ears of the Health Ministry, which wanted all hospitals to hire consultants who could come up with cost savings. In Stratford, that task fell to Naus and Newlyn, an Erie, Penn., company whose principals claimed they could save any hospital 15 per cent of its payroll costs with no loss in the quality of service. They said the savings for SGH would be more than $400,000, and guaranteed their claim to the extent that their fee would not exceed the savings, whatever they were, as determined by the hospital accountants. The Stratford board and the ministry were eager to see if N and N could deliver on its promises.

For nearly a year the firm conducted a management training program, designed to show managers how to accurately measure the amount of work to be done and how to calculate the number of employees required to do it. Nothing was imposed on hospital personnel except the method of studying workload requirements. In the end, all departments except two were able to reduce staff costs, and the hospital began to save hundreds of thousands of operating dollars annually. "The staff worked a lot harder, but quality was maintained," says Cameron. "Savings came about by the attrition of full-time staff, reduced overtime, and reduced part-time hours. In order not to lose the benefit of the study and instruction over the years, the hospital contracted for a representative of the company to come to the hospital one day per year to monitor the continuing application of the program, to reinforce the lessons learned, and to instruct new supervisory staff in these techniques. The hospital continued to be one of the most efficient in the province based upon cost-per-patient-day."

Eventually the hospital computerized the system in some departments, notably nursing. It was used to determine staffing levels on each nursing unit, each shift, each day. The determination began with the staff on the unit assigning a numerical category to each patient, to identify the amount of nursing care required on the next shift. Thus, staffing levels were determined by the staff working on the individual nursing unit in accordance with a previously, and jointly, determined set of criteria. The numbers were fed into the computer two or three times a day, as required by the work schedule, and the unit was staffed according to the results. If more staff were scheduled than needed, the extra would be reassigned to other units, which were short. To help cover shortages, the position of "float nurse" was created, and filled by those with long and varied experience. The float nurse, it was reasoned, should be able to perform well, on short notice, in any unit.

Cameron says the system, which could be overridden by nurse supervisory staff in the event of unforeseen situations, worked well at SGH. But, he says, ministry officials liked it only when it revealed a unit was overstaffed. "They could not agree to the reverse, that is, if the computer said another nurse was needed and should be added," says Cameron. "That's when they said, `No one staffs a nursing department by computer.' To which we replied, `Stratford General does, and if the computer program can tell us when to reduce staff, it can tell us when to increase it when needed. It's a two-way street.' We had expectations of eventually marketing the system to other hospitals and generating revenue for our hospital. But that goal proved evasive and elusive, a real loss to the industry, for it was an effective and accurate non-confrontational method of arbitrating a sensitive issue."

In 1978 the hospital spent $69,840 for an ultrasonic grey-scale diagnostic machine for the X-ray department. And it agreed to dispatch a team of specialists to Listowel to provide partial psychiatric day care and consultative services. If those were considered progressive steps, they were out of line with what the Health Ministry did for SGH in 1978: namely, reduce its beds from 188 to 177 and decree that number be down to 166 by April 1, 1981.

In 1979, members of the SGH board met with Health Ministry officials to discuss the budget constraints imposed by the government. It was suggested by the ministry that SGH hire management consultants and have them recommend where and how severe the cutbacks should be at the hospital. In any event the board decided that in May it would close 10 beds in the north wing of the third floor and use that space for outpatient day surgery.

It also decided to establish a new department, specifically a medical staff unit that would oversee the RECU. Dr. David Williams was named the department head. By now, ultrasound service was available in radiology, and the hospital received $75,000 from the Rotary Club of Stratford to help pay for the necessary equipment.

Health Minister Dennis Timbrell toured the RECU in 1979 and declared, to no one's surprise, that the facilities needed upgrading. He said SGH would be placed on the government's list of hospitals that were in line for capital renovation funds,

which were expected to be available in the mid-1980s.

In 1980 more beds were closed, this time in the west wing of the third floor. As well, a director of volunteers was appointed.

In January 1981 about 100 of the 230 members of Local 424 of the Canadian Union of Public Employees at SGH opted to take part in a two-day provincewide illegal strike, while their leaders continued to negotiate with Ontario Hospital Association officials in Toronto. The workers, unhappy with the OHA's demands for binding arbitration, had staged two information pickets in front of SGH. The walkout, which officially started in Stratford at 5 a.m. Jan. 29, affected about 40 Ontario hospitals.

At Stratford it forced closure of the 24-bed wing known as 4 South, a medical ward for patients not requiring surgery. Patients in 4 South were moved to beds that became available when about 35 patients – 10 to 15 more than the daily norm – were discharged. As well, scheduled operations at the hospital were reduced from the usual 15 or 16 a day to just four or five. And only emergency cases were being admitted to

SGH. As far as working staff members were concerned, they dealt only with essential duties. At the RECU, patients were cared for by part-time registered nursing assistants, who were not CUPE members, and by part-time registered nurses who were called in for extra duty.

On the second day of the walkout, picketing in Stratford began at 6 a.m., just a few hours before Justice J. D. Cromarty of the Supreme Court of Ontario granted an injunction which ordered the workers back to their jobs, at least until Feb. 6. "We've been expecting it (the injunction) all week," said Pat O'Donovan, president of Local 424. Still, he said, "I figure we gained something by the pressure we put on the OHA." O'Donovan was referring to reports that the OHA, which represented 65 of Ontario's 235 hospitals, had increased its wage offer. The Stratford workers voted to obey the injunction. Early in February the hospital reopened 4 South.

The hospital also levied suspensions against 106 CUPE members for their parts in the illegal walkout. Ninety-eight employees were given one-day suspensions. Four others were given two days and four

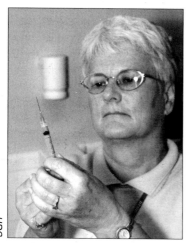

Nurse Gerry Wilhelm, now the regional co-ordinator occupational health and infection control.

others three days. SGH said the suspensions were to be arranged by department heads at the convenience of the department. CUPE grieved the suspensions, and they remained unresolved until late in March, when provincial Labour Ministry officials negotiated an eight-point agreement. The settlement, reached about a week before the matter was to go to arbitration, reduced the three-day suspensions to two and the two-day suspensions to one. The 98 one-day suspensions were upheld. As well, record of the suspensions was to be removed from the employees' personnel files within 24 months from the time the suspensions were issued. "I think we came off relatively light compared to other hospitals," said O'Donovan. He was referring to outright dismissals and suspensions of up to 10 days for workers who struck illegally at other Ontario hospitals. "I don't think the membership expected miracles. They were prepared to accept the consequences," he said.

A few months later, an arbitrator resolved the contract dispute between the hospitals and the union.

As they did in 1977, off-duty nurses at SGH staged a one-day information picket in October 1981 to protest a situation that had left them without a contract since Oct. 1, 1980. "People are madder now than they were earlier," said Gerry Wilhelm, president of Local 23 of the Ontario Nurses Association. "We go to arbitration, follow all the rules and we get stuck again." More than 100 issues, common to 134 hospitals in Ontario, had been in the hands of an arbitrator since March.

In non-labour news in 1981, the RECU held its first annual staff-patients barbecue. And volunteers were recruited to assist with occupational therapy and in the pediatric wards. As well, SGH hired Pat Hopwood as its director of volunteer services. After more than 20 years in that role, she retired in November 2002.

A flag for all seasons

The 50-foot (15-metre) galvanized flagpole that was erected in the circular lawn in front of Stratford General Hospital was paid for by a donation from someone who wished to remain anonymous. The donation also covered the purchase of a nine-foot (2.7-metre) Union Jack that was first raised by Harold W. Strudley, former chairman of the hospital's board, on Nov. 12, 1954.

Bob Cameron says one of the first things he noticed when he took over as administrator of the hospital in March 1969 was that a flag was never raised on the pole.

"When I asked about this I was told there was no one to do this chore," recalls Cameron. "One staff member, grateful for

Harold W. Strudley, chairman of the board 1939-1952

the opportunity to live the remainder of his life in Canada, volunteered to come in early and raise the flag in the ceremonial fashion he had been taught in the army of his homeland. Another staff member volunteered to lower it daily on his way home, at supper time. That arrangement

lasted for months until one of them tired of it, and it stopped. So I suggested it be flown all the time in spite of the protocol that says not to fly it in the dark without a light on it. Finally, a scheme was devised to light it at night in spite of the great push to conserve energy."

Snowmobile enthusiasts have often come to the aid of the hospital when winter storms have made normal modes of travel impossible. Snowmobilers have logged hundreds of hours transporting employees, and occasionally patients, to and from SGH. It was during one such emergency situation, in the early 1970s, that the hospital's flag served as more than patriotic ornamentation. Cameron says he was in the lobby of the hospital, as snowmobile operators were summoned and dispatched. During a lull in the activity he noticed a female employee come through the main door alone.

"I rushed over to her and inquired as to where she had come from," says Cameron, "for no snowmobile or other vehicle had approached the hospital. `Oh,' she said, breathlessly, `I walked from home. It was not too bad until I got to the corner of St. Vincent and West Gore. I started across the open field to the front door of the hospital. I got halfway across when the wind blew so hard it caused a whiteout and I couldn't see the hospital anymore. I didn't know which way to walk. I stood still and I could hear the metal rings on the ends of the rope of the flagpole banging against the metal pole. So I walked in the direction of the noise, and I got to the front door. But if it were not for that flag I'd be out there yet walking in circles in the snow.'"

When the winds of January and February blew like that in Cameron's days, many SGH employees took overnight bags to work rather than risk trying to get home and not be able to return the next day. They

The flagpole in 2002.

slept in the residences, in empty patient beds, at the homes of colleagues who lived close to the hospital, on exercise mats in physiotherapy – wherever there was a comfortable, quiet spot. "Without this extraordinary effort of the staff and friends of the hospital, staffing at the hospital would not have been possible," says Cameron. "The military offered their support with four-wheel-drive vehicles, ambulances and communications equipment. The public works departments of both the city and province provided snowplow backup, if needed, to assist an ambulance to reach its destination. The co-operation and support of the entire community was excellent and appreciated by all members of the staff, who were made to feel their efforts were important to the citizens – as indeed they were."

Strong winds in the early 1980s were almost too much for the venerable flagpole. During a morning coffee break in the cafeteria, says Cameron, he was joined by

the hospital's director of maintenance, who proceeded to tell him how the flagpole had been fixed. Not knowing there had been anything wrong with the pole, Cameron said, "That's great, but what happened to it, and how did you fix it? `Didn't you know?' said the man. `The wind blew so hard last night it bent the pole over about 10 or 15 feet from the bottom, until the top half was parallel with the ground. To straighten it we got a truck with a boom on it, fastened the top end of the pole to the end of the boom, raised the boom, and straightened the pole as much as we could. Then we lined up the pole, the boom and the truck, put the truck in gear, and pulled the pole until it was straight again. We were afraid that pulling on the pole might break it off at the bend point, but it didn't. Then we took two pieces of steel rails or bars three or four feet long and bolted and welded them over the point where the pole bent.' A little aluminium paint and the repair was complete."

Campaigns and cutbacks

In 1981 Stratford General Hospital made an expansion-renovation pitch to Health Minister Dennis Timbrell that called for replacement of the 90 beds in the RECU and the establishment of a 60-bed nursing home. The price tag had not been determined. In October 1981 the proposal was revised, and the hospital asked the government to pay for two-thirds of the cost of an 86-bed rehabilitation unit and renovation of the 190-bed acute-care facilities. It was to be a long-term project and cost about $12 million. The nursing home, it had been decided by then, would be financed through local fund-raising. Government response was typically slow, and made slower no doubt by a cabinet shuffle in which Larry Grossman replaced Timbrell as health minister in February 1982.

In January 1982 hospital officials interviewed architects for its proposed changes even though no official provincial approval had been received. Eventually they settled on plans submitted by the Toronto firm of Zeidler Roberts Partnership, a company whose credits included the Eaton Centre, Ontario Place, McMaster University Medical Centre and a number of other hospitals. The ZRP plans included a $3.3-million safety upgrade of existing facilities. After dispatching a consultant to survey the hospital and make recommendations, the government agreed to grant $1.25 million for safety improvements. Zeidler Roberts was engaged by SGH to make the changes.

By this time the Women's Hospital Auxiliary had changed its name to the Hospital Auxiliary Association of Stratford General Hospital. And it pledged $250,000 to SGH's building fund, over five years.

There were now about 100 doctors tending to patients in 294 beds (100 of them at the RECU). It was estimated that the cost to open one new bed was running at about $100,000.

By March 1983 the hospital had in place the Stratford General Hospital Foundation, to accept and direct donations from the public for its most ambitious expansion

From left, dietary aid Judy Dietrich, orthopedic tech Brian Le Souder and sous-chef Claude Bernier, dressed for a Halloween day celebration in the early 1980s.

ever. To solicit those donations the hospital's fund-raising committee was reactivated the next year.

Also, by this time, the hospital's lab had been accredited by the College of American Pathologists – one of just a few labs in Canada able to boast of such distinction.

Amid all the talk of the hospital's renovation-expansion and its need to streamline services, there was some suggestion from the Health Ministry that patients requiring chronic care could be more economically served by the private sector. The board, under the chairmanship of Rev. Jim Williams, flatly rejected the notion of selling off the RECU. In May 1983 the board learned that the ministry was ready to assist in the replacement of the RECU.

A year later, the ministry said there was $6 million available to Stratford for the replacement of the RECU if SGH could come up with a like sum. Stratford officials took up the challenge and recruited their board chair, Williams, the priest at St. Joseph's Church, to head their fund-raising committee. They also recruited Jeff Preston, the well-known head of a family-owned office equipment supply company, to co-ordinate their campaign, which they decided would stretch over five years. The campaign slogan, they decided, would be For Your Health. For part of that campaign, one of the campaign co-ordinator's sons, Jim Preston, was chair of the hospital board.

On April 1, 1985, the health minister of the day, Alan W. Pope, visited the hospital. A month later his ministry approved the Stratford master plan, which outlined the size and use of every room to be built, and the relationship of those rooms with each other and with the facilities already in place at the hospital. But the ministry also denied a licence request from SGH to operate 30 nursing home beds. Instead, it granted that right to Hillside Nursing Home in nearby Mitchell.

As far as the day-to-day operation of SGH was concerned, a pet visitation program for shut-ins was initiated, and the home oxygen program was expanded. And an endoscopy room was set up and equipped for day surgery.

Williams and Preston were persuasive, and the community, for the most part, supportive. In relatively short order they had a pledge of $5 million from the City of Stratford. They secured the promise of another $3.5 million from local and area businesses, organizations and individuals. Initially, at least, they were counting on the provincial government for $6 million. From Perth County they had pencilled in $2.5 million – but that proved to be the toughest target of all, and one they could not meet.

The fund-raisers based their county request on statistics that indicated Perth residents outside Stratford accounted for about 40 per cent of the hospital's use. Their numbers did not impress all county councillors, among them Listowel Reeve Elsie Karges, who said the figure of $2.5 million was about $2 million too high.

The hospital's funding request was the subject of about two dozen votes at several county council sessions. It was debated privately and publicly, and prompted editorials and letters to the editor. Finally, on March 21, 1985, in a 17-16 vote, the councillors decided on a pledge of $1 million over 10 years.

"I think health care in Perth County has been dealt a very bad blow by this decision," said Williams. "If county council is telling us to wait for more money from the (health) ministry, they're wrong. I don't agree with that philosophy. I heard people stand before me and say quite openly that they agreed in theory and in principle with what we were doing – then they turn around and vote against it. Yesterday's vote does not represent the feelings of the people of the county. It might represent certain areas, but it does not represent overall opinion in the county. I'm not going to give up because of this decision."

The councillors also endorsed a suggestion by Karges that they no longer deal with hospital grants, that such requests be handled at the local level. As Wallace Reeve Hans Feldmann put it, asking the county to discuss a matter which is in the realm of municipalities and the province is like "trying to take the family car to the mill to pick up two tons of chop."

Meanwhile, fund-raising news from the hospital's auxiliary was far more favourable. Three days before the county made its decision, the auxiliary announced a pledge of $250,000 and said the total could run to $350,000 if its 285 members hit their target of $100,000, which had been established months earlier. As of mid-January 1985, 48 of those members had donated and pledged $30,000.

Even without all they had hoped for from the county, Williams and Preston rounded up close to $10 million in local money. That prompted Williams to think about other needs at the hospital, which included improvements in the emergency department and an upgrade of the fire safety systems that had been introduced over the years and was to become mandatory in 1988 under retrofit legislation. All the while, Williams wondered why other health-care bodies seemed to qualify for two-thirds funding while Stratford was limited to 50 per cent. At opportune times

Rev. Jim Williams

SGH

The house built in 1903 by Thomas Ballantyne, who donated it to the hospital as a nurses residence. It was demolished in 1985 to facilitate the building of a parking lot to the north of the original SGH.

he made that point with local and provincial officials. He also began to multiply the community-raised funds by a factor of three instead of two. Eventually the government agreed to fund two-thirds of an $18-million project that covered the replacement of the RECU and improvements to emergency facilities.

In June 1985 the hospital proposed a $25-million multi-phased renovation-redevelopment program for the acute-care section of the hospital, a program that would extend into the 1990s. It was also a program that would require Stratford officials to come up with $17 million.

In July, SGH submitted drawings to expand and update its outdated and overworked emergency department, which had served 27,000 patients in 1983. By then the minister of health was Murray Elston,

and he said his government would support that project for two-thirds of its cost, up to $200,000. The contract was awarded to Nith Valley Construction out of New Hamburg, and work began on May 12, 1986.

On Nov. 15, 1985, an arbitration ruling gave members of the Ontario Nurses Association a two per cent wage increase. It also awarded more pay for statutory holidays. That meant nurses working 12-hour shifts had to be paid for 12 hours for each of the year's 11 statutory holidays. When hospitals went to 12-hour shifts from seven-and-a-half-hour shifts in October 1982, they had continued to pay nurses for just seven and a half hours for statutory holidays.

The arbitrator decided nurses would have to be paid for another five and a half days each year. According to executive director Bob Cameron, for SGH that equated to a hike in the annual payroll of about $100,000. It was a hike the hospital elected to avoid by deciding that, as of Feb. 9, 1986, it was going to discontinue 12-hour shifts. The nurses, who preferred the longer shifts because they made possible consecutive days off and enabled them to live what they considered a more normal lifestyle, responded by threatening to withdraw about $100,000 in pledges to the hospital's building fund.

The two sides met in mid-December, but when there was no resolution, about 50 of the 250 nurses made good on their threat. The ONA followed through on its promise, too, by filing unfair labour practice charges against SGH and four other provincial hospitals. Just before Christmas, SGH withdrew the notice that would have returned the nurses to seven-and-a-half-hour shifts. Cameron said the hospital wanted clarification of what it felt was some ambiguity in the wording of the arbitration award. "After it is clarified, if most hospitals stay with a 12-hour shift, then Stratford will probably do the same," said

Cameron. That was positive news as far as the nurses were concerned. Gerry Wilhelm, president of Local 23 of the ONA, said, "We've won a battle but not the war." She said they were not withdrawing their grievance but they were putting it on hold while they awaited SGH's next move.

By the end of February, however, they had withdrawn their grievance, as well as the charges of unfair labour practice against SGH.

By Nov. 19, 1986, ambulances were able to pull up to a new and larger emergency entrance. Beyond the double set of automatic doors was an expanded reception-waiting area with offices for the head nurse and health nurse. The new facilities, which had cost $335,000, were officially opened Nov. 28 by Elston. On the same day, he also helped turn the first sod for construction of a new power plant, incinerator and chimney, expected to cost $1.2 million. Elston's ministry was to provide $333,000 of that money. Another $480,000 was to come from the provincial Environment Ministry and the rest from the SGH building fund. The Environment Ministry had been pressuring the hospital to upgrade its incinerator for about a decade, but a shortage of funds had always forced postponement of the project.

At about this time, SGH officials were also seeking a new ambulance. But because the ministry had by then gone to a cube-style van for its ambulances, the SGH ambulance garage was not large enough to house a new vehicle. In time it was decided that Stratford would get a new ambulance and a new garage, as designed by the ministry's ambulance services branch.

Stratford officials, at the urging of their medical staff, were also proposing the

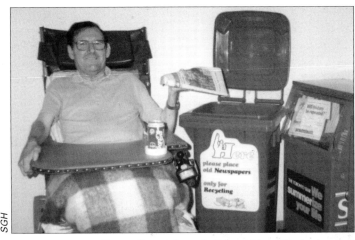

SGH

Longtime patient Bruce (Soup) Campbell does his bit in the interest of recycling at the hospital. He was at SGH from the mid-1980s to April 2001. Since then he has been a resident at Hillside Manor, at Seebach's Hill.

acquisition of a computerized axial tomography scanner, better known as a CAT or CT scanner. Technology had now made available the expensive tool, one that could help in the diagnosis of tumours and hemorrhages, and of structural problems in the back, brain, lungs, bronchi and pancreas. And, since 1977, provincial lotteries had made available some money that had been used for such tools. SGH thought itself ready for and deserving of such an innovation, but the ministry had reservations. In short, Stratford did not meet the ministry's criteria, which Stratford's CT committee argued were outdated. The ministry said SGH's population base was too small, it had no neurologist on staff, and no budget surplus to cover the scanner's operating costs.

By December the $17-million fund-raising goal had been reached but, for a variety of reasons, pledges of about $85,000 could not be collected. "Regardless of the committee or organization, you never collect 100 per cent of the pledges," conceded board chair Jim Preston. That left the Stratford-and-area part of the campaign short of its $11-million target. Some of the shortfall – about $8,500 –

was wiped out with the proceeds of a fund-raising dance at the Stratford Coliseum.

Shortfall or not, the local campaign had been successful beyond the expectations of most. It was a cause well understood and well supported. Said fund-raiser chairman Jim Williams on the eve of the door-to-door canvass: "When three small children walked into my office last August and gave me $1.25 from the sale of lemonade for our hospital campaign, I knew at that moment there was no turning back. The actual $1.25 was a far cry from the $17 million we had established as our goal, but it was the beginning of a continuous outpouring of generosity that I would experience from every sector of the community over the next eight months." The efforts of Williams and his committee were considerable, in step with a game plan that was downright bold. The SGH board chair in 1988 was Bob McTavish, who said, "During our first meetings with the ministry, a few of us almost fell off our chairs when Father Jim said we could raise $6 million locally. But, thanks to the people who dug deep in their pockets, we raised much more than that."

At about that time, the hospital revised its smoking regulations and banned the practice everywhere but in a section of the cafeteria and in the coffee shop, and in rooms where patients had been given letters of permission by their doctors.

In December 1987 the hospital and its nurses reached a negotiated settlement for a three-year contract that was to begin April 1, 1988. The deal was unusual in that a third party had not been required to arbitrate the terms, as had been necessary in a number of the previous talks.

Work on the power-plant phase of the redevelopment began in 1987 and was completed in the spring of 1988. In late-March 1988 construction was started on a $16.3-million three-storey, two-wing addition to the east and south of the hospital, to replace the RECU. The contractor was a familiar name in SGH history – Pigott Construction Ltd. of Hamilton. Plans called for a 33-bed extended-care nursing unit on the third floor in each wing, and a central area comprising lounges, a dining room, an exercise room and general-purpose rooms. The second floor on each wing was to be unfinished in the short term but become operational later in the development to serve medical and surgical patients. The first floor of the south wing was to be finished and house a 32-bed rehabilitation nursing unit for patients in more active rehabilitative programs. The first-floor location would allow patients easy access to an outdoor garden and lawn area, to be located between the old and new buildings.

The first floor of the east building was allocated for occupational therapy and physiotherapy, but budget cuts forced delay of its completion. A small surgical outpatient facility was also planned for the first floor of the west wing, as well as an ambulatory care unit where orthopedic and cancer clinics could be held. The budget cuts also determined the basements in each wing would go unfinished for the present, but that eventually they would be used for staff lockers, the personnel department, computer services and work rooms for volunteers and the hospital auxiliary. Both wings were to be connected to the original hospital by a corridor containing a reception area.

Health Minister Elinor Caplan was in Stratford on April 22, 1988, to share in sod-turning ceremonies for the addition with Jeff Preston. By then, construction was well underway, and Caplan told the crowd of about 150, "It looks like some gremlins got here before me." She also said, "In a short two years, in the spring of 1990, you'll have two beautiful three-storey wings on that site. And there's no question those facilities will greatly improve the hospital's capabilities." She also praised Williams:

Jeff Preston, 1988

"He's knocked on a lot of doors, and his persistence paid off." A long-held dream, she predicted, was soon to become a reality.

During her visit, Caplan was asked about Stratford's application to purchase a CT scanner. Her political response included: "When it comes to the purchase of expensive equipment, one of my concerns is the ability of a hospital to manage its operating costs. Since this hospital is one of 22 in the province with chronic operating deficits, we're looking at how to solve those problems first."

In addition to its plea for money for a CT scanner, SGH was also seeking an increase of $200,000 in its operating budget to cover the costs of running a pediatric neonatal unit. That request was made soon after Dr. Shamim Tejpar became the hospital's first staff pediatrician in almost two decades. For the last five of those 20 years SGH had been actively advertising the position. The ministry's immediate response to the application for more money was negative,

primarily, it said, because 20 other Ontario hospitals were providing neonatal care. But that set up a catch-22 situation, said Dr. Van Woolnough, because London hospitals were not anxious to take Stratford patients. "They're under as much financial pressure in London as we are but we can't get the funding to provide the services," said the Stratford family physician. "I can't understand these huge cutbacks in health funding when children's health is at stake."

Upon completion of the east building, SGH had about $5 million on deposit in treasury bills, to start its second phase of improvement – specifically a retrofit of the west (old) building for fire safety, and for acquisition of a CT scanner. Stratford had sought and received a two-year extension, from 1988 to February 1990, of its deadline for the retrofit. In February 1990 that deadline had to be extended again, this time to December 1992.

The hospital's fiscal position, its upgraded facilities and its improved services resulted in a $2.6-million increase in funding from the ministry, and an additional $509,000 because of the increased care rendered in 1989. Part of that money was directed to renovations of the obstetric and pediatric departments, which were completed in 1994.

Soon after the hospital's budget recovery plan had been approved by Caplan's ministry, SGH board members announced – on Feb. 23, 1989 – that a fund to acquire a CT scanner was officially in place. Until then, without ministry approval for the scanner, there had been only an unofficial campaign. A move to make the fund official was presented by finance committee chair Ken Hall, who said, "The motion will tell the community we're actively pursuing a CT scanner and is a soft way of telling the Ministry of Health that this community supports it and is willing to fund it." Some board members and executive director Bob Cameron questioned the timing of the motion. "This is the kind of thing they (ministry officials) can get annoyed at," said Cameron. "Maybe they won't work against you, but they might stop working for you. I'd wait another month or two, after we see the deputy minister or the minister herself."

Art vanWalraven, chief of the medical staff at SGH and an ex-officio member of the board, said the motion was not meant to pressure the ministry, but rather an attempt to obtain standard medical equipment for

Dr. Art vanWalraven, internist

the hospital. "There's nothing magical or unproven about a CT scanner," said the doctor. "It was new technology 20 years ago and 20 years ago is an extremely long time when you're talking about medical technology. We'll be falling behind if we don't obtain it. I think the people in this community need the kind of health care a CT scanner can provide; that is our motivation." He said an official fund would speed up the process of getting a scanner – making it possible for the hospital to

purchase one the day after ministry approval was received.

At the time the fund was made official, the scanner was expected to cost up to $1 million to purchase, and between $300,000 and $350,000 annually to operate – exclusive of professional fees, which would be billed through the Ontario Hospital Insurance Plan. In its unofficial state, the fund had managed to attract $340,000. When the ministry finally changed its criteria for funding CT scanners, Stratford was at the top of the list among those wanting one. Cameron says that while the hospital's repeated requests under the old guidelines fell on deaf ears, he's convinced Stratford's persistence led to changes in those criteria.

To help the official fund along, the hospital's foundation launched a campaign to raise $1.25 million. Actually, just $900,000 was to go towards the scanner. Of the remainder, $13,500 was for an incubator, $45,000 for four new electrocardiograph telemetry units, $45,000 for an electromyography machine and $11,500 for a second birthing machine. "With government constraint, most of the equipment is beyond our reach without private funding," said Dr. Doug Thompson, president of the foundation. "The equipment will help bring the hospital up to date, so our patients don't have to run all over the countryside for diagnosis and treatment."

In March 1989 the hospital's smoking policy was again revised. The main-floor area across the hall from the switchboard was declared off-limits to smokers. Smoking was still allowed in the cafeteria and in rooms where patients had been given written permission by their doctors.

In May 1989, Fanshawe College in London began sending respiratory therapy students to Stratford for clinical training at SGH. A year later, one of those students, Michelle Steckly, received the highest marks in the provincial registration exams and won several awards in the process.

Also, in 1989, board members awarded a $602,000 contract to D. W. Lorentz Construction Inc. of St. Agatha for the building of a three-bay ambulance garage. The project, to be two-thirds funded by the provincial government, was to include training facilities for ambulance attendants, locker rooms for male and female attendants, an office, a kitchen, an exhaust system, an air intake system, air conditioning, improved sewer system, a central vacuum system, an intercom to the hospital, a public address system, and a computer and radio system linking Stratford to a dispatch agency in London. "Some thought the hospital might have settled for a little less building," says Cameron, "but the design was set by those charged with providing an integrated provincial ambulance service." By judicious location of the new garage, the costs had to include between $75,000 and $100,000 to replace the retaining wall near the hospital's incinerator on John Street. Had the construction package not included money for the wall, which had taken on a precarious lean, the hospital might have had to pay for its replacement without government financial assistance. The price tag also covered the construction of storage space for a tractor, a wagon and snow removal equipment. Work began May 1, by which time the three-storey, double-wing addition to the hospital was about 65 per cent completed.

Also on May 1, 1989, parking fees were introduced at SGH. Visitors began to pay $1 each time they exited controlled-entry lots. There were no charges for taxi drop-offs or for handicapped parking. And the lots just east of John Street remained reserved for employees and medical staff though they were now required to buy parking passes for $10 a month. "The board, after careful deliberation, felt generating additional revenue by this means is preferable to

cutting service or staff to help balance our budget," said Cameron.

Almost immediately, visitors and patients for the hospital's clinics created a run on the 18 free parking spaces outside the entrance to the emergency department. The hospital responded by announcing it would tow any vehicles parked there illegally.

Also about that time, it was decided that staff and physicians at the hospital should wear photo identification badges, in an effort to restrict the access and movement of unauthorized personnel.

Telephone service was now available in 150 of the hospital's rooms, which cost about $22,000 to install. It was estimated it would cost a further $2,600 a month to operate, but that the phones would generate about $35,000 in revenue each year for SGH. Patients were to be charged $5 for hookup plus $1 a day for the first 14 days and 65 cents a day thereafter. Outgoing calls would require patients to reverse the charges or use a credit card.

Late in May the hospital board budgeted for an operating surplus for the first time in four years – specifically $71,000. Its grant from the province for 1989-90, $25,340,000, was up four per cent over the previous year.

In late summer 1989 the Health Ministry approved a grant of $290,087 for the establishment of a psychogeriatric assessment clinic in the Special Services Unit at SGH. It was estimated that the clinic would handle 300 patients annually, with 35 in active treatment at any one time. The money came 11 years after the hospital first applied for it.

A medical manpower plan approved by SGH in October 1989 satisfied the Ministry of Health, which required it as part of the hospital's financial recovery plan, but it won no friends among the medical staff. The plan called for no reductions to the staff but it required a cost-impact analysis be done before any new doctors were hired. "We prefer to let the marketplace determine the number of physicians, not the ministry," said Dr. Paul Weir. Colleague Steve Marchuk added, "The government is limiting the access of patients to the health-care system by limiting the number of physicians."

Bob Cameron suffered a stroke on Nov. 27, 1989 – four days before the official opening of SGH's $18.7 million Phase I redevelopment project, something he'd worked towards for two decades. While he recovered in Victoria Hospital in London, the health minister and a handful of other politicians and dignitaries were among about 500 gathered at SGH for the ribbon-cutting ceremony. As Caplan praised the efforts of those who had helped make the dream come true, she cautioned that Phase II "won't happen as quickly as we would like. It's important to make sure we plan well in these changing times and get the best advice we can. We can't always give everyone everything they want but we try to respond with what they need." In Cameron's absence, the hospital administration was represented by Terry Fadelle, assistant executive director.

On Valentine's Day 1990, Cameron was among 28 patients who were moved from the RECU and became charter patients of Unit 1 South in the hospital's new east building. The remaining 98 patients were moved over in the next three weeks as the completion of construction

allowed. The areas housing those patients was renamed the continuing care and rehabilitation unit.

In March 1990 the hospital offered its first pre-surgery education classes, to familiarize children and their parents with scheduled surgery procedures. "We really believe that the more they know and see, the better prepared they are," said Lynn Strugnell, assistant director of nursing at SGH. The Sunday afternoon classes, which included videos and tours, grew in popularity, and in December of that year the hospital added a similar program for adults.

In June 1990 the hospital stepped closer to a smoke-free environment by banning smoking in its cafeteria. It also decided to close 35 beds for three months to help generate a $539,188 operating surplus for 1990-91 – its second surplus in as many years. The bed closures, scheduled to begin July 20, were expected to reduce expenditures by about $150,000.

In October 1990, Bob Cameron told the board he would not be coming back to work. Because of a stroke, he had been on medical leave for more than 10 months. "It's

Linda Gowing, head nurse Unit 1 east building, Valentine's Day 1990

SGH

The montage presented to Bob Cameron upon his retirement as executive director of SGH in 1990. The artwork was done by Todd Mulligan of Stratford.

Bob Cameron

SGH

been pretty stressful the last few years," said Cameron. "The question was whether or not to go back to all that stress. The pressure has been the worst during the last five years with the restrictions on government spending and the board trying to maintain services with decreasing funding." Board chair Colleen Misener said, "I've worked with Mr. Cameron for the past 17 years and he has really provided the hospital with great leadership. His driving force led to the hospital expansion. A lot of good things at the hospital are attributable to Mr. Cameron."

Also in October 1990, the board renamed the original hospital once again. The RECU became Avon Crest – which is what it was rechristened soon after the new hospital was opened in 1950. As well, a committee was formed to find new tenants for the

building, which fell silent when the last of its patients were moved to the hospital's new east building. By early in 1991 four medical services were operating out of Avon Crest, which by then had soaked up $120,000 in renovation costs. An occupational therapy clinic for children, the Stratford Physiotherapy Community Clinic, an audiology clinic – a first for Perth and Huron counties, and the Speech Language Pathology Clinic, designed to treat children from birth to age five, were in the 100-year-old building. Hindering the tenant search somewhat was an outdated electrical service, which meant the building could not support offices in need of an abundance of electricity.

The ceremonial re-opening of Avon Crest was held on May 15, 1991, and was highlighted by the presentation of a cheque for $42,000 by Paul Hunt, president of the Rotary Club of Stratford. The money was earmarked for equipment in the physiotherapy clinic. Also on that day, the public was able to tour the refurbished facilities.

For the 1990-91 fiscal year the board had budgeted for an

Garry Brodhagen of purchasing and assistant director of nursing Lynn Strugnell, 1990.

operating surplus of $500,000. Late in November 1990 it announced it would likely miss that target because of a 15 per cent wage increase over two years for the hospital's Canadian Union of Public Employees members. That settlement was reached in September, and the board's finance chairman, Chris Thomson, said he expected it to cost the hospital an additional $300,000 in wages. As well, there was an unexpected tab of $44,000 for non-union employees – the result of pay equity legislation, and a federal tax of between $50,000 and $80,000 for goods and services. The pay equity settlement represented an annual salary increase of $4,816 for each of the 3,000 Ontario Public Service Employees Union members at 50 provincial hospitals. At Stratford, where officials had anticipated a five per cent salary increase, wages for each of the 40 registered technologists went up 12.6 per cent.

Medical history was recorded at SGH on Jan. 15, 1991, when chief of surgery James Hardwick used laparoscopic methods to remove Marie Finnie's gall bladder. He repeated the operation later in the day on another patient, and the next day performed a third such procedure. At the time, the technique had been used in the United States for only two years, and just once during that time in Canada. "It will become one of the standard operations," Hardwick predicted. He said two-thirds of the patients undergoing gall bladder operations at SGH would be candidates for the new method of removal.

Also in January, the hospital received $687,000 from the estate of Lawrence Arthur W. East, who died in December 1989 at the age of 87. This gift, the largest private donation in SGH history, was not the first from the East estate. The hospital received $225,000 in 1990. East was born in England but moved with his family to Stratford, where his father worked in the repair shops of the Grand Trunk Railway. The younger East earned a degree in engineering at the University of Toronto and spent most of his working life in New York and Montreal. He returned to Stratford in 1971 to retire and marry Catherine Jane Ryerson, who predeceased him in 1981.

On Feb. 1, 1991, SGH was visited by

Perrin Beatty, the federal minister of health and welfare. He spent the day in Perth County meeting with various groups.

Eighteen days later, the board announced the name of Cameron's replacement. Forty-year-old Bernie Schmidt was the chief executive officer at the 80-bed Sensenbrenner Hospital in Kapuskasing, Ont., when he joined 51 others in applying for the Stratford job. He was one of five people interviewed for the position.

Cardiorespiratory technician Anne Forsyth takes the blood pressure of Sammy Good Health (SGH for short) in the early 1990s. Sammy was created in the late 1980s or early 1990s after the hospital agreed to take part in a week-long health fair in the Stratford mall. The committee struck to decide the nature of that participation created the Sammy persona, and Grace Untucht fashioned the costume from assorted fabrics and notions. Through the years she has also been one of Sammy's many inner selves, as the SGH mascot has attended staff barbecues, children's Christmas parties, strawberry socials, flu shot clinics and McHappy Days.

Another of the five was Fadelle, who had been running the SGH ship as acting executive director since Cameron's stroke. Shortly before the Stratford board made its decision, Fadelle, who had spent 15 years at SGH, accepted the job of executive director at St. Marys Memorial Hospital in St. Marys, Ont. "Their (the SGH board's) timetable and mine were different," said Fadelle, a St. Marys resident. He said the Stratford board members had had 14 months to decide if they wanted to offer their top job to him on a permanent basis, and they chose not to. Thus, he added, he had to make a decision of his own when the St. Marys job became available.

In anticipation of a "very difficult" year, the hospital took some cost-cutting measures on Feb. 11 when it closed 35 of its 294 beds and laid off eight nurses, the first such layoffs in its history. As well, it reduced the hours worked by part-time staff. At the same time, it offered a free dinner to any of its 198 full-time nurses who didn't miss a scheduled shift in a three-month period. "Sick time is very expensive," said nursing director Doug Pinder, who claimed 80 per cent of absenteeism at SGH could be attributed to 20 per cent of the staff.

In April 1991 the hospital received some good news about its fiscal years 1988 and 1989, which also had been difficult. The provincial government came through with $1.3 million so SGH could wipe out the deficits it had accumulated in those years.

Schmidt's first official day on the job at SGH was May 21, 1991, though he had attended the April board meeting as an observer. His wife Heather remained in Kapuskasing with their two-year-old son and 15-year-old stepdaughter until after the birth of their second child. Schmidt was born in Germany but moved to London, Ont., with his family before he was a year old. A registered nursing assistant, he also had a bachelor of arts degree from the

University of Waterloo, a master's degree in social work from Wilfrid Laurier University and a master's of health sciences from the University of Toronto. He worked at University Hospital in London and at York Finch Hospital in Toronto before taking the Kapuskasing job in 1988. With the arrival of Schmidt, SGH changed the name of its top administrative post from executive director to chief executive officer. Two days after his arrival, Schmidt was at his first board meeting as CEO. He told the board he had been meeting continually with staff members and had found them to be "very supportive, helpful and understanding."

In June 1991 the hospital stepped up its mother-child bonding program by implementing a 24-hour rooming-in policy for births that were free of complications. No longer were newborns required to spend time in the hospital's nursery, unless they arrived in the evening or during the night. It wasn't a new concept, said Sheila Knechtel, head nurse in obstetrics, "It's the trend in maternal care. There has been a really positive response so far. The change wasn't made to save money but it has made for more efficient use of staff." She said nurses were looking in on each mother and baby every half-hour. By then the hospital was delivering close to 700 babies a year, up about 100 from 1981. In the mid-1980s an 18-hour rooming-in policy had been introduced at SGH.

The hospital celebrated its centennial in 1991 in a number of ways, but few more lasting than by the creation of a donors' wall in the main lobby. On the wall, oak-trimmed brass plaques recognize the municipalities, businesses, service clubs, volunteer groups and individuals that have contributed to the hospital's expansion program. Many of those contributions had been solicited by Jim Williams and Jeff Preston, and to honour them SGH commissioned relief portraits of the fund-raising pair, to be displayed in the new wing. To help keep the donations coming, the Stratford General Hospital Foundation hired its first full-time employee. Andrea Weiner (later Page) signed on in 1992 as development officer.

The donor wall was unveiled at the conclusion of the hospital's 1991 annual meeting, a meeting highlighted by good news on several fronts. First, the 1990-91 fiscal year resulted in an operating surplus of about $190,000 – despite negative predictions about seven months earlier.

Outgoing board chair Colleen Misener

Looking south at the courtyard and garden between the east and west buildings of SGH.

said the turnaround was possible because of an additional $588,100 in funding from the Health Ministry. As well, the ministry provided a one-time adjustment of $1.35 million to the hospital's capital fund.

Misener also announced that part of the Lawrence East money would be used to landscape the expansive outdoor courtyard south of the main lobby. And that donations from the Schulthies family, in memory of Dr. Lloyd G. (Peter) and Alona Schulthies, would go towards a quiet garden in the courtyard, which was to include a sculptured horse, donated by board member Gordon J. Steed. More than 40 people joined hospital officials and members of the Schulthies family in dedicating the garden on Oct. 12, 1991.

Also at that 1991 annual meeting, Misener received a donation of $66,000 from the auxiliary association and another $64,823 as a bequest. The more than $130,000, she said, would cover the cost of an expanded gift and coffee shop (which opened in March 1992), the cost of landscaping the children's therapeutic playground, and the cost of two laparoscopes.

The next meeting was handled by new chair John Callan, who praised Misener for her two-year effort as chair. "Your dedication to the hospital has seen us through difficult times," he said. Also at that meeting, Callan and Schmidt were able to announce that SGH had received a favourable assessment in gaining two-year accreditation from the Canadian Council on Health Facilities.

As the year wound down, the hospital celebrated the 10th anniversary of its birthing room with a party for Faye Davidson, the first child born in the room. The Grade 5 student at Central Perth public school near Wartburg was accompanied to the party by her parents. Also on hand was Judy Fuhr, who gave birth to son Reece in the birthing room just hours before the party began. Maternity ward staffers had hoped to celebrate in the birthing room, but they were forced to move the cake, juice and coffee to the nearby waiting room when their original choice was called into service.

The birthing room was designed to create a home-like atmosphere, complete with comfortable furniture, a stereo system and wallpaper. In its first decade it had been used for about 1,000 births, all involving women with normal labour and delivery. That number represents about 20 per cent of all births at SGH in those 10 years.

It was on April Fool's Day 1992 that the hospital became a smoke-free environment, under a policy whose lone exception was a specified area in the psychiatry department.

Difficult times were not long in presenting themselves to Callan which, in reflection, he says he knew were coming before he became chair. In a prepared statement at the hospital on April 23, 1992, he announced the layoff of the equivalent of 44 full-time positions. Few job areas among SGH's 900 employees were spared, in a sweep that covered 17 positions in management, 18 in nursing and nine in professional support services. The 17 management employees received their notices and severance packages the day the announcements were made. It was also announced that seven more management positions – nursing co-ordinators – would be eliminated beginning June 15. Those cuts, it was said, would save the hospital $1.5 million and, coupled with a reduction of $600,000 in supplies and expenses, would make possible a $50,000 surplus on SGH's $38.8-million budget for 1992-93. Submitting a deficit budget would risk government takeover of the hospital, said Callan. "It would no longer be a community hospital." Too, it was announced that 10 more in-patients beds would be closed, and nursing floor areas were to be consolidated.

Most of the blame for the drastic measures was directed at Bob Rae and his

A friend indeed

It was in 1995, when Stratford General Hospital established a palliative care unit, that the hospital hired its first full-time chaplain. The idea had been under discussion for some time, and the move was recommended by the pastoral care committee of SGH.

The hospital has long enjoyed the support of Stratford and area clergy, and for years the committee has hosted an annual clergy luncheon to show its appreciation.

The chaplain hired by SGH was Bill James-Abra, a Baptist minister who came to Stratford from St. Joseph's Health Centre in London, Ont. He has remained the hospital's chaplain, or pastoral care co-ordinator.

Rev. James-Abra says the staff and patients of SGH and their families are his congregation, and that his role is to provide pastoral care in times of crises, particularly for those who have no parish minister. For patients who are church members, he will contact their clergy.

Prior to his coming on board, pastoral care at the hospital was provided by the ministers and priests of churches throughout Perth County; each was responsible for visiting his or her church members while they were patients in SGH. There is still an active pastoral care committee, which includes at least six clergy from Stratford and Perth County, as well as representatives from the hospital's staff, administration and board.

Rev. James-Abra is also assisted on occasion by master's students, who work at SGH as part of their field training. One of those, Rev. Marion Jackson Tyler, is now at Grace United Church in Tavistock. Another, Rev. Ririe Mitchell, is at Hensall United Church.

"The idea of having a chaplain in a hospital is based on the notion that we are all, in fundamental ways, spiritual beings," says Rev. James-Abra.

"Whether we express that formally, as dyed-in-the-wool Presbyterians or Baptists or Lutherans or whatever, or more informally in ways that do not seem obviously religious, we are all of us guided in our living by hopes and longings, and supported by our faith and sense of purpose."

New Democratic government, which had reduced its increase in annual funding of hospitals to one per cent. Traditionally, it had been four or five per cent. The ministry money was to account for 86 per cent, or about $33 million, of the 1992-93 SGH budget. Hospital officials said their payroll alone required $28.5 million.

Schmidt described the mood at the hospital as sombre. He said employees had known for a month that $1.5 million was going to be eliminated in wages and salaries, but until the announcement was made they didn't know how and where. The cuts were decided after a review of programs and services, said Schmidt, but from the services that remained, there would be quality delivery. Psychology was among those that remained, but in a reorganized state.

Schmidt said admissions at SGH had remained constant, at about 9,000 annually, but in the year preceding the cuts, the hospital had managed to pare 7,000 patient-days by reducing the length of stays and by increasing outpatient services.

A week later, the board announced a budget of $39.5 million and predicted an operating surplus of $100,000, despite a promise of just $324,000 from the Health Ministry. It also announced an increase in parking rates for the SGH lots, from $1 to $1.50. The hike was expected to boost annual parking revenues from $230,000 to $330,000.

By that time the hospital unions had identified all the people to be laid off, a process that took time because of their seniority-based bumping procedures.

By the end of May the hospital and its nurses union were interpreting the job losses and reduced services in different ways and with different numbers. Wilhelm said the hospital was closing 16 beds, not 10. She also said that would bring the number of recent closures to 56, not 35. Amid such cutbacks, she expressed concern about the quality of patient care. Schmidt denied the accusations and said the hospital was adhering to the numbers announced in April. The 21-bed discrepancy was a paperwork foul-up, he said, and it had been resolved with the ministry. According to Schmidt, those beds had never existed. He also said three-day workshops were planned to help laid-off union employees with resumes and job searches.

By then, some of the management employees fired by the hospital had filed lawsuits related to their dismissals. Their severance packages created a $214,540 deficit in the hospital's operating budget for the first quarter of the year. Their lawsuits dragged on for years.

More than 100 people – many of them disgruntled employees – packed the hospital's annual meeting at the end of June. "With everything that's been going on in the last year and a half, we just figured it's time to come out and have a little input," said Wilhelm, on behalf of the nurses. The board had hoped to adopt numerous revisions to its bylaws with one motion. But when the assembled protested, Schmidt had to outline each bylaw in the 67-page document, one by one. The chief of staff, Dr. Art vanWalraven, walked through the changes made to the bylaws affecting the hospital's medical committees. Wilhelm noted that an agreed-to procedure for the representation of nurses on the committees was missing, and she proposed an amendment. It was adopted.

Mark Hopkins, president of the OPSEU local, voiced opposition to the hospital's plan to "axe" the four-member psychology department. "At no time have we talked about axing," said Schmidt. He said the hospital was considering cutting the department but "at no point do we want to leave a gap in service."

Memberships, which allow holders to vote at SGH meetings, were increased at that June meeting. Annual fees went from $1 to $5. Lifetime memberships went from $100 to $1,000 for individuals and from $1,000 to $5,000 for corporations.

Late in 1992 the provincial government dealt the hospital two pieces of bad news, both costly. First, the Ministry of the Environment said SGH's incinerator – installed three years earlier at a cost of about $600,000 – would have to be eliminated in the next five years. No longer was it an environmentally friendly way to dispose of bio-medical wastes, said the MOE. "Ours was the most modern up-to-date, efficient incinerator when it was installed," said Misener, who noted that the Ministry of Health had approved it and had paid for it.

Second, the hospital was informed that its promised two per cent increase in funding for 1993-94 had been reduced to half a per cent. That, said Schmidt, would mean delaying the purchase of new equipment, worth about $1 million, as well as trimming about $500,000 from its operating budget, which was certain to reach $40 million. He also said he was "fairly positive there won't be any staff cuts."

However, there were further layoffs, in September 1993 and January 1994. Schmidt said most of them came after contracts had expired.

By September 1993, less than six months into its two-year funding drive, the hospital had donations and pledges of $1.8 million – about 75 per cent of its $2.5 million goal for the CT scanner. The most recent $25,000 had come from the Toronto-based J. P. Bickell Foundation, which was administered by National Trust. Another $4,000 came in the next month from local Bell Canada employees.

While the funding news was good, the target date for having the scanner in place had to be moved from October 1993 to January 1994. Schmidt said the ministry's step-by-step planning process involved a lot of red tape and working through that process was taking longer than expected.

The scanner on order was a spiral model, the most up-to-date diagnostic imager available, according to Schmidt. He said Stratford would be the first hospital in the province to have such a machine, which could do a full-body scan in less than six minutes, just a fifth of the time required by other models. "This type is known for both its speed and its accuracy," said Schmidt. "There are very few of these in all of Canada." He also said it was estimated that one in three people will need a CT scan at some point in their lives.

In photo-opportunity-type ceremonies on Oct. 14, 1993, Schmidt signed documents that committed SGH to expenditures of $2.3 million – for the purchase and installation of its scanner. One contact, for $1.1 million, went to Ron Zehr, owner of Nith Valley

Construction of New Hamburg, the same company that for months had been doing a retrofit that would help the hospital meet fire safety standards. Nith was one of six companies that bid on the construction of a 3,000-square-foot (288 square metres) addition to house the new scanner.

The other contract, for $1.2 million, went to Elscint Canada Ltd., the company that was supplying the machine. Elscint general manager Kenneth Giles was on hand to accept the order and a cheque for $120,000, which represented a 10 per cent down payment. The cheque came from Frank Romano and Colleen Misener, co-chairs of the CT scanner campaign fund. Upon receipt, Giles reassured Stratford officials they had made a wise choice in their selection of scanner when he told them fewer than 10 per cent of the scanners in Canada had the advanced capabilities of the spiral model destined for SGH.

In January 1994 the Ministry of Health recognized Stratford as one of the province's top 10 hospitals in terms of operational efficiency. It also said SGH was the best when it came to handling patients with heart and chest problems. Thus, Schmidt was summoned to Toronto, along with the heads of the other nine top-10 institutions, to offer suggestions that the ministry could pass on to other hospitals.

To further encourage better operation, the ministry reorganized its funding process, to take $21 million from hospitals identified as least efficient and redistribute it among the most efficient of the remaining 200 hospitals in the province.

In March 1994, SGH made a pitch to the Health Ministry for more money, this time to proceed with its $12 million redevelopment master plan, which had been approved in the 1980s. At the top of the project list was completion of its three-storey east building, which would bring into use 200,000 square feet (about 19,000 square metres) of vacant space. The hospital was also hoping to renovate its aging west wing and transfer active-care beds and related support services to the medical-surgical ward on the second floor of the east building. That, it was reasoned, would create expanded and improved conditions for the departments left in the west wing, namely obstetrics, gynecology, pediatrics and the special-care nursery. Other proposed changes included renovation of the operating suites on the second floor of the west wing, as well as expanded laboratories on the fourth floor. The changes would update the older main portion of the hospital, said Schmidt. "It will bring the (hospital) environment into the 21st century."

Plans for the special-care nursery accelerated when the Rotary Club of Stratford donated $60,000 to the project. The cheque was presented in June by Rotary president Norm Bird at the hospital's 13th annual chronic care and rehabilitation unit barbecue for patients and staff. The Rotary money went towards a neonatal intensive care unit, designed to provide special treatment for high-risk infants such as those born premature or to diabetic mothers. The unit could accommodate up to six infants. Local decorators helped with the project by donating time and materials.

In February 1994 the hospital announced it had finished its 1993 fiscal year with another operating surplus.

In April 1994 the board approved a plan to revamp its chronic care and rehabilitation programs. Changes were necessary because the use of chronic care beds had dropped from 100 per cent a few years earlier to about 70 percent – partly because other health-care services in the community, such as nursing homes, had replaced hospitals in that area of treatment. Four months earlier, SGH had temporarily closed 33 of its 78 chronic care and 20 rehabilitation beds on the first two floors of the east building. What the hospital now wanted to do was

maintain 20 rehabilitation and 33 chronic care inpatient beds, reallocate eight chronic care beds to palliative care, reallocate four chronic care beds to respite care, and establish a rehabilitation and geriatric day hospital. Local approval for the changes was just the first step. The plan then needed the blessing of the Health Ministry, even though all funding for the changes would be covered through the reallocation of existing resources.

But in 1994 at SGH, talk of the future was overshadowed by developments of the present, specifically the arrival and installation of the long-awaited dual-slice spiral CT scanner, the first of its kind in Canada. Medical staff chief Art vanWalraven said the machine was "a generational leap over what was available five years ago." The hospital took delivery of the Israeli-built Elscint CT Twin on April 4. Its 18 pieces were off-loaded in the emergency parking lot. At three tons (2.7 tonnes), the largest and heaviest of the pieces, the gantry, was towed to the door by a mini-van owned by the installer. Within three weeks, the scanner was operational and the training of hospital personnel was underway.

On May 5, H. N. R. (Henry) Jackman, the lieutenant-governor of Ontario, was in Stratford to cut a ribbon and officially open the portion of the hospital renovated especially to accommodate the twin dual-slice scanner. Jackman told the crowd that acquisition of the scanner was "a tribute to community feelings and volunteerism at is best." He was joined in the spotlight by city and hospital officials, as well as by MPP Karen Haslam and MP John Richardson. Haslam said that one of her first acts as a provincial member of parliament – even before she had established a riding office – was to phone Queen's Park on behalf of the hospital and seek support for the scanner from the health minister. Singled out for special thanks on that May day were

Frank Romano

Colleen Misener, a longtime board member, and Frank Romano, who co-chaired the fund-raising committee for the scanner.

The $2.5-million scanner was first proposed about eight years earlier and was an idea warmly embraced by the community. The hospital auxiliary gave a cornerstone donation of $100,000, and later a further $26,000. Money came in from all sectors of the community. But on the day the scanner was unveiled, the hospital still needed about $200,000 to cover its cost. Within three months that figure was cut in half. More than $9,000 came in from a Cats Can Variety Night and another $10,000 from Henry and George Kalbfleisch as they celebrated the 100th anniversary of their Stratford car dealership. Other donations were received from throughout Perth County – from junior farmers, Royal Canadian Legion branches, service clubs, Bell Canada employees, women's institutes, and teenagers who took part in a dance recital. The campaign goal was reached in September 1994.

While the scanner was the most

significant capital addition at SGH in 1994, it was not the only one. Down the hall from emergency, and next to the scanner, a `quiet room' was built. It was designed as a place where friends and relatives of hospital patients could seek privacy and, in some cases, await the news or prognoses of loved ones in emergency-care situations.

The room was furnished by city businesswoman, alderman and hospital board member Marg Wade, in memory of her husband Frank and daughter-in-law Judith. Mrs. Wade said her husband had furnished the old chapel at the hospital with fresh flowers from their flower and gift shop, and that he was upset when the chapel was converted to a records room. She also said the Wade's shop would supply the new room with fresh flowers on a weekly basis.

While most attention was on the installation of the scanner, there were facelifts underway in three other departments, namely pediatrics, cardio-respiratory services and surgical ambulatory. All areas were `re-opened' in September.

As the hospital began its last six years of the century, most board members continued to focus on money, in particular how to get along with less. At the 1994 annual meeting, board chair Chris Thomson said SGH's provincial funding had been reduced by $2 million. He also said the funding shortage was being offset, in part, by improved technology – which in turn was reducing the average length of stay for many patients.

Indeed, patient days at SGH in 1993-94 numbered 61,544, down from 85,903 in 1990-91. For acute care, the average stay dropped from 6.5 days in 1990-91 to just more than five days in 1993-94. In that time there was also a significant reduction of activity when it came to X-rays, nuclear medicine examinations, ultrasound examinations, occupational therapy and physiotherapy visits, surgical operations and emergency visits. Still, said the hospital's CEO, with fewer beds than in 1990-91, SGH was serving more people. Schmidt said the ratio of patients had increased – more of them were being treated, but they were staying fewer days.

By now, each year the hospital was helping to: deliver 700 babies, perform 5,500 operations, see 36,000 emergency/ambulatory patients, host 3,600 speech therapy visits, conduct 32,000 X-rays and 1,000 nuclear medicine examinations, respond to 2,000 ambulance calls, perform 4,500 ultrasound exams, serve 183,000 meals to patients, and clean 415,000 kilograms of laundry.

Whatever the activity, it was happening with more than 70 fewer staff members than were on the payroll in 1990-91 – a fact that some continued to say threatened the quality of care and led to low morale among the employees who remained.

Schmidt blamed the layoffs on the provincial government, which he said had ordered the hospital to balance its books. Those layoffs, he said, reduced the hospital's costs by about $2.8 million over two years. He also said a more aggressive bed management policy had allowed SGH to retain its patient volume but also to handle that volume with reduced staff and beds.

The Health Ministry now bases its hospital funding on patient volumes instead of beds. Schmidt said the reduction from 294 beds to 211 beds actually improves SGH's position when it comes to funding.

"Some patients might feel they were being rushed if they had previous stays in hospital," said Schmidt, but those patients were often admitted on the basis of empty and available beds. Now, he said, admissions are based on clinical need, and the savings have been significant. He said the cost of keeping a patient in a SGH bed is about $425 a day.

"We will not serve our community by burying our heads in the sand," said Thomson. "We will not serve our community by resisting change. We will serve our community by keeping an open mind and working together with all our health-care partners to achieve the best possible health-care solutions for our community . . . solutions we can afford."

Affordable solutions continued to dominate many hospital board discussions. In October 1994, spurred by a recommendation from its finance committee, the board agreed to use if necessary its long-standing but heretofore unneeded $3-million line of operating credit. Were cash required, said SGH's assistant director of finance David Hughes, the hospital could realize savings in interest payments by using its line of credit.

On Nov. 18, 1994, with party hats and fanfare, the hospital announced the successful end of its fund-raising drive for the CT scanner. The $2.5-million diagnostic tool was paid for, by which time it had been used for about 1,500 scans. "It's like making the final payment on your car or burning your mortgage," said the technical director of imaging services, Ken Dale, during a ceremony in the hospital's main lobby. Dale also said he and SGH director of development Andrea Page had made almost 200 speaking engagements in the previous 14 months to generate funds and help bring the campaign to a close.

"It's a day to be proud of for Stratford General Hospital and its foundation," said Colleen Misener, co-chair of the fund-raising committee. She directed special praise to the hospital's auxiliary, which pledged $100,000 to the scanner project. The other co-chair, Frank Romano, thanked the volunteer canvassers, and singled out the efforts of Bob Mountain, who had been a chairman of the SGH Foundation.

Mountain, a prominent Stratford lawyer and tireless community worker, as well as a

The hospital later recognized the support of the 219 staff members who donated $50,000 for the scanner, by dedicating the CT exam room to them.

It was also in 1994 that SGH fiscally amalgamated its community mental health programs. Specifically, those programs were Listowel Mental Health Outpatient Services, seniors mental health and sexual assault counselling. The amalgamation enhanced the clinical resources available for service delivery across Perth County. The visits for those programs in 1994-95 numbered 1,433 for Listowel, 1,067 for seniors and 500 for sexual assault.

As well in 1994, former mayor of the city, had died of cancer in May 1994. Less than a year later, Jeff Preston who, like Mountain, had been one of the hospital's most ardent supporters in the time of its greatest financial need, also died. He was 78.

In a full-page newspaper ad to announce the completion of its scanner campaign, which realized $2,764,378 in cash and pledges, the hospital said that to maintain its level of service it needed $1 million annually to purchase new and replacement equipment. And it urged continued support.

the hospital's home oxygen program received a vendor status that allowed it to offer to the community respiratory care that included oxygen therapy, home ventilators, aerosol medication, apnea monitors, nasal airway pressure care, tracheostomy care and humidity care.

SGH's physiotherapy community clinic was awarded the highest accreditation status by the Toronto-based Institute for Work and Health. No doubt that designation was a reflection of the program expanding to include injuries associated with motor vehicle accidents, sports and the home. In addition, the SPCC established partnerships with local industries, a partnership that generated on-site analysis and education, assessment and treatment.

It was in 1994-95 that the hospital revived its heart-to-heart program for patients and families with heart disease. It comprised an eight-week training session with members meeting for two hours each week. The program was organized and taught by critical care nurses, assisted by Dr. Art vanWalraven. They also enlisted the help of dietitians, pharmacists, and psychological and social services.

The hospital remained committed to continuous quality improvement initiatives, and in this fiscal year it created a patient processing team, whose job was to examine how patients flowed through SGH. The project took the group into areas that included billing, bed assignments, registration and records.

In September 1994, SGH opened a medical ambulatory care unit, which was able to facilitate electroencephalograms (EEGs), electromyograms (EMGs), chemotherapy and outpatient nutritional counselling, as well as provide the services offered by medical clinics, the allergy clinic and cardiorespiratory services

Also in September 1994, the hospital unveiled a surgical ambulatory care clinic, and patient volumes were soon exceeding 1,100 visits a month. Patients were encouraged to attend pre-admit clinics to learn more about their surgery, which could range from the removal of bumps and lumps to ear, nose and throat procedures to the treatment of gynecological or urological problems.

In like fashion, the hospital began a pre-admit clinic for women in their seventh to ninth month of pregnancy.

Co-ordinated by those in the critical care program, the dissemination of cardiac information became formalized. The contents of information packages were reviewed with patients and their families,

and two days after discharge, patients were phoned by SGH staff. If necessary, a return to the hospital for a visit with critical care staff was arranged.

In January 1995 the Health Ministry approved SGH's reprogramming initiatives for its east building. Those plans called for the establishment of a palliative care unit, a rehab geriatric day program and respite care.

In February the board members approved a 1995-96 operating plan which forecast a surplus of $9,800 over expenses of $38.5 million. At the same meeting, they were told that staff numbers would return to pre-1992 levels of 545 full-time equivalent positions. That was possible, said David Hughes, because the hospital made some tough decisions in the early '90s to satisfy the budgetary demands of the Health Ministry.

"We have had our bad time," said Bernie Schmidt, who noted the current budget would enable the hospital to hire back employees previously laid off, and to staff new programs in the east building. SGH, he said, would be adding a palliative care program, complete with a full-time chaplain, and a geriatric day program. The position of full-time chaplain would be new to SGH, as would be that of a leisure activities co-ordinator.

"One thing is very clear," said Chris Thomson. "This is a very tight (budget) plan." But he was optimistic because of how SGH had finished the three previous years with surpluses of $5,500, $44,000 and $35,000.

Other things were also clear – health-care delivery and the role of hospitals in Ontario were undergoing changes that were going to tax more than budgets. For instance, there was the newly formed Huron-Perth District Health Council, which was to formulate a long-term plan for health care in Perth and Huron counties. SGH was named as one of eight hospitals represented on a committee established to help guide the DHC when it came to mandating and directing those hospitals.

On another front, Health Minister Ruth Grier appeased the College of Family Physicians, temporarily at least, by agreeing to have an independent panel review the licensing of nurse practitioners in Ontario. Worried about the erosion of what to then had been

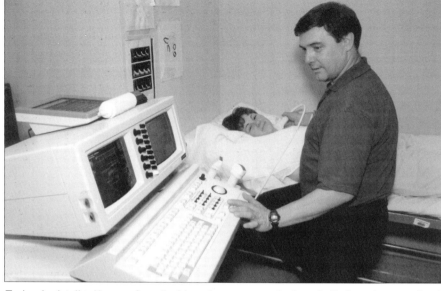

Technologist Jim Houze of medical imaging operates the hospital's first ultrasound unit that could map in colour the blood flow in the body, spring 1995.

their medical domain, the college's 5,000 members threatened to take legal action to stop the government from fast-tracking the licensing and hiring of more nurse practitioners.

In May 1995 the hospital started a rehabilitation day hospital, which offered service to adults and their families from a multi-disciplinary team of leisure recreation, occupational therapy, physiotherapy, nursing, social work and speech language pathology.

In June SGH opened its new pediatric unit, with a brightly coloured hall mural and newly decorated rooms. Also redecorated was the special care nursery, which included space for parents who wished to stay overnight with their children.

By then the hospital had also begun to develop new computer facilities, and was in the throes of amalgamating its two power plants into a single contemporary facility. It was also assessing its food preparation and delivery systems, with an eye to updating the kitchen in 1996.

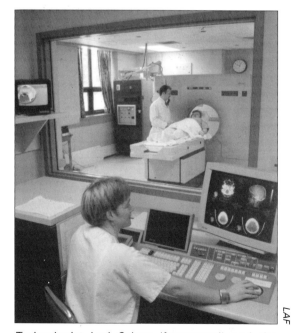

Technologist Lori Selves (foreground) and the director of cardiorespiratory, medical imaging, Ken Dale, use the hospital's new CT scanner, spring 1995.

Caring clowns

It was while they were working on nursing degrees at the University of Western Ontario in London, that Cheryl Yost and Saralyn Lichty sought to initiate a humour therapy program at SGH, where they worked. Initially, their focus was on the palliative care unit, but they were encouraged to involve the entire hospital.

In pursuit of their interest in care clowning, they took courses, and at a clown conference in Toronto they met Pat Willows,

SGH

Surgeon James Hardwick awaits more abuse in the dunk tank during a fund-raiser for the SGH humour project in the summer of 1994. Through the years, the good-natured Hardwick, usually armed with a water gun, has been a regular in the fund-raising tank.

also known as Beany, a professional clown who lives in Carlingford, about 15 kilometres from Stratford.

Yost and Lichty enlisted Willows as a fellow instructor, promoter and leader for their endeavours at SGH. From hospital staff and the public, they formed a volunteer committee, whose immediate job was to raise funds to buy a humour cart and the likes of funny books, videos and audio cassettes to stock it. Among their fund-raising efforts were raffles, bake sales, barbecues and guest speaking.

In 1995 Willows, Yost and Lichty trained about a dozen volunteer clowns. Apart from the first two sessions, the recruits had to pay for their training and their costumes and props. They learned how to be clowns, but also about hospital protocol and how to approach the ill.

While the Yost-Lichty project got underway in 1994, it wasn't until February 1995 that the first care clowns graduated. In April 1995 the committee and the clowns officially launched GAGS (Giggles and Get Well Service) at SGH. Guest speaker for the occasion was Ken Shonk, the doctor who had started the same program in Kitchener.

Beany, Beaney 1.5 (Yost) and and Sunnyside (Lichty) and their friends soon became happy fixtures in the halls and patient rooms of SGH.

In February 1996, Mayor Dave Hunt proclaimed Lighten up Stratford Day, during which GAGS held a graduation ceremony for its newest clowns. It also staged some fun and fund-raising activities, among them red-nose day and crazy-hat day.

By 2001 there was a need for more clowns, and the training classes resumed, though not through SGH. New trainees are encouraged to volunteer for the humour therapy program at the hospital. They are also free to take on other clown jobs, perhaps as a career. Some choose to forego the costume and be "plain clothes" bearers of good cheer.

Care clowns Gumdrop (Patricia Freeman) and Flossy the Cow (Barb Elg).

Yost, Lichty and Willows continue to promote their humour and health concept among hospital staff and with the public. Willows is still training clowns and has helped establish programs in Woodstock and Seaforth. Based on the Stratford model, there are also care clowns in Tillsonburg, Goderich, Brantford, St. Thomas and St. John, N.B.

"The whole persona of a clown walking in (on a patient) breaks down barriers," says Willows. "It's the last thing they (patients) expect to see in a hospital corridor. We realize we can't visit anyone's space if they don't want us, but when we take their attention off their illness, they feel better, research has proven."

"We believe that as individuals we need to be more connected to our human experiences," says Yost. "Humour is a must to support balance in life today."

NAME THE HUMOUR OPTION CONTEST

A "Humour Option" program is being developed for staff and patients at Stratford General Hospital. A Steering Committee is currently working on this project.

The Humour Option project will be a free service available to all patients, visitors and staff at the hospital. It will entail a video cart with humorous video and audio cassettes, books, gag items etc. It is planned this program will be run by volunteers and a group of newly trained clowns. Not only will the clowns work within the hospital area but also plans include working with outreach facilities within Perth County and surrounding area.

We need your help in choosing a new name for this special project which will bring humour to those who need it most.

Look for your suggestion form the last week of July. Submit your suggestion by August 20th to Cheryl Yost, Co-ordinator, Educational Services. A special vote will be held at a fundraising BBQ August 25th in the Hospital courtyard.

Beany presents Andrea Page of the Foundation with the first donation cheque dedicated to the Humour Option project. Donations to fund the Humour Option are gratefully accepted and go towards supplies needed for the humour cart and the program. The first donation was given by Optimist Club of Downie.

From the July-August 1994 issue of *Generally Speaking*, the SGH newsletter.

More turbulent times

It was in June 1995 that voters elected Mike Harris the premier of Ontario. The successful platform for him and his Progressive Conservatives had been something they called the Common Sense Revolution, which emphasized lower taxes and less government; education, health and welfare reform; job creation; and a balanced budget within four years. While not everyone was sure what the revolution held, few would be unaffected as it was visited upon them. Over the next three years, Harris and the Tories would cut income taxes by 30 per cent, shift welfare responsibilities to local municipalities, slash education spending, repeal labour laws, begin a program of urban amalgamation and close hospitals.

Their health reform included the formation of a body known as the Health Services Restructuring Commission. But, says Ken Haworth, SGH's director of finance, its impact in Stratford was not significant because he and his colleagues had anticipated what was coming and had the changes in place before there were any directives from the commission. Within the Huron-Perth District Health Council, they formed a restructuring task force of their own in anticipation of the hospital closures

SGH

Orthopedic tech Brian Le Souder demonstrates attachments for the fracture table to Ellen Young of the physiotherapy department during a health fair in the fall of 1995. The table that replaced this one cost $40,000.

they were sure would be ordered by the government-appointed body.

It was the report of that task force that precipitated the development of an alternative approach by the eight chief executive officers in Huron and Perth counties. Their alternative ultimately ensured the

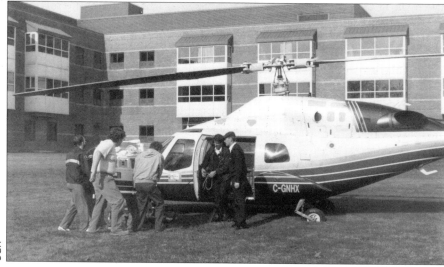

SGH

Early in November 1995, SGH transferred a patient by helicopter for the first time. A premature baby was airlifted to the children's hospital in London, a 12-minute flight. The chopper, a Bell 222, landed on the southeast lawn.

survival of their eight hospitals.

In November 1995 SGH launched Equipped to CARE (with CARE standing for community and regional equipment), a campaign to raise $5 million for the purchase of about 150 pieces of surgical, medical and diagnostic equipment. Co-chairs for the sizeable undertaking were John D. Lawson, manager of the local branches of the Royal Bank of Canada, and Barb Culliton, a longtime member of the hospital board and its auxiliary, as well as the SGH foundation. Almost immediately, money began to come in, some in the form of one-time cheques, some pledged over periods of up to five years.

Among the first Stratford businesses to come up with a fund-raiser for the hospital was the Olde English Parlour, which in February 1996 hosted a dinner for 150 SGH supporters and had minstrel Peter Shaw on hand to entertain them. To the hospital went $10 from each $20 ticket.

By then, downsizing and restructuring were fueling a winter of discontent at SGH. There was a sign of that during a hospital board meeting in January. According to

medical staff representative Dr. Van Woolnough, some doctors were unhappy with the termination of one of the hospital's four pathologists by chief executive officer Bernie Schmidt.

In February, SGH was declared highly efficient when it came to treating heart attack patients. That declaration came from a study looking at how heart attack victims were treated upon their arrival at hospitals. SGH's director of patient care services, Lynn Strugnell, attributed the positive report card to teamwork. In Stratford, that team was able to recognize patients experiencing a heart attack, notify a physician, and initiate clot-dissolving medication within 30 minutes. SGH was caring for about 200 heart attack patients a year, said Strugnell.

Near the end of February, the hospital learned its cut in funding from the provincial government was to be 2.8 per cent, which amounted to $909,000. Four months earlier, Ontario treasurer Ernie Eves had suggested an across-the-board slash of five per cent for all of the 200 hospitals in the province. But he and the Tories eventually opted to fund each hospital on the basis of efficiency, size, services provided and demand for those services. SGH director of finance David Hughes said the reduced funding would negatively affect salaries and medical supplies, and that more layoffs could be an option as the hospital struggled to come up with a budget acceptable to the Health Ministry by the end of April. If that budget did not identify savings, there was to be a penalty of $10,000 for the first week and $5,000 for each week thereafter that the budget was not submitted. Soon, it became apparent that SGH was faced with reducing its expenditures by $2 million.

On March 7, at a meeting of administration and some 120 staff, five options for cutting wages were presented: retirement, resignation, leave of absence, changing from a five-day week to a four-day week, and moving from full time to part time. Later, a sixth option was added, namely working six to 12 shifts without pay. The last idea was a throwback to the social-contract-era of Bob Rae and his New Democratic government, from which the province had only recently emerged.

By 1996, SGH's budget was about $40 million, of which about $24 million went to wages and salaries. The lifting of the social contract was adding about $400,000 to those wages and salaries. Human resources director Barry Cameron said the impending pain would not

be unlike that which was induced at the hospital in 1992.

The three unions at SGH had little appetite for the hospital's options. The Canadian Union of Public Employees filed seven grievances. There was another from the Ontario Nursing Association. Mary Lou Wukinic, president of the Ontario Public Service Employees Union local, wanted some assurance that the collective bargaining agreement was not being violated. OPSEU wrote a letter of protest to the hospital's administration.

On April 23, during National Volunteer Week, the hospital honoured its many volunteers with an afternoon reception. Two days later the SGH board approved a 1996-97 operating budget of $37.7 million with a projected surplus of $1,600. To make those numbers work, it was closing 20 of its 184 beds and eliminating the equivalent of 34 full-time staff positions. The loss of jobs was not the blow it could have been, in that 90 employees had responded to the options presented to them in March. Twenty were taking early retirement; eight were quitting; five were reducing their work week from

SGH

Hospital employees Kathy Mutch (left) and Grace Untucht show off a fund-raising sweatshirt in the spring of 1996. Available in navy or white, the shirts were selling for $20.

five days to four; eight were going from full-time to part-time employment; and 49 were take leaves of absence of between six and 30 days. The savings from those moves totalled about $1.4 million of the $2.1 million that the hospital needed to find. The rest was to come from

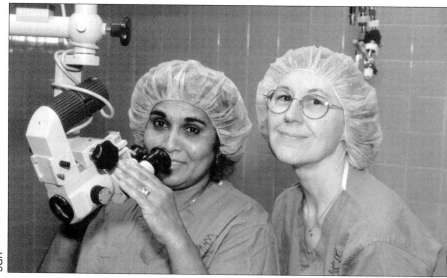

SGH

Mariamma Powath (left) and Anne Rolleman, registered nurses.

cutting expenses in other areas and increasing revenues. One revenue source that was tapped on a regular basis was parking, and it would not escape this round of belt tightening. Fees at hospital lots were hiked from $2.25 to $2.50 a visit.

Also in April 1996, hospital staff began using a Coherent XA 50 CO2 laser for the removal of pre-cancerous cervical lesions and warts, the freeing of abdominal lesions, and for treating endometriosis in women. The laser and accessories were purchased with a $100,000 donation from Stratford optometrist Don Larkworthy and his wife Betty.

In May the hospital began accepting MasterCard and Visa for charges not covered by the Ontario Hospital Insurance Plan and other insurance carriers, as well as for those incurred by non-residents of Canada. Those credit cards also became acceptable in the SGH gift shop.

Near the end of May the hospital learned that it had received a three-year, unqualified stamp of approval from the Canadian Council on Health Services Accreditation. Three surveyors from the council had determined the hospital "is operating in a

consistent and progressive manner" and that any weaknesses were minor in nature. "The institution is generally outstanding," said their report.

In June the hospital held an open house to showcase its refurbished pediatric rehabilitation services wing in Avon Crest. In the spotlight were eight refurbished rooms on the second floor of the storied building. The nine staff members had previously dealt with their caseload of 150 in three crowded rooms on the first floor. The cost of making the move came to $10,000, mostly for redecorating. It was covered by a grant from the Ronald McDonald Children's Charity. "The expense is minimal but the benefit is quite great," said Jeannette Eadie, SGH's director of rehabilitation services.

In September the hospital's Equipped to CARE campaign was given a $50,000 boost by the St. Marys Memorial Hospital Foundation. The money was to help pay for four intensive care unit monitors.

By October the hospital's projected deficit of $1,600 had increased by $426,000. CEO Bernie Schmidt attributed the bad news to an arbitrated wage settlement for CUPE workers at SGH ($127,000), the Ministry of Health reneging on an agreement to cover benefits for employees at the hospital resigning their jobs or taking early retirement ($154,000) and an unusually high percentage of acute care patients requiring more expensive treatment ($145,000). With five months left in the fiscal year, Schmidt told the board, "I can't assure you we are going to achieve a balance (balanced budget)."

As tough as times had become, the hospital still waived all parking fees for its open house on Nov. 24. Dubbed the "SGH For Your Health Fair," the Sunday afternoon open house gave the public an opportunity to see everything from an operating room to the medical imaging department and the CT scanner. The 400 to 500 visitors were invited to have their heart rate and blood pressure checked, to watch the demonstration of procedures, and to answer quizzes. For children, there were games and face painting.

Soon after that public relations exercise, the hospital started a six-week slowdown, designed to help reduce some of its projected deficit by as much as $60,000. SGH had traditionally slowed down for two weeks over the Christmas and New Year's period. Department heads were asked to look for expenditures that could be eliminated or deferred, and employees were encouraged to take holidays or leaves without pay. All concerned, including SGH board chair Dave Rae, conceded the extended slowdown was a stop-gap measure at best. He noted the hospital would likely face another six per cent cut in funding in the next year, under the Health Ministry's three-year plan to slash spending by 18 per cent.

In a letter to the editor in December, Rae assured readers that SGH would again end its fiscal year with a small surplus. He went on to cite the hospital's accomplishments and its importance not only to residents of Stratford, but also to those in Perth and

Bentley's Inn sponsored the float, and SGH staff took their plea for $5 million to Stratford streets in the rainy, windy 1996 Santa Claus parade.

Huron counties, and beyond. "As consumer of health care," he concluded, "you can be assured that the excellence of the programs and services delivered will always remain our No. 1 priority."

On the same day that letter appeared in the *Stratford Beacon Herald*, Schmidt, chief of staff Dr. Randy Gonser and SGH's assistant executive director of planning and hospital services Andrew Williams delivered an aggressive pitch to a 19-member Huron-Perth District Health Council's restructuring task force. They wanted SGH designated a major referral centre.

As Christmas approached, Schmidt delivered the best gift he could to his SGH board. He told the directors the hospital operation would be deficit-free by March 31, 1997, the end of its current fiscal year. The bold prediction, he said, was based on a number of factors, among them an increase in chronic care fees; the deferral, reduction or elimination of some supply purchases and other expenses; a reduction in medical and surgical supplies; and the depreciation of equipment.

But as 1996 ended, the directors had more than a balanced budget to look forward to in 1997. In their plans was a five-station kidney dialysis unit in the east building, and trained staff to run it. It was one of three satellites planned by the London Health Sciences Centre.

The board was also looking at relocating the hospital's maternal-child program, which included pediatrics, the special care nursery, birthing-recovery and postpartum. All were bound in 1997-98 for the second floor in the south wing of the east building.

Also flagged for relocation and expansion were SGH's critical care and emergency facilities. Plans for that upgrade were to begin unfolding in the summer of 1997.

When the district health council announced in January 1997 that all eight hospitals in Huron and Perth counties would remain open, its restructuring report contained some good news for SGH. The council endorsed Stratford's mandate as a district referral centre and called for its maintenance of all existing programs and services, and an increase in in-patient bed capacity from 134 to 157. It also identified necessary capital redevelopment for Stratford – to the tune of $13.6 million, and pointed to the importance of consolidating administrative and support services throughout the two counties.

The DHC thought its survival plan would result in savings of 13 per cent, or $10.5 million, of the $78.3 million it cost to operate the eight hospitals in 1995-96. Implementation of the plan was to be staged over two years, with April 1999 as its completion date.

It was in 1996-97 that SGH forged a formal link with the United Ostomy Association and Perth County Home Care, and members of the hospital's surgical unit began to provide clinical expertise at the association's regularly scheduled monthly meetings. It was in July 1996 that that surgical unit was moved from the west building to the east building. In the same month, chronic care and rehabilitation were amalgamated and moved to the east building. As that unit evolved, the length of stay for both chronic and rehab patients was growing shorter. Many long-term patients were being transferred to long-term care facilities.

In January 1997, a consolidation of surgical services resulted in gynecology surgery and short-stay cases being moved to the east building. To modernize its 1949 vintage maternal-child unit and move it to the new east building, SGH sought $8 million from the Health Ministry. Actually, some of that money was required to expand and upgrade the critical care unit. And some of it was already in place. As SGH's director of planning and hospital services, Andrew Williams, explained it, the $2 million needed for the maternal-child unit

Dr. Chris Arciszewski,
orthopedic surgeon

building were halted, the money had been sitting, available for east wing causes only.

Still, for the hospital to proceed with either capital project, it required approval from both the Health Ministry and the Huron-Perth District Health Council. SGH, then, was asking the ministry to share the $6 million in costs for upgrading critical care. Traditionally, the government covered 70 per cent of such shared projects.

On a daily basis the hospital was coping with a flu epidemic that was showing no signs of abating. Patients began showing up at the emergency department en masse during the Christmas period, and they kept coming. Emergency visits in December 1996 totalled 2,498, 10 per cent more than in December 1995. "It's one of the worst (flu strains) on record," said Randy Gonser, SGH's medical chief of staff.

In February, Hospice Services, Family Services Perth-Huron and SGH began a

had already been raised and was in the hospital foundation's capital reserves. In fact, there was twice that amount in the reserves. The money was acquired in the campaign to put up the east building in the 1980s, and since plans to complete the

Greg Eldridge is flanked by colleagues in the medical imaging department on the occasion of his retirement in the spring of 1997, after 31 years at SGH. Back row, from left: Louanne Plain holding her son Douglas, Golda Wilson, Irene Simons and Jane Heatherly. Middle row, from left: Sharon Eghoetz, Laurie Brown, Carol Mason, Jan Atchison, Michelle Carter and Nancy Clark. Front, from left: Dave MacIntyre, Greg Eldridge and Ken Dale.

joint hospice-palliative care volunteer training program for those interested in helping people with life threatening illnesses live as comfortably and fully as possible. Volunteers for that kind of help were needed at the hospital, in patients' homes and throughout southern Perth County.

In March 1997, ambulance personnel at SGH began working with Stratford firefighters for calls to the likes of car accidents and heart attacks. Tiered response was the terminology used to describe the new system. In a provincially funded program, SGH personnel were among those helping the firefighters through four days of training designed to upgrade their skills in terms of a first-response team. In addition to first aid and cardiopulmonary resuscitation, the firefighters were required to learn more about victim assessment, anatomy, airway management and ways to control bleeding.

Later that month, Health Minister Wilson returned to Stratford to announce a $2.1 million reinvestment for community-based mental health services for southwestern Ontario. SGH was named the lead agency to sponsor a Huron-Perth crisis intervention program and a full-time crisis-case management service for North Perth, and to that end, Huron-Perth's share of the minister's offering was $647,245.

It was also in March that the hospital's palliative care unit hired music therapist Karen Hughes of New Hamburg to provide eight hours of music therapy a week. Having completed her requirements for graduation from Wilfrid Laurier University at SGH, she was no stranger to hospital personnel and many of its patients. When she resigned, her placed in the palliative care unit was taken by Michelle Holst of Tavistock, who signed on early in 2001.

Meanwhile, the seniors mental health program at Stratford General was preparing to implement psychogeriatric clinic days at

SGH

Bill Smith, a patient on the third floor of the east building, feeds a furry friend during his almost-daily rounds in the hospital courtyard, 1997.

four long-term facilities, to provide on-site psychiatric assessment and consultation. And the sexual assault counselling program was co-sponsoring a dating violence prevention program in four Perth County secondary schools.

It was in May of that year that Fides Coloma, manager of the Ontario branch of the Eye Bank of Canada, was guest speaker at SGH's grand rounds, a gathering of doctors, interns and nursing personnel. In the audience was John Pyper of Stratford, the first physician to send donated eyes to the repository, which was established in 1955. Dr. Pyper was instrumental in the establishment of the eye bank, at a time, he said, "when it was not socially acceptable to remove the eyes of a loved one." At the end of her talk, Ms. Coloma presented the hospital with an award for it being the top eye donor centre in Ontario. The plaque was placed in the SGH lobby. In 1996 the bank received 240 eyes from Stratford, 126 more than from runner-up Milton. "It has gone from being offensive to ask for eye donations to being offensive not to be asked," said Dr. Art vanWalraven, former chief of the hospital's medical staff.

It was also in May that the Huron-Perth District Health Council approved the hospital's $2.5 million plans to build a new maternal-child care department in the east building.

On June 6, Minister of Health Jim Wilson was on hand to officially open SGH's new dialysis unit, which was good news for patients who until then had been required to go out of town for such treatment.

When members of the board met later that month for the hospital's 107th annual meeting, there was talk it might be the last such gathering. The interim governance authority, the committee charged with governance and administrative reform of the eight general hospitals in Huron and Perth counties, had been studying an umbrella board model. Outgoing Stratford board chair Dave Rae described the restructuring process as "a great leap into the unknown." But, he said, it was an essential step if clinical programs were to be maintained, and that SGH continued to support the process.

In September, members of the Stratford and Area Builders Association donated their expertise to create a quiet room and education area in SGH.

Late in October, the hospital officially opened its chemotherapy unit, which had

SGH

SGH board members 1997-98. Front row, from left: past chair Dave Rae, chair Anne Lake, vice-chair John Lichti, chief executive officer Bernie Schmidt. Middle row, from left: honorary director Colleen Misener, Chris Thomson, Mary MacPherson, Marg Wade, Helen Anderson, Ruth Lawson, Barb Culliton and Pat Young. Back row, from left: Dr. Randy Gonser, David Jutzi, Ray Waller, George Schroeder, Dr. David Parratt, Dr. James Hardwick and George Skowby.

been operating for about three years. This opening was to recognize an agreement signed with the London Regional Cancer Centre, which made SGH, as its chief executive officer, Bernie Schmidt, put it, "part of a broader regional effort" against cancer. "We've become very active players in the battle against

To kick off their 1997-98 season the Friends of the Cullitons held a meet-the-Cullitons car wash and raised $150 for the hospital foundation's Equipped to CARE fund. From left: Stratford Hockey Club president Paul Smith, Culliton captain Greg Van Bakel, campaign co-chair Barb Culliton and FOTC president Perry Reibling.

cancer," said Schmidt. "This is an important step for the region, the hospital and most of all our patients."

It was his salary of more than $115,700 that had garnered Schmidt some attention a few months earlier. Under the provincial government's newly established Savings and Restructuring Act, public sector employers were required to disclose the names and salaries and benefits of all employees paid $100,000 or more in the previous calendar year. The hospital's lone employee in that bracket was Schmidt, who also received taxable benefits of almost $1,600.

When a regional diabetes program for Huron-Perth was established, SGH was identified as the intermediate teaching centre for the education program. In November 1997 it was announced that the hospital would receive $160,050 from a $2.5 million Health Ministry program aimed at improving diabetes programs and services.

As 1997 wound down, SGH and the other seven Huron and Perth hospitals were embarking on a patient-focused food

service delivery program that was to run for 18 months. It was to feature heated and chilled food carts and a more efficient and effective delivery of food to patients, who were to have some input on the size of servings. "Our directive was to define opportunities for cost savings without

Dee Innes, nutrition and food services.

compromising quality, programs or service," explained Barbara Collins, the hospital's director of nutrition and food services.

Also by the end of the year, the Equipped to CARE campaign had raised $1,956,244, which represented about 40 per cent of its $5 million goal. More than $24,000 of that money was generated by the sale of a compact disc featuring the vocal and instrumental contributions of dozens of Stratford and area residents. The ambitious project was developed and co-ordinated by Karen and Earl Filsinger, who enlisted the production help of recording engineer Paul Benedict. The CD, titled *A Reason for Giving*, includes 17 traditional Christmas songs, and was available at several outlets for $20 ($15 for the tape version).

Several months earlier, Doug McNall of Stratford had recorded 11 songs, most of them written by himself, and promised $3 from the sale of each tape to the hospital's fund-raising campaign.

Less musical but equally enthusiastic were the Stratford Optimists, who gave $60,000 to the campaign. The money, bound for the maternal-child unit, was more than half of the $110,000 the Optimists raised in their Dream-a-Reality Lottery.

From the Perth Regiment Chapter of the Imperial Order Daughters of the Empire came a cheque for $2,800, which was used to buy a portable ultrasound machine.

Never far from the front lines when it comes to supporting SGH, the hospital's auxiliary association pledged $220,000 to the campaign, and that resulted in the purchase of a state-of-the-art Bennett Contour mammography unit. Another $30,000 or so from the auxiliary was spent on three high-tech beds for the intensive care unit and a laser printer for electrocardiograms (ECGs).

A pledge for $50,000 came from the Canadian Imperial Bank of Commerce and from the RBC Foundation and the Royal

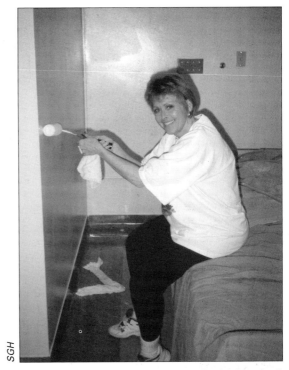

SGH

Employee Laurie Brown (medical imaging) volunteers her painting skills to help ready the new mammography suite, spring 1997.

Bank, and one for $37,500 from each of the Toronto Dominion Bank and the Bank of Nova Scotia.

The $10,000 donated by the Huron-Perth lung association was used for the purchase of equipment for a new pulmonary rehabilitation program.

Standard Products (Canada) Ltd, with factories in Stratford and Mitchell, pledged $100,000 through 2001. From the Knights of Columbus in Mitchell came $1,500.

Also in 1997, there was a spring social and dance, which included a taster's delight table, at the Church Restaurant. And when comedian Simon Cotter of Toronto returned to Stratford to perform at the Royal Canadian Legion Hall, he donated the proceeds to the Care campaign in memory of his father-in-law Emil Ruf.

When members of the housekeeping and linen services staff at SGH received a new buffer from the campaign's equipment wish list, they celebrated with two bake sales and three cheese sales and raised $1,530.

The hospital's Christmas mailout to donors generated about $98,770, just short of its $100,000 goal. "We're really pleased to have this kind of support from the community," said SGH Foundation's development director Andrea Page. "We're very pleased to see that outcome, especially when other charities are reporting a 30 per cent drop from their mailouts."

In January 1998 the Bank of Montreal presented a cheque for $12,500 to the campaign's co-chairs. It was the first instalment of a four-year $50,000 pledge.

In February came a cheque for $8,500 from the Stratford branch of the Royal Canadian Legion. Some of that money was used to buy a critical care stretcher, and the rest went to the intensive care and emergency units.

In March the Olde English Parlour hosted another Equipped to CARE fund-raising surf and turf dinner. Half of each $29.95 ticket went directly to the campaign. In the same month, Elaine Gibb donated laparoscopic instruments and a flexible cystoscope to the hospital's surgical department in memory of her husband Ron, who had died about seven months earlier, at age 63. "I wanted to do this from the bottom of my heart," said his widow. "The hospital has been there for me and my family many, many times, and I wanted to do this in Ron's memory."

The Stratford and Area Regional Council of Registered Practical Nurses raised about $500 and used it to buy a commode chair for the surgical floor in the east building. They made their presentation on May 13, RPN day.

That summer, the family-owned Beaulieu of Canada company pledged $24,000 to the Care campaign for the purchase of a security system for the new maternal-child unit. By the time the 19,845-square-foot,

SGH

Obstetrician Nancy Whitmore with a newborn in SGH's new maternity unit, September 1997.

child-friendly unit was officially opened, on July 27, its price tag had crept to $3 million. The hospital had tried without success to have the Ministry of Health share in the costs of the new unit.

The state-of-the-art birthing facilities in Stratford played a part in St. Marys Memorial Hospital's decision to close its obstetrics unit in September 1998. In 1999-2000, a record 1,050 babies were born in SGH, and that total was surpassed in the following year.

In January 1998 SGH learned it was getting $477,600 from the province to help offset the costs it had incurred in following the government's order to restructure in 1996-97. Stratford's CEO, Bernie Schmidt, called the news bittersweet, in that the hospital's costs had been closer to $1.1 million. The costs associated with restructuring, which he said SGH had started as far back as 1992, related mostly to early retirement packages for employees who chose to leave, termination benefits for those who were told to leave, and shortened work weeks. As well, there were costs to take part in the many meetings with other hospitals in Huron and Perth, as the

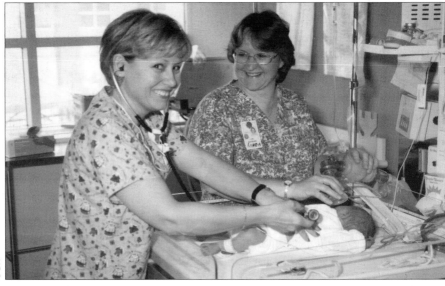

SGH

Nurses Dianne Youmans (left) and Linda Reid with a patient in the maternal child unit.

trustees and administrators of each wrestled with the establishment of a joint board charged with sharing services and reducing expenses.

It was also in that January that the Ontario government ordered the Huron-Perth District Health Council to amalgamate with its counterpart in Grey and Bruce counties. The new Grey Bruce Huron Perth District Health Council, within whose jurisdiction fell 20 hospitals, was one of 16 such amalgamated councils across the province. The government gave all of them until Aug. 14, 1998, to respond to the restructuring commission's choices in creating the amalgamated councils.

In February 1998, SGH was taken to task for renting out the dormitory-style rooms in the former Youngs Street nurses residence. Specifically, the hospital had been making the 165 rooms available to tourists through the Stratford Festival season. In fact, said Schmidt, SGH had been doing that for close to two decades, and he couldn't understand why the city's hotel-motel association was suddenly in a flap about it. "It (the residence) has never been as strongly

promoted as it is now," explained Mike Mitchell, the association's lawyer. He suggested the hospital was targeting all tourists with its advertising, not just students and seniors, and that it was unfair competition for his clients.

Schmidt said SGH was not out to make a profit with the room rentals, but that it needed to generate revenue to cover the building's maintenance costs. He also said the residence had been averaging about 7,000 bed nights a season, 88 per cent of them from groups, mostly students and seniors. That business, he added, meant an estimated 14,000 tickets for the Festival.

Initially, the debate between the hospital and the hotel-motel association, at times heated, played out in the council chambers at City Hall because what SGH was doing was illegal. Under the existing zoning bylaw, rooms in the residence could not be rented out by the hospital. Its lawyer, John Skinner, argued for an amendment to the bylaw.

For this year the hospital was allowed to continue renting the rooms under a temporary-use bylaw. But the hotel and motel operators were not about to roll over, and the matter wound up before the Ontario Municipal Board. It ruled in their favour and told the city to repeal its temporary-use bylaw. In March 1999, with the help of a mediator, the two sides were able to strike a compromise, albeit one they chose not to disclose, and the hospital continued to rent out the rooms in the residence.

In March 1998 SGH received $100,000 from the Ontario Health Ministry to expand its speech and language services for preschool-age children in Huron and Perth counties.

By April, 10 family doctors had started an after-hours clinic in the medical building at the corner of John and Cambria streets. "The idea is to take the pressure off the emergency department by looking after the routine, daily stuff," said Dr. David Williams. "With regionalization coming down the road, waiting times can become quite protracted for things like kids with sore throats. This is a means of addressing that and providing easier access to the emergency department for more serious cases." The clinic is now at 93 St. Vincent St. N.

In May the hospital announced an operational shortfall of $192,810 for the fiscal year that had ended on March 31. But, said George Schroeder, chair of the board's finance committee, that loss was well below the projected deficit of $987,000.

It was also in May that the hospital took part in Operation Twister, a city-wide exercise designed to test the emergency services in Stratford. Twenty volunteer "patients" with assorted injuries were processed through emergency.

In June 1998, SGH received a further $600,000 from the Health Ministry to help with its restructuring costs. In light of a projected $1.6 million operating loss for 1998-99, Stratford board chair Anne Lake said, "We're happy with anything we can get at this point. It means we won't have to cut our programs." However, she added, SGH had reduced its staff by 25 per cent since 1992 because the provincial government had slashed the hospital's budget by $3 million over the previous two years. In October the Health Ministry came up with another $563,000 – to be shared among the three hospitals in Perth.

By the end of October 1998, the Huron

SGH chief executive officer Bernie Schmidt (serving inside), nurse manager in maternal-child Sheila Knechtel and director of human resources Barry Cameron (doing windshields) work McHappy Day at the Stratford McDonald's outlet, May 6, 1998. Half of the $4,440 raised was directed to equipment for the hospital's new maternity unit.

Perth Hospitals Partnership had been formed, an extension of the alternative approach developed by the chief executive officers of the eight hospitals within the two counties.

The first official day on the job for the HPHP's president and CEO, London native Bonnie

SGH

In the summer of 1998 a duck and her brood settled in at the SGH residence on John Street, where they particularly enjoyed the pool. Jarod Smellie, recruited by his mother Brenda of housekeeping and linen services, could not corral the mother but did round up the ducklings and relocated them at the Smellie farm near Harrington.

Adamson, was Nov. 1. That was the day after Bernie Schmidt, by then being paid $155,540 a year, had left his job as CEO at SGH. Lake said she was saddened by his decision to not be a part of the team required to guide and ease SGH into the partnership. By the end of November the site administrator at Stratford was 36-year-old Andrew Williams, who had joined SGH in 1991 as assistant executive director of planning and hospital services.

By year's end, Adamson, who came to the partnership from the London Health Sciences Centre, was looking for five vice-presidents to do the work of her eight site administrators. One of those V-Ps would be named chief financial officer for the partnership's $100-million budget. "We're just beginning down the road of a series of changes we hope will positively impact all communities involved," she said. "The fear of any hospital closures is behind us now, but it's too soon to say how much money we'll be saving yet." Adamson was working out of the HPHP's offices in Seaforth, for the partnership's 24-person executive committee, which comprised three

representatives for each hospital.

All the while, personnel at SGH continued to plan for the relocation of the operating rooms and intensive care unit to the second floor of the west building, and for doubling the size of the emergency department.

Service in the medical imaging department was broadened with the addition of bone mineral densitometry equipment. It's used to measure the calcium content of bones and help in the diagnosis

SGH

Dr. Yale Erenberg, former director of medical imaging

91

of osteoporosis.

Surgeries such as gall bladder removal, hernia repair, cataract extraction with lens implants, and tonsillectomies – previously performed as in-patient procedures – were by now being done on an out-patient basis.

The kidney dialysis unit, which opened in May 1997 with two patients, was now treating 10. Admissions to the chronic care unit had jumped by 96 per cent and in the rehabilitation unit the numbers were up by 50 per cent.

By mid-February 1999, Adamson and the partnership had hired their five vice-presidents, and two of them, Williams and Barry Cameron, were from SGH. Williams and Janice Cosgrove each was named a V-P multi-site administration with system-wide administrative and clinical responsibilities. He was to directly oversee SGH, Seaforth Community and St. Marys Memorial. She was to run the hospitals in Goderich, Clinton and Exeter.

Cameron, who had been director of human resources at SGH since 1987, was appointed V-P human resources and organizational development. His duties also included the development and maintenance of system-wide labour relations, occupational health and safety, and learning services.

John Sutherland became V-P finance and information management, including the development and maintenance of integrated system-wide information technology, information systems, tele-health services, utilization and risk management.

Margrét Comack, from Toronto East General, was the lone hire from outside Huron and Perth hospitals. As a V-P multi-site administration, she became directly responsible for the hospitals in Wingham and Listowel, as well as the development of continuing quality improvement and professional practice leadership programs system-wide.

The eight hospitals had been spending $5

million each year on 70 management positions, said Adamson, but with the new system there would be no more than three levels of management and in some cases just two.

The English-born Williams, who had been the site administrator in Stratford and Seaforth, said he was "happy to continue working in Stratford and very excited about working in St. Marys. I know about the programs and services in St. Marys, but there's still going to be a learning curve."

In March SGH was looking at a deficit of $2.4 million for 1998-99, and, while the Health Services Restructuring Commission supported the formation of the eight-hospital partnership in Huron and Perth, it was allocating no capital funding. "Continuing requests for these essential funds will be an ongoing priority," said Adamson. The partnership was projecting a deficit of $3.1 million over the next year. According to Williams, SGH was looking at a shortfall of $2.4 million in 1999 and $2.8 in 2000. Those projections were lowered later in March when the government came up with $715,000 in new funding for the partnership.

In April the same government excluded Stratford from the list of 49 hospitals in line for a share of $83 million in capital funding for emergency room renovations. The shutout didn't surprise Adamson because the restructuring commission had only recently evaluated SGH and its partners. "We were late in the process," she said. "The Stratford board is continuing to work diligently with the (health) ministry . . . to bring their attention to how the sequencing has affected Stratford's needs."

Within a couple of weeks the pain of that slight was soothed somewhat when the ministry came up with a further $2,362,000 for SGH. Most of it, $1.49 million, was to help it eliminate its deficit. The remaining $872,000 was for the hiring of more nurses.

It was early in 1999 that the Equipped to

CARE campaign reached $2,569,528 – better than half of the $5-million goal. SGH workers, who had set their goal at $60,000, raised more than $71,000.

Other money came in from the Stratford Professional Firefighters, who raised it through the sale of a calendar for which they posed. City photographer Terry Manzo volunteered her time to shoot the pictures, and other donors covered the production costs.

The Tavistock Jets women's hockey team played the Revs on Ice at the Tavistock arena and donated all proceeds from the exhibition game.

Stratford and area Masons gathered for breakfast at the Garden Grove Restaurant and raised $1,163 for the campaign. That was double what they had been able to collect at their breakfast in 1998. To increase the donation, staff at the restaurant worked the breakfast without remuneration.

For the second winter in a row, SGH workers found themselves battling a flu outbreak. In an effort to control the spread of what was identified as Sydney-strains A and B, the hospital isolated the chronic care and rehab ward and restricted group activities and ward visits.

It was in January 1999 that SGH hired its first full-time emergency physician, Miriam Mann.

SGH

Site administrator Andrew Williams and campaign co-chair Barb Culliton hold the ladder as Dr. James Hardwick uses a brush to paint the $5-million Equipped to CARE campaign past the halfway mark, March 1999.

In March the government pledged $27 million to allow new mothers the option of remaining under hospital care for a guaranteed 60 hours after childbirth. Stratford's share of that pledge was $152,852. Premier Mike Harris said he wanted to quash the perception that new mothers and their infants were being pushed out of hospitals. The 60-hour guarantee caused more than a little consternation at SGH, where the new maternal-child unit had been designed, approved and built around stays of 24 and 48 hours. About half of the mothers and their newborns were staying 24 hours, the other half about 48 hours. Difficult deliveries could require longer stays, said Lynn Strugnell, assistant director of patient care services, but "no one is thrown out the door."

With the Harris mandate, the Stratford maternal-child facility became undersized within about eight months of its official opening. If that weren't bad enough, SGH had still received no government funding to help pay for building and equipping the unit. In an effort to remedy the latter, board chair Anne Lake sent letters to the health minister, the deputy health minister and to Bert Johnson, Perth County's representative in the Ontario legislature. She complained that the government's restructuring commission had give SGH short shrift, or "it would have confirmed that we have had too much money removed from our funding base. Unlike most urban hospitals in Ontario who have had billions of capital dollars allocated to them and have been sized operationally by the ministry, SGH continues to operate in isolation with limited assistance from your government." Specifically, she sought retroactive funding for the maternal-child unit as well as for other capital projects. Eventually, the hospital received about $160,000 for the maternity ward, says Andrew Williams.

In June, he and Adamson took part in a public forum at St. Marys Memorial Hospital. Its purpose was to sell the partnership idea and to give citizens some insight into what the new arrangement would mean to them. The vision of the partnership, said Adamson, was "to be an innovative patient and family focused health care system characterized by excellent quality in co-ordinated care programs and supportive services, appropriate standardization, enhanced access to care and services, and a

commitment to quality, unity, integration, leadership and teamwork." She also said, "Maintaining all sites is a given. About 25 people took in the St. Marys presentation. Similar get-togethers were planned for the other seven hospitals within the partnership, said Adamson.

It was also in June, at its annual meeting, that SGH reported its operating deficit for 1998-99 was $1.2 million, much of which it attributed to negotiated wage increases, pay equity payments and the fact that the hospital had treated an increased number of patients, for which it had received no additional government funding. For 1999-2000, Stratford officials were predicting their budget of about $44 would be about $2.8 million short on the revenue side. Still, the meeting was told, SGH was outperforming the Health Ministry's cost-per-patient benchmark by $91 per case. "I believe Stratford General Hospital has a wonderful future," said outgoing board chair Anne Lake.

By August that future included a lot of concern for bugs and viruses of a different sort.

Like much of the wired world, SGH was preparing for the challenge of something dubbed Y2K. Specifically, officials were worried about how their computers and computer-operated equipment – most of it date sensitive – would handle the calendar rolling over to 01-01-2000. To ease that worry, they conducted tests, updated their installations, ran backups, audited systems, reviewed and revised contingency and emergency plans, and stocked up on medical supplies, food, water, blood, linen and fuel. "By the end of October I expect everything will be at 100 per cent," said Andrew Williams. Well before the deadline, all hospitals in the HPHP were declared prepared for the new millennium.

In October SGH became the 48th site in the province to offer the Ontario Breast Cancer Screening Program, which was expected to serve between 1,500 and 2,000 city and area women a year. Women 50 to 69 years of age were invited to simply phone for an appointment; they needed no doctor's referral. After a first examination, each was to be recalled for re-examination every two years. Results were to be sent to each patient and to her physician.

In November the HPHP received a grant from the Change Foundation and directed the money to a rural medicine program linked to the University of Western Ontario and the London Health Sciences Centre. Over four weeks, the HPHP was able to train 10 medical students "in health informatics and evidence-based preventive medicine" and then send them into the field for six weeks. There, they were expected to train and support three rural physicians in "identifying and accessing appropriate resources for addressing practice-related questions; searching and evaluating evidence-based medicine and Internet sources; and accessing and using the resources on the project Web site. As well, they were to provide each physician with a computer device and "train the physicians in its uses as well as in the use of the project-specific tools installed on the device."

At the same time, the medical students would be spending two summers learning about rural family medicine. The Change Foundation, part of the Ontario Hospital Association, disburses money from fund-raisers such as lotteries.

Early in December a deer that had been grazing in the south courtyard crashed through a double-glass window and wound up in the main lobby of the hospital. It then slammed into some other windows in an effort to escape. It was eventually coaxed out through the doors leading to the courtyard and headed west towards the Old Grove. Its injuries included a broken antler and cuts to its head and mouth.

Later that month the HPHP drew high praise from the Health Services Restructuring Commission. "After our review of the hospital network in Huron-Perth, we would probably direct that the joint executive committee be given a collective Order of Ontario," said lead commissioner Duncan Sinclair. That review included no visit to SGH. Rather, Dr. Sinclair met once with the partnership's eight board chairs, in Mitchell, and delivered some governance requirements. As Lake puts it, there was a "lack of restructuring directive" from the commission to the hospitals in Huron and Perth.

Also in December, the HPHP scored "above average" in patient satisfaction in the Ontario Hospital Association's 500-page report card on the province's hospitals. Far from a friendly user guide for taxpayers, the report was intended more to help hospitals than their patients, said the OHA. While the Ontario Health Coalition slammed the report, Adamson said, "We are extremely pleased with the results of this groundbreaking study. Our overall above-average score in patient satisfaction is particularly gratifying. It is excellent news for all our partner hospitals."

Then, two days before Christmas, the partnership received $552,000 from the Health Ministry for "front-line patient care and transitional expenses." SGH's share was $284,000, but, said Ken Haworth, the hospital's director of finance, "We don't know what, if any, strings are attached." He said, if allowed, the money would likely go towards the hospital's projected deficit.

From supporters closer to home, the hospital received another Christmas gift. Brothers Chuck and Stan Dingman, who five months earlier had sold the *Stratford Beacon Herald*, forwarded $10,000, which they earmarked for new furniture for the patient waiting area in the mental health services department. They made the donation as a gesture of thanks to their former employees, which numbered about 100 at the time of the sale.

Bringing comfort to the dying

By Diane Sewell
Staff reporter

MAR 1 8 2000

Eugene Dufour has been in the palliative care field for 15 years now. That represents a lot of grief, but a tremendous amount of experience as well.

Eugene Dufour

STRATFORD BEACON-HERALD

As palliative care co-ordinator at Stratford General Hospital, Mr. Dufour has worked with hospital administration, local physicians and staff to create a standard of palliative care renowned throughout Canada and the United States.

He points out that SGH provides 12 palliative care beds for a population base of about 60,000 people, while London provides 22 beds for 400,000.

The palliative care unit at SGH is currently the model for North America and continues to attract eager-to-learn palliative care workers from far afield.

In recognition of Mr. Dufour's knowledge and contribution to the field, he was recently elected vice-president of the Canadian Palliative Care Association. "It was quite an honour," he says.

After serving a two-year term in that role, he'll automatically become its president. For the past three years he was president of the Ontario Palliative Care Association.

In December he was also hired to fill the newly-created role of regional palliative care co-ordinator for the eigh-hospital Huron-Perth Hospitals Partnership, which includes SGH. Part of his job will be to train palliative care teams throughout the two counties, helping them do what he and his team at SGH already do. Much of the focus will be on long-term care facilities.

That new job is supposed to take up 30 per cent of his time, while his role at SGH takes up the remaining 70 per cent. He admits the time often adds up to much more than 100 per cent. Forty-hour work weeks are virtually non-existent.

Mr. Dufour entered the field 15 years ago at a London hospice. It was the beginning of the AIDS epidemic. When he started he had a caseload of 72 patients. Nine months later they were all dead.

Since then, he's encountered every kind of situation imaginable. His involvement with the dead and the dying, and their families, has brought him face to face with the top issues surrounding the field of palliative care.

No doubt his involvement at the national and provincial levels will serve the field well.

Meanwhile, he and his local team members will continue to do the grassroots work of serving those most in need. As he's fond of saying, "we're not focused on cure. We're focused on comfort."

A foot in the new millennium

Stratford General, like the rest of the world, ushered in the 21st century without a hitch. The Y2K bug, as everyone learned, was more fiction than fact, more talk than balk.

So, when Feb. 29 came around as the calendar said it would, medical assistant Bernie Van Herk celebrated his birthday as he always had at SGH – by giving a card and $10 bill to the parents of babies born in Stratford on that day. "I thought it was a special day and felt that for children born on the same day it was a nice idea to share my birthday with them," he said. Since SGH had become a regional centre, his number of gifts had grown. In this leap year he helped welcome six new Canadians – four boys and two girls – into the world. But, at age 64, and after a quarter of a century at the hospital, it was his last such celebration. Even leap-year babies retire.

This year was the first for Eugene Dufour in the newly created role of regional palliative care co-ordinator for the Huron Perth Hospitals Partnership. As palliative care co-ordinator at SGH, he had also just been elected vice-president of the Canadian Palliative Care Association and was finishing a three-year term as president of the Ontario Palliative Care Association. He said Stratford's unit, with 12 beds for a population base of about 60,000, had become the model for North America. His new role called for him to train palliative care teams at the other seven hospitals in the partnership. But it was a role he would fill for only a year or so, before taking a job in Vancouver in the spring of 2002.

Meanwhile, his team in Stratford was bolstered by the addition of Van Woolnough, a 59-year-old Stratford doctor who had been paralyzed in a kayaking accident in 1999. "We're just thrilled to have him," said Dufour. "As a family physician for over 30 years, he already has many of the skills we need. With that kind of background and a little extra training in grief theory, he'll be perfect for the job." Dr. Woolnough had started his training in palliative care during his rehabilitation at

Parkwood Hospital in London, and it had helped to pull him from "the depths of despair."

Another addition to the unit was a one-year pilot project called Pain and Symptom Management. Funded by a $45,000 grant from the Health Ministry, the program was headed by Judy White, co-ordinator of the North Perth Community Hospice and a part-time nurse in the palliative care unit at SGH. The aim of the project was to connect people and their families with the kinds of services they need when they are dealing with a life-threatening or terminal illness. "It's the whole team approach," said White. "My job is to offer the care – emotional, physical, spiritual, everything. At the end of it I'm going to prove to the ministry we need a program."

In March 2000 the Huron Perth Hospitals Partnership and the medical school at the University of Western Ontario in London formed an education partnership designed to better train doctors by using various skill sets that exist in Huron and Perth counties. "It's nuts to think that the only expertise is in the City of London," said Dr. Carol Herbert, UWO's dean of medicine and dentistry. She also said she was most impressed by the palliative care and maternity units at SGH. The trade-off for the HPHP, it was hoped, would be more new doctors choosing to set up rural practices.

In May 2000 the provincial government's Health Services Restructuring Commission released its *Report on Rural and Northern Hospital Networks: Advice and Recommendations*, and it declared the HPHP to be "in an excellent position to deliver quality benefits" to its member communities. The authors said they were "encouraged by the achievements they saw." HPHP president and CEO Bonnie Adamson called the report good news: "We've had a vision and that vision has been recognized. We've met with their

SGH

Former board chairs John Callan (left) and Dave Rae at a tree-planting ceremony in June 2000.

approval and we are very pleased about that." But, she added, there is much work yet to be done, and a lot of it depended on securing more capital funding for the partnership generally, as well as more operating monies, in particular for SGH, which was facing a projected deficit of $1.3 million for 2000-2001.

In that same month, McDonald's Restaurants' annual McHappy Day generated $4,280 for SGH. The hospital had a number of volunteers helping at McDonald's that day, which "gives us a chance to do some friend-raising, as well," said Linda Jones, executive director of the Stratford General Hospital Foundation.

Early in June, the Health Ministry did a little friend-raising as well, in announcing it was giving the partnership another $2,118,729, of which the lion's share, $942,920, was addressed to Stratford General.

After two straight deficits, SGH ended its 1999-2000 fiscal year with a surplus of $400,347, according to the report prepared by the hospital's resources committee (previously known as the finance committee). Not lost in that report was the role played by one-time funding from the Health Ministry in achieving the surplus. "Stratford General Hospital, in its capacity as the regional referral centre, will continue to face challenging financial environments in the coming years if it is to maintain the existing services now in place, as well as deal with issues such as patient repatriation from larger urban centres without financial recognition from the Ministry of Health and Long Term Care," noted the report.

On Oct. 14, 2000, Stratford joined more than 500 towns and cities in 38 countries in a worldwide hospice concert. Sponsored by British Telecommunications, its purpose was to support hospice and palliative care. The concert in St. John's United Church in Stratford featured the Perth County Children's Choir, the 1939 Casino Band, the Stonetown Entertainers, the Amazing Grace Jazz Choir, the Stratford Male Chorus, the St. Mary's Children's Choir, the Stratford Spirit Singers, the Perth County Youth Choir, Cow and Sow, and the Stratford Concert Choir. It was a timely event, in that about two weeks earlier those running the hospice and palliative care facilities in Stratford had appealed for volunteers.

Also in October, the Health Ministry came through with another $3.6 million for the Huron Perth partnership. The $900,000 directed to SGH would allow that member to eliminate its projected $1-million deficit.

In December, officials at SGH learned they were in line for a further $147,263 in government money, to expand their specialized services. Stratford site administrator Andrew Williams said the money would go to the hospital's special-care nursery and orthopedic programs.

In March 2001 the Festival Jubilee and Perth Regiment chapters of the Imperial Order Daughters of the Empire gave the Equipped to CARE campaign $34,000 for the purchase of a gamma probe, a

diagnostic tool used to detect the spread of cancer.

In April, SGH staffers put on a fashion show, dinner and dance and raised more than $2,800 in support of the campaign. The Stratford on Avon Shrine Club donated $2,000 and directed the money towards a pulse oximeter for pediatrics. Shortly, the CARE fund had passed the $4.3-million mark, and the money kept coming, $24,000

STRATFORD BEACON HERALD

Dr. Miriam Mann (left) and Marilyn Finnigan do some rehearsing for the fashion show they and other SGH staff members put on, April 6, 2001, to raise money for the Equipped to CARE campaign.

of it from the first two Golf for the Health of It tournaments sponsored by Royal LePage Hiller Realty.

It was also in March 2001 that the hospital got another $646,275 from the

Clinical leader Wayne Priestap serves assorted treats to volunteer Verna Maitland during the hospital's annual volunteer appreciation tea, April 2001.

Health Ministry, this time to upgrade its CT scanner and to modernize other medical equipment. Actually, the funding was reimbursement for money SGH had already spent on improvements.

When its 2000-2001 fiscal year ended on March 31, the hospital found itself with an operating surplus of $887,864. That was due in no small part to a savings of $800,000 across the Huron Perth partnership in food services. The partnership initiative is "a stroke of genius," declared outgoing board chair John Lichti at the SGH annual meeting in June. Partnership president and CEO Bonnie Adamson said the hospital had "lots to be proud of."

"That surplus is significant for us," reasoned Stratford site administrator Andrew Williams. "It allows us to have some money available to invest in things we need to do. And you can't do that when you operate in a deficit position." He praised the SGH employees and volunteers for helping to put the hospital in the black.

In general, volunteers everywhere were getting a bigger share of the spotlight, in that 2001 was the International Year of Volunteers. SGH acknowledged theirs in newspaper ads and held an appreciation reception for them in April. In Stratford, the appreciation reception had become an annual event.

In July, when the provincial government allocated $200 million to its 164 hospitals, the share for SGH amounted to more than $1.6 million. Williams said $617,000 would be spent on six new beds, already approved by the Health Ministry. The hospital was also going to establish some "flex beds," which could be used when needed – in the flu season, for instance.

It was about then that beds were much on the minds of those working in the maternity ward, where births were expected

Nurse Jean Aitcheson at a staff association barbecue, August 2001.

to reach 1,000 by year's end. In 2000 there were 816 births at SGH. Donnalene Tuer-Hodes, clinical leader for the ward, attributed the increased activity in part to the new year-long maternity leaves available to parents. But she also said the hospital's "baby-friendly" maternal unit was appealing to more than just Stratford and Perth County residents. "We're drawing from a larger area," said Linda Youngblut, the ward's clinical resource nurse. "I think part of our appeal is that we have a new unit and great doctors here."

In September 2001, SGH qualified for $226,143 in government money to upgrade and modernize some of its medical equipment. In the same outpouring of funds, Perth County ambulance services were given $34,521 to replace vehicles and equipment such as defibrillators. Two other hospitals in the Huron Perth partnership, St. Marys and Listowel, also received some of the money.

In November, HPHP project manager Gwen Devereaux effused the partnership's philosophy at a brainstorming session involving municipal and education officials from Huron and Perth counties. Mostly, the participants were discussing the worth of unified promotion for economic development. "When you promote regionally, you become stronger," Devereaux told them.

Indeed, unification was a hot topic within the HPHP about then, but not everyone was buying tickets for the same train. In January 2002, six of the partnership's eight hospitals announced they were studying the possibility of uniting under one board of governors. The two sitting out were Listowel Memorial and Wingham and District.

Spokesman for the six was Paul Howley, the SGH board chair as well as a member of the partnership's joint executive committee and the chair of its governance task team. "A single organization with six sites may be

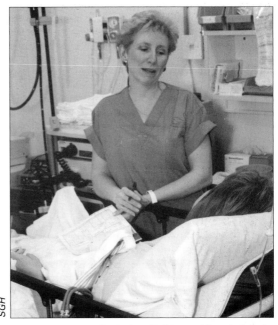

Registered nurse Ruth Ann Robinet with a patient in surgical day care, 2001.

better able to address the human resource, fiscal and other challenges confronting our hospitals," he said. He also said the six boards involved in the study had retained health care experts to seek the views of all interested parties.

In March, after receiving two reports from those experts, the six hospitals decided to forego amalgamation, at least in the near future.

All the while, SGH's Equipped to CARE campaign was creeping close to its $5-million goal, helped by the likes of a 24-hour marathon of squash at the Stratford County Club and a seemingly endless number of cheques from the hospital's auxiliary.

By March, the total stood at $5.09 million, and, in the spirit of the recent Winter Olympics, the SGH Foundation presented gold medals to six key players in the five-year drive: Barb Culliton, campaign co-chair; Pat Million, the auxiliary president; Anne Reintjes of the employee campaign council; Lori Stewart of the staff association; Brenda Smellie of housekeeping and linen services, the top fund-raising department; and Andrea Page, executive director of the foundation. Page said the successful campaign was "a real milestone for the foundation."

SGH

Sharon Crozier (left) and Kelly Dubrick, patient registration.

But the fund-raising continued. In April, SGH staffers put on another fashion show, dinner and dance, this one called *A Feast for the Eyes*. It raised more than $3,200. And there was another evening of music at St. Andrew's Church, also in April.

In the same month, the hospital once again found itself in the news for renting out the rooms in its former nurses residence. The compromise reached in March 1999 by SGH and the city's hotel-motel association didn't last past the end of the 2001 Stratford Festival season. And once again the matter wound up at Stratford City Hall. This time the councillors formally approved a bylaw and official plan amendment that allowed the hospital to continue using its 165-room facility as a hostel.

In May the mood was more celebratory than confrontational when SGH unveiled a four-sided kiosk bearing the names of those who contributed $1,000 or more to the Equipped to CARE campaign. Foundation chair Chris Thomson told the assembled that it was 24,271 donations from 5,500

donors that took the campaign past its goal of $5 million. "Your generosity is simply overwhelming," he said. The kiosk is in the main lobby of the hospital, and on it are the names of 350 individuals, groups, foundations, businesses and corporations. Auxiliary members Anna Walkom and Bob Dawson pulled the cords that facilitated the unveiling.

Also in May, Bonnie Adamson resigned as president and chief executive officer of the Huron Perth Hospitals Partnership for a job with the same title at North York General Hospital in Toronto. "This is an excellent career opportunity, and I look forward to the challenges that lie ahead," said Adamson, whose resignation took effect Aug. 16. The job she left with the HP partnership paid her $184,003 plus taxable benefits of $7,890 in 2001.

Near the end of June, Adamson was at SGH's 2002 annual meeting to deliver some farewell remarks. She urged the Stratford board to continue recruiting health care professionals, and then work to retain them.

She also stressed the importance of providing educational opportunities for staff.

At the same meeting, the board members learned they ended their 2001-2002 fiscal year with an operating deficit of $576,624, which was a little more than one per cent of their $52.4 million budget. Williams and the hospital's director of finance Ken Haworth blamed that shortfall on the inflationary pressure of not being completely funded, increased volumes of acute patient care, additional physicians bringing in more patients and the repatriation of patients living in Perth and Huron counties who previously would have been cared for by hospitals in London.

"We're a bit concerned we haven't got cash in the bank, and sustaining a deficit over a long period is difficult," conceded Williams. Within 24 hours he was breathing a little easier, after the government announced it would be giving the Huron Perth partnership an additional $3.2 million in funding.

Dr. Brian Hasegawa, plastic surgeon

Within two weeks, SGH announced it was pulling out of that partnership. "We are a very progressive board looking to improve, and we're examining ways to do that," said SGH board chair Paul Howley. He said the move had nothing to do with the failure of an amalgamation proposal that called for the hospitals in Stratford, Exeter, Goderich, St. Marys, Seaforth and Clinton to come under one administration.

To leave the highly touted HP partnership, Stratford was required to give a year's notice, which it did in a letter dated July 10, 2002.

In August, Seaforth Community Hospital followed SGH's lead and gave the partnership its withdrawal notice. Then St. Marys opted out, then Exeter, Clinton and Goderich. "The partnership is fully operational and working and doing the job it is supposed to do, at least until July 10 next year, when Stratford's notice period is over," said Howley. He predicted that before then, the partnership would re-invent itself with a modified set of responsibilities.

With Adamson gone, the running of the HPHP fell to John Sutherland, who was named acting president and CEO, and to four vice-presidents, of whom some, like Williams, were also site administrators. In 2001 their annual salaries ranged from $118,923 to $128,495 plus taxable benefits of between $1,363 and $1,517.

Still in place was the joint executive committee, comprising three members from each partner. The SGH board members on that committee were Howley, Jo Deslippe and physician Laurel Moore. More than 11 decades after it opened, the hospital they represented had 142 beds (97 acute, 30 chronic, 15 rehabilitation) but no cow or chickens. Its range of services included obstetrics, pediatrics, psychiatry and internal medicine. Numbered among the specialities in its surgical unit were orthopedics, urology, gynecology, ophthalmology, plastic surgery and ear, nose and throat procedures. The SGH of 2002 had maternal-child facilities that were second to none, and a satellite dialysis unit. And it was providing 24-hour emergency services.

Clinical resource nurse Cathy McCarroll (left) and acting nurse manager in the operating room Donnalene Hodes-Tuer.

About 72 per cent of the patients now treated at SGH by the 72 physicians associated with the hospital are from Perth County. Another 13 per cent are from Huron County, seven per cent from Oxford County, three per cent from Wellington County and five per cent from other counties.

By year's end, SGH had signed a letter of intent to join three other hospitals – in

Emergency room nurse Marilyn Finnigan with surgeon Randy Gonser.

Seaforth, St. Marys and Clinton – in a new arrangement. At the same time, the hospitals in Wingham and Listowel were said to be pairing up. In December 2002, Andrew Williams was named chief executive officer of the proposed alliance that would include SGH.

The HPHP said its eight members were moving from a partnership to a network of voluntary co-operation. The network is not to be involved in any aspect of direct patient care, but members are to continue sharing administrative and support services.

While Huron and Perth partnership members were meeting inside their hospitals to map out the future, some of their employees were parading outside in an effort to right what they considered to be wrongs of the past. Social workers, therapists, and X-ray and lab technicians – members of the Ontario Public Service Employees Union – held rallies to press for a new collective agreement and to protest working conditions. The workers, from 40 hospitals across the province, including SGH, had been without a contract for about nine months, and they said they would continue job action until they ratified a new deal with the Ontario Hospital Association.

Also by year's end, officials at SGH were focusing on a $20-million critical care redevelopment that includes reconfiguring and doubling the size of the emergency department; relocating the operating rooms, recovery room and intensive care unit to expand their size and configuration; expanding the maternal-child unit; and increasing the space in its 18-bed inpatient psychiatry unit.

"Our current emerg (department) has 14 beds and we're now seeing 28,000 patients a year," says Dr. Miriam Mann, chief of emergency services. "That's far greater than we used to see."

"It's like anything that was built in the 1950s," says site administrator Andrew Williams. "It's like a car built in the '50s. It meets the needs of 1950, but it doesn't meet today's needs."

To facilitate those upgrades, SGH officials plan to complete and maximize the space in the east building; expand the emergency department east to the tree line in the courtyard; and enlarge the second floor of the west building with additions atop the CT scanner facility and the new section of the emergency department.

As well, the plans call for overhauling the mechanical and electrical systems in the 50-year-old west wing (an overhaul that includes the addition of air-conditioning), and relocating and expanding the medical ambulatory care programs and the materials management department.

The cost estimates are to be updated early in 2003, and the rest of the timeline is to be established after SGH receives Ministry of Health approval for the project.

The proposed cost sharing for the project has been summarized in the following chart. The hospital is hoping the Ministry of Health will come through with about half of the required money.

Redevelopment areas	Estimated costs	MOH grants	SGH community campaign
Emergency addition/renovation	3,308,572	1,654,286	1,654,286
Operating room addition/renovation	5,746,277	3,125,720	2,620,557
Surgical ambulatory care	1,593,167	858,716	734,451
Intensive care/telemetry	1,950,982	1,092,550	858,432
Psychiatry relocation	1,852,313	926,156	926,157
Cafeteria relocation	1,008,324	329,824 *	678,500
Medical ambulatory care/obstetrics	2,352,206	1,317,235	1,034,971
Sub-totals	**$17,811,841**	**$9,304,487**	**$8,507,354**
Furnishing/equipment	2,000,000	1,044,800	955,200
Totals	**$19,811,841**	**$10,349,287**	**$9,462,554**

* The MOH portion of this component relates to the infrastructure required for the emergency and operating room expansions.

The nurses of SGH

There were nurses in Stratford soon after the first settlers arrived, but there was no formal training for them until the public, general hospital, above the Old Grove on the west side of John Street, was opened in 1891.

Anna Fennell

The new facility necessitated the hiring of a "lady superintendent," namely Anna Fennell, a native of Guelph, where she had received her training as a nurse. When the Stratford job came up Miss Fennell was working at Bliss Hospital in Saginaw, Mich. She turned down the superintendent's job at Bliss to move to Stratford and be closer to her home town.

With her came two young women who had received part of their training, and to get the rest they became the first students of the Stratford Training School for Nurses, which was established early in 1892. Dressed in freshly laundered student uniforms, Georgina Stevenson and Sadie Laughlin were graduated in 1893 during a ceremony in a patient's room. There was just one graduate in 1894, H. Innis Huber, and two in 1895, Mattie McIntyre and Helen Malloy.

In those days the students lived in rooms on the top floor of the hospital, logged 12-hour shifts and received their lectures from members of the medical staff. They also were sent into city homes, where they assisted and learned from families caring for the sick. When patients were isolated because they had contagious or infectious

Nurses and hospital officials gather on the front steps of the Ballantyne residence, soon after it was built in 1903.

diseases such as typhoid, smallpox or diphtheria, nurses and nurses-in-training were on duty around the clock. For a while, those isolation cases were housed in a tent on grounds behind the hospital; it was not until 1910 that an isolation hospital was built.

Originally, student nurses were required to train for two years. In 1898 the program was changed to three years. It was also in that year that Anna Fennell resigned from her Stratford post, after helping graduate 18 nurses. Each had been given a gift of $25 from the hospital's board of trustees – a custom that eventually gave way to a monthly stipend.

The new hospital and its modern facilities no doubt fuelled the dreams of Perth County schoolgirls who longed

to become nurses. In 1902, 65 of them applied to become probationers. Five were accepted, but three left before graduation.

Superintendent Emily Chilman (centre) and her nursing staff in 1906, from left: Lizzie Kidd, Bessie Harrison, Agnes Keller, Annie Turnbull and Lily Fleming. Fleming graduate in 1907, the others in 1906.

The graduation ceremony for nurses Jessie Munro, Pauline Thompson and Gertrude Young, in front of the Ballantyne residence in 1908. The grads are seated together in the front row.

As the hospital added to its facilities and expanded its services, it needed more staff. By the turn of the century the living quarters in its attic were inadequate. Enter Thomas Ballantyne, who in 1903 became a part of Stratford nursing history when he had a house built just to the north of the hospital and donated it as a nurses residence. One of the founders of the cheese industry in Ontario, Ballantyne started the Black Creek Cheese Factory in 1867, the same year he became reeve of Downie Township. In 1875 he turned his South Perth riding Liberal nomination into a seat in the legislative assembly of Ontario. From February 1891 to April 1894 the honourable member served as the legislature's speaker, the first from Perth County. Ballantyne had shown more than a passing interest in the planning and building of Stratford's hospital, and he was chairing its board of trustees when he donated the residence. It was named after his wife Mary, who had been a nurse, and it was furnished by the Women's Hospital Aid. The residence, a stately white brick structure with verandas facing north over the Old Grove, stood until 1985 when it was quickly demolished to make way for a parking lot.

In 1910 a group of graduate nurses formed a Stratford alumnae association, intended to promote unity and fellowship among graduates, as well as advance the interests of the nursing profession. To that end the association was instrumental in amending the nursing school's curriculum.

Alexandra M. Munn, lady superintendent at SGH from 1919 to 1924.

Five of the nurses who graduated from SGH in 1915. From left: ???? Hueghan, Agnes Ballantyne, Margaret Warren, Helene Hodges and Ada Buckle.

It also promoted the provincial registration of trained nurses. Miss Alexandra M. Munn, a 1913 Stratford graduate and the hospital's superintendent from 1919 to 1924, pushed tirelessly for registration. In 1924 she took a job with the Ontario Department of Health in Toronto and worked for what eventually became the Nurses' Registration Act. Later she became an inspector of training schools in the province. Graduate nurses presented her portrait to the alumnae association, and for many years it hung in the reception room of the Stratford nurses residence.

In the days before health insurance, each hospital furnished a room in which graduate nurses could receive free care. Too, there was a nurses lounge. In Stratford, alumni members donated money to the Alexandra Munn Library Fund, which eventually became the Alexandra Munn Loan Fund. For years that fund provided no-interest loans to students and graduates for education expenses and other financial obligations. In later years there was the

Alexandra Munn award for proficiency in bedside nursing. The SGH nurses alumnae association disbanded in 1975.

Elizabeth McArthur and four of her nurses. Miss McArthur was the lady superintendent at SGH from 1916 to 1919.

By 1917, superintendent Elizabeth MacArthur and her assistant, Miss Munn, were overseeing 20 student nurses: nine senior, five intermediate and six junior. That year they collectively used 16,000 yards (14,630 metres) of material to roll bandages. The following year they were tested as never before, when more than 150 patients were admitted to the hospital because of a flu epidemic. Many of them died, and their bodies were tagged and loaded on wagons by men of the Canadian National Railways, who carted them off for burial. Among the victims were two student nurses who contracted the disease from patients; the names of Frances Jean Matheson and Sarah Edna Brigham were later inscribed on a plaque that read "Faithful and efficient members of our nursing staff who in our hour of need stood at their post, giving all and losing all so that humanity should gain.

Died of influenza Oct. 27 and Nov. 4, 1918."

At the same time, at posts far away, were Stratford graduates serving in the war to end all wars. Their name tags read French, Haynes, Burt, Heughan, McLenaghan, Buckle, Robb, Ferguson, Petty, Abel, Cudmore and Southern.

In 1919 a life-size Chase hospital doll was acquired by the hospital to help student nurses practise their procedures. X-ray equipment was added in 1920 and helped improve diagnostic facilities. It also provided valuable training for the student nurses.

With the first addition to the hospital in 1910 came an operating suite, and with it the need for operating room nurses. The O-R speciality became a fixture at Stratford's school of nursing in 1922.

A second major addition was opened in 1923, and it included a classroom. Soon

NURSING SCHOOL ARCHIVES

The class of 1925. Back row, from left: Beatrice Cavell, Elsa Steffan, Myra Britton, Hanna Ballantyne, Mary Slimmon, Eleanor Huras and Jessie Case. Front, from left: Edith Kopas, Clethe Staples, nursing superintendent Allie Mickle, Louise Sippel and Hazel Crerar.

after, formal instruction was given to nursing students for the first time. A part-time instructor of nurses was hired to lecture probationers and provide procedural demonstrations for junior students. These were significant steps for what in 1925 was changed from a "training school" to a "school of nursing," for which applicants needed at least two years of secondary school as an academic requisite. Eventually that requirement was changed to secondary school graduation, and a preference was shown to those with Grade 13.

Also in 1925, a three-month course affiliated with the sanatoriums for tuberculosis in Weston and London was adopted by the school. As well, students began to broaden their field study by nursing with the local public health department and with the Victorian Order of Nurses. Probationary students were now admitted and recognized as a class. This was also the year graduates began writing provincial registration exams in Toronto. The age of haphazard nurses' training was fast fleeting.

In 1922, Aillie Mickle graduated from SGH's school of nursing. In October 1924, she became the hospital's superintendent. It was during her two-year reign that the title of "lady superintendent" was replaced by "superintendent of nursing." (Later Miss Mickle married Dr. David Smith of Stratford). But whatever the position was called, whoever held it carried a lot of weight when it came to the care and control of those enrolled in the nursing program. As discipline for defiance, indifference, inefficiency or neglect of roll-call, a student could be dismissed or sent home for a period of time. Such discipline, it was thought, was necessary for the building of character.

While the part-time instructor was providing early classroom instruction, supervisors of the departments were supervising students on the wards. The curriculum for those students included subjects such as practical nursing, anatomy, materia medica, solutions, ethics, surgery, contagions and infections, general medicine, pediatrics, obstetrics, dietetics, first aid, bacteriology, eye, ear, nose and throat, mental diseases, urinalysis, physics, chemistry, venereal diseases and dentistry. The aspiring nurses took some of those courses at Stratford Collegiate.

Two classes of nursing students were enrolled each year – in March and in November – but both graduated in one ceremony. Prior to entrance, girls with diseased tonsils were to have them removed. Upon entrance there was a thorough physical examination, as well as chest X-rays and tuberculin tests. Students were vaccinated against diphtheria, smallpox, scarlet fever, tuberculosis, typhoid and tetanus.

Miss Zeta Hamilton replaced Mickle as superintendent in 1926 and in her 1927 report to the hospital's board of trustees she stressed the need for a new residence for the 40 nurses in training. The trustees were listening, and a new nurses residence off the southeast corner of the hospital was opened in 1929. Built at a cost of $50,000, it included modern demonstration and lecture rooms. It also contained an apartment for the superintendent of nurses and rooms for some of the supervisors and instructors. Students who stayed there were closely observed and supervised. Today the building houses SGH's Special Services Unit.

In 1930 an obstetrical supervisor was added to the nursing staff. In 1931 nursing students began taking chemistry classes at the Collegiate. A year later they began to observe and assist patients attending chest clinics. They assumed similar roles at the crippled children's clinics organized by Dr. David Smith. In 1936 the school affiliated with the Ontario Hospital in London, which meant students from Stratford could

Graduation day at SGH, 1932. The nurses were picked up at the hospital and driven to the bandshell on Lakeside Drive for the ceremony. It would appear that whoever had been cutting the lawn in front of the hospital elected to take a break while the nurses were assigned to cars for their ride to the Avon River. The push mower is at rest near the front steps. The graduating class on this day included Charlotte Attwood, Anna Beadle, Marie Felpusch, Agnes Greason, Helen Halliday, Mary Hart, Hazel Morrison, Mary McMaster, Lavina McNairn, Annie Patterson, Merle Wilson, Anna White, Florence Weicker, Laura Wagner, Lila Youngblutt and Delores Klassen.

observe or take part in school visits or clinics covering areas such as mental health, chests and babies. In 1950 these clinics became compulsory for Stratford nursing students.

In 1934 the hospital hired three young women as ward helpers, or aides. They were interested in nursing care but did not have the academic requirements for entrance to the nursing school. One of them was Irene Burt, who was assigned to the children's ward. She remained a helper until 1941 when she enrolled in the nursing school. She finished her training at the Seaforth hospital.

Also in 1934, Johnena Gall became the third student nurse to die while in training at SGH.

And it was in that year that nurses at Stratford began to receive X-ray experience under the supervision of the hospital's first full-time radiologist. They were also assigned to the newly renovated pediatric ward. A day supervisor of nurses was appointed in 1935.

In the mid-1930s, students at Stratford were working shifts that ran from 7 a.m. to 7 p.m. and from 7 p.m. to 7 a.m., with a half-day off each week. That was changed upon recommendation from the Ontario inspector of training schools. In 1938, on a trial basis, an eight-hour day, or a week of 56 hours of day duty (58 hours of night duty), was introduced in the obstetrics department at SGH. The provincial health department was anxious to reduce hours of duty in all Ontario hospitals to 58 a week.

The hospital in Stratford opened a medical wing on May 12, 1938, and it provided jobs for three additional graduate nurses – two to work days and one for the night shift. The night nurse was required to relieve students, which allowed them to get some sleep. Also that year, the nurses in training organized a student government to "guide and conduct the affairs of the students in their residence life and to encourage and promote higher ideals." In the main that meant rules and regulations, which were revised with changing times and fashions. At one time, students were never to be seen in public in slacks; their "proper" attire was to include a hat and gloves (white in summer) and stockings or leg paint. For lectures they were to wear full uniforms. In 1950 they were granted one sleep-out per month, and seniors could have three late-leave cards (to midnight) a month. One day off a week was allowed. Those working nights were confined to their rooms from 9 a.m. to 3 p.m. unless permission to leave was granted by the training school office. There were prayers, roll call and inspection at 6:30 each morning in the chapel. While in uniform, students were forbidden to smoke, and they could not wear jewellery.

But amid the rules and routine there was some time for recreation, mostly dances and parties. There was the mid-winter formal and the blue-band (senior year) dance. Capping, which came after six months of probation, was a big event for students, who until then wore nothing on their heads. The graduation dance was always the highlight of the year. During the Second World War, savings bonds generated some revenue for the students council treasury. Money from car washes and bake sales helped sponsor the school's foster child. There was a yearbook in 1946 called *The Mirror* (edited by Alice Schiedel and Genevieve Smith, both of the class of '47), and another, first published in 1958, called *Bibs and Blue*. The 1959 *Bibs and Blue* sold for $1 and was available from any member of the graduating class.

In the late '30s and well into the 1940s, student nurses at SGH, unless they were on duty, were required to attend, in uniform, an annual Anglican Church service in Elora. It was a Sunday evening service as close as possible to May 12, the birthday of Florence Nightingale, the founder of trained nursing as a profession. Graduate nurses could also attend the service, which attracted people from numerous area hospitals.

Nightingale's cousin, John Smithurst, was rector at the Elora church from 1852 to 1867, the year he died. A communion set donated to the church by Florence Nightingale is still on display in Elora.

The SGH school's first full-time nursing instructor was appointed in 1939, namely Miss Emma Marentette. She replaced Miss Bessie Jeffrey, the last part-time instructor, who had to step down because of illness. Actually, Elizabeth (Mrs. Hiram) Moulton first replaced Jeffery, but only for a short period.

In November 1940 Stratford hospital introduced patient-assignment nursing, whereby nurses were assigned to specific patients and focused their care and attention on the needs of those patients. However, meeting the demands of such a system required more nurses, and after about six months the hospital returned to efficiency nursing. Total patient care was reintroduced in later years, and then, by more fully using para-medical personnel, team nursing was established.

By 1941 – the year of its 50th birthday – the hospital was being operated by a staff that comprised a superintendent, six supervisors (obstetrics and pediatrics, operating room, night shift, X-ray and two on day shifts), a nursing instructor, an assistant instructor and supervisor, 51 student nurses and five ward aides.

The hospital celebrated its half-century birthday on June 11, 12 and 13 in 1941, and for the most part it was a celebration of the nursing school. Among those invited to attend the anniversary reunion were four women who had gone on to make outstanding contributions to the nursing profession. Miss Charlotte Aikens, who had lived in Detroit since 1907, was an 1897 grad who wrote four textbooks which, by 1941, were being used by SGH's school of

nursing. From Stratford she had gone to the Polyclinic Hospital in New York City for postgraduate work and received a diploma in 1898. She was superintendent of hospitals in Pittsburgh and Des Moines, and for 15 years she was editor of the Trained Nurse and Hospital Review. She was also an associate editor with the National Hospital Record.

Miss Jessie Murdoch graduated from Stratford in 1902 and became such a fixture at Jersey City Hospital, in Jersey City, N.J., that a residence for nurses opened in that city in May 1941 was named after her. As she mingled on the lawn in front of the Ballantyne residence, which was built a year after her graduation, Murdoch reflected, "When I was here we had 35 beds. Sometimes we could get 50 patients into the hospital if we did a bit of squeezing and it was absolutely necessary. A Mr. McPherson (lawyer George G. McPherson) took part in the ceremony this afternoon. He used to drive the finest team of spirited horses I ever saw around here."

Jessie Murdoch, 1904

NURSING SCHOOL ARCHIVES

Alexandra Munn, the superintendent at SGH from 1919 through 1924, had become the director of nurse registration for the provincial department of health. And there was Mrs. Anna M. Stabler, who then lived in Los Angeles. The superintendent at Stratford from 1908 through 1911, she had

The class of 1941. From left: Jean Bailey, Muriel Farrish, Alma Finnigan, Lorna McKellar, Ellen Turkheim, Hazel Jamieson, Edith Howald and Fuschia Whitehead.

founded the New England Industrial Nurses' Association.

Miss Aikens did not attend the Stratford reunion, but the other three did. So did about 100 other women, mostly former students of the Stratford school. They came from across Ontario and from the states of New York, Ohio, Michigan and Oregon. All were invited to witness that year's graduation of eight students in exercises at the Collegiate Vocational Institute. On that day the pins and diplomas were presented by Miss Zeta Hamilton, superintendent of SGH. She was assisted by Misses Myrtle Gibb of Port Hope and Florence Kudoba of St. Thomas, former members of the hospital staff. In her congratulations, as representative of those who had gone before, Miss Murdoch said, "I have been

associated with many Canadian nurses in my work in the United States, and I have been very proud of them, and also of the graduates of this hospital who have filled places of prominence in the nursing profession in that country."

Then the clock was turned back as Margaret (Buchan) Woods of Bayfield read the valedictory of her 1896 graduating class. She was followed by Dr. Lorne Robertson, who read the address which had been prepared and delivered by his father, Dr. James A. Robertson, to the hospital's charter graduate nurses in 1893. "The world heralds the trained nurse as one of the most valuable productions of civilization," read the doctor. He also said such a person should be "endowed with refinement, intelligence and culture; that she should possess the qualities of kindness and sympathy; that her supreme duty should be her patient; and that she should be tactful, firm, strong and vigorous in order to perform her duties capably and efficiently."

Valedictorian in the golden jubilee year was Miss Fuchsia Whitehead of Kitchener, who also attained the highest marks in general medicine and obstetrics. Miss Edith Howald of Listowel was the top award winner with four. Miss Jean Bailey picked up the other of the five annual prizes. As he did at many of the graduation exercises, George McPherson administered the Florence Nightingale pledge to the newly qualified nurses, each in her crisp white uniform, standing among baskets of red and white (the school's colours) peonies. For much of the ceremony they also held bouquets of red and white roses, which were presented by Nancy Kirkpatrick of New Hamburg and Sonja Sinclair, young daughters of area doctors. The little flower girls also presented corsages to the special guests, among them Misses Murdoch, Munn, Hamilton, Kudoba and Gibb, and Mrs. Woods.

Harry W. Strudley, president of the Stratford General Hospital Board of Trustees, and Rev. W. Tillmann Corcoran, of Church of the Immaculate Conception, also took park in the ceremony. Musical entertainment for the afternoon was supplied by the Aeolian Trio, specifically Miss Anna Trethewey, her brother Charles and Felix Walker. Miss Florence Lawson was on hand to sing "I Love all Lovely Things." Though the accompanist and violinist changed, Charles Trethewey and his cello were a musical staple at the nurses

Nurses Ellen Turkheim (left) and Edith Howald assist Annie [Woods] Wighton plant a mulberry tree in the Shakespearean Garden during golden jubilee celebrations in 1941. At right are Charlotte Attwood and Rev. Francis Lightbourn.

Nursing graduates at the Stratford County Club, 1941. They had gathered to help Stratford General Hospital celebrate its golden jubilee.

graduation ceremonies from the early 1930s, when he was still a student at the Collegiate, until 1964.

On the night of the 1941 renewal, the graduates and their friends and members of the SGH medical staff and their spouses gathered for a dance at the Stratford Country Club, where music was provided by Collegiate students Bob Small, Laurie Wren, Earl Robinson, Mervin Doerr and Bill O'Loughlin. The evening was sponsored by the hospital trustees.

The next morning the alumnae and current students reassembled in the city's Shakespearean Garden to commemorate the anniversary by planting a mulberry tree. Special guest of honour at the tree planting was Annie (Mrs. John) Wighton of Toronto, who, as Annie Woods, graduated from the school in 1898. She delivered a brief speech as she placed the tree in the ground. The first few handfuls of dirt to support the tree were tossed by Miss Howald, gold medallist

of the class of '41. Classmate Ellen Turkheim of Exeter was the flag-bearer, and Rev. Frances G. Lightbourn of St. James' Anglican Church, who arranged the ceremony, read the Scripture and offered a closing prayer. Miss Charlotte M. Attwood, a 1932 graduate still nursing at SGH, opened the proceedings by saying, "It is quite fitting that we should pick a mulberry tree to plant on this occasion. Shakespeare planted a mulberry tree in his garden in 1609 and today a mulberry still stands there." (The tree matured and stood until 1968, when it was taken down during a revitalization of the Garden. But a seedling was taken from the tree and planted on the island which is attached to the Garden by a footbridge. More than 30 years later, the offshoot of the original jubilee tree, now about 10 metres in height, continues to bear fruit.)

After the ceremony there was a sightseeing tour of the city in automobiles, a

SCHOOL FOR NURSES 1941

PHOTO taken by DENTON (KITCHENER) FOR ROGERS STUDIO STRATFORD On

DENTON-ROGERS

luncheon attended by about 150 at the Country Club and a walk through the hospital and nurses residence in the afternoon. At night there was an anniversary banquet at Knox Presbyterian Church, and those at the head table included doctors, hospital staff and trustees, politicians, nurses and representatives of the Women's Hospital Aid and the local ministerial association. Bessie (Mrs. Thomas) Ballantyne, honorary vice-president of the WHA, was chosen to cut the jubilee cake. Alight with candles, the cake was carried to the head table by Misses Mae Wettlaufer and Hazel Johnson, student nurses.

There were customary speeches from the special guests and musical entertainment from the Orpheus Girls Choir, under the direction of Irene Joceyln. With war raging in Europe, the choir's selections included God Bless the Shores of England. Later in the evening everyone joined in singing *There'll always be an England.*

The jubilee banquet also included the showing of a series of lantern slides by Dr. William M. (Mac) Gilmore. His pictures showed early-day hospital staff and nurses on the job, working with equipment that by now seemed obsolete. Many of those pioneers were at the dinner and happily shared their memories. The slide show was followed by a live pageant that recreated the history of the training school from the days when one superintendent oversaw two probationers. Charlotte Attwood, a key organizer for the three-day reunion, wrote the stage history and directed the 25 students and one graduate who performed it. Their characters ranged from Florence Nightingale to a 1941 wartime nurse. The narrator was Annie Ballantyne, a 1935 graduate of the school. Music was provided by nursing students Misses Evelyn Edgar (piano), Mary Grafton (violin) and Jean McDonald (cello).

The next day, the nurses gathered for a picnic in Queen's Park in the morning and for a farewell tea at the Erie Street home of George G. McPherson in the afternoon. McPherson, a lawyer, was chairman of the hospital's house and grounds committee. He had also been an active member of the board of trustees for more than 25 years. For a number of years, teas for the school's graduating class had been held at the McPhersons'. Organizers had hoped to have the jubilee tea on the ample and landscaped grounds of the McPherson home, at the northwest corner of West Gore and Erie streets, but chilly weather forced the proceedings inside. While they sipped their tea, the guests were entertained on the piano by Mary Manson, whose mother, Elizabeth McArthur, was superintendent of the hospital from 1916 through 1919. And there was a vocal duet by Miss Eleanor Nelson, daughter of a nursing school graduate, and Miss Shirley Doherty. They were accompanied on piano by Miss Helen Humber.

In its first 50 years, Stratford hospital's nursing school had graduated 323 students. By 1941 the residence was housing 51 students and staff, 11 more than its designed capacity of 40.

In 1942, Hilda Bennett, the provincial inspector of nursing schools, put an end to the use of student nurses on a round-the-clock basis in Stratford's isolation unit. She said the students needed to be supervised, and they need some free time. They should have time off and be permitted to live normal lives, as well as eat in the staff dining room and sleep in the residence, said Bennett. Under the 24-hour duty roster, nurses were required to spend the entire length of a patient's illness with the patient, which meant sleeping on a couch near the patient's bed and being available when needed. In the case of death, it was up to the nurse to notify next of kin, prepare the deceased for burial and disinfect the room.

Bennett suggested another graduate nurse be added to the staff to ensure 24-hour supervision, and that more nurses be hired for the night shift so students could get at least two hours rest. She said until the staffing problem was resolved, no student was to spend more than a shift at a time with a patient in isolation.

In 1944 a community nursing registry was organized in Stratford by Viola Byrick, which meant the nursing school office no longer had to field calls for special nurses. Because most of the hospital was staffed with students, there was a large surplus of graduate nurses. Some found work in private homes, where they worked 12- or 20-hour shifts. In 1940 the pay for a 12-hour day was $5. For 20 hours it was $6. In such arrangements, nurses ate with family members, not in the kitchen with the servants. In theory, at least, they were not responsible for doing housework. Into the 1940s, surgery was still occasionally performed in homes, and babies were still being born there. Some nurses also did private duty nursing in the hospital. Still, the Depression years were as lean for many nurses as they were for those in other walks of life.

Also in 1944, a supervisor for the training school was hired. That was the year the provincial inspector suggested student nurses not be used for night emergencies, and that a graduate surgical nurse live in the residence and be available for those calls. That didn't happen in Stratford, where a student and the night supervisor continued to serve at night in the operating room.

In 1946 a committee was formed to outline and oversee the nursing school's curriculum. Representatives of the nursing classes began to attend nursing conventions. And about twice a month there were staff conferences, designed to promote better working relationships and a more efficient administration. Problems related to nursing service and to the education of students often were on the agenda.

An almost eight-hour schedule was established for students working days in 1947, though the night shift remained 7 p.m. to 7 a.m. with two hours off-duty during the night until 1955. A committee was formed to assist students with spiritual and social leadership. A year later the school's training committee affiliated with Toronto's Hospital for Sick Children so Stratford students could get better training in pediatrics. Also in 1948, SGH officially added nursing assistants and orderlies to its staff.

On Nov. 5, 1949, a 22-year-old Stratford nursing student, Claribel (Clara) McMillan, died from head injuries received in single-car accident the previous night, half a mile west of Seaforth. A native of North Easthope Township and graduate of Stratford Collegiate, McMillan had been in training at SGH for about 16 months. None of the other six people in the car was seriously injured. They included two other SGH nursing students, Marilyn Riches and Peggy Whiteman, and university student Barbara Sproat, daughter of Dr. William and Ruth Sproat, Stratford. The three males in the car, one of which was charged with dangerous driving, were from the Royal Canadian Air Force bases at Clinton and Centralia. The following year, in memory of Clara McMillan, a large stone barbecue was erected at the northwest corner of West Gore and John streets – in the backyard of the nurses residence.

The post-war years between 1945 and 1950 were boom times for hospitals in Ontario, and a natural outgrowth of that flurry of activity was a demand for nurses. At the provincial government level, the nurses' registration division was renamed the nursing division of the Ontario department of health, and became responsible for the supervision of nursing schools and the training and registration of certified nursing assistants. It also improved the curricula of nursing schools. At least nine Ontario centres built new nurses residences, while others improved their quarters.

With the opening of the new building in 1950, SGH was employing 200 people. The school of nursing staff comprised an assistant director of nursing education, a nursing arts instructor, clinical instructors, unit supervisors and medical staff lecturers. Not only did students no longer provide the sole nursing care for patients, but patients were chosen to provide a learning experience for the students. Greater emphasis was placed on learning, and students followed a rotation designed to give them experience in all of the hospital's departments.

And in 1951 there were record numbers of them – about 65 – taking advantage of that training. Enrolment was up considerably over previous years. The students' recreational activities included the formation of a choir.

Margaret (Peggy) Hoy [later Heinbuch] was among the school's 1951 graduates and joined SGH as a charge nurse in September of that year. Upon her retirement in 1993, Heinbuch reflected upon her 42-year association with SGH. She said her starting salary was $100 a month with an additional $10 for living expenses, and that she was able to keep her expenses low by sharing a $40-a-month apartment with five other nurses. She also said the most recent of her colleagues made more in one shift than she did in a month in her early years.

In 1952 the hours for formal lectures at the nursing school totalled 1,087. Students were allowed three weeks of sick time for the three years they were in the program. They were also allotted three weeks of vacation, annually.

The Ballantyne residence was renovated in 1954, and in the next year 22 students moved into a new residence – on the third floor of the old hospital, which had been

The class of 1951. From left: Kathryn Parrott, Karina Whiteman, Madeline Wilson, Mary Proctor, Marilyn Riches, Margaret Hoy, Rhea Durnin, Grace Murr and Mary Fisher.

renamed Avon Crest. Where possible, each student had a room to herself. Also in 1955, the graveyard shift (7 p.m. to 7 a.m.) was abolished. In 1956 the workweek was down to 44 hours; in 1959 it was reduced to 40.

In 1955 there were 68 student nurses enrolled at Stratford and, with the works of Shakespeare enjoying new life in a tent down by the Avon River, many of them took part in what became an annual theatre night. In August 1959 the school lost its fifth student when Alice Lauretta Hayes, a native of Kincardine Township, drowned during an outing with classmates at Grand Bend. They were celebrating their first anniversary in training.

By 1961 the hospital had 303 full-time employees and another 85 part time. It also had 72 students in its nursing school. An advisory committee was established to provide a communication bridge between the school and the hospital.

The reception to welcome incoming nursing students in September 1962 was much like those in years previous – with one landmark exception. Among the 30 newcomers was a male, the first to attend the Stratford school. That night he was the first male student to be invited to the orientation party hosted by the senior and intermediate students in the recreation room of the residence. And, almost three years later, on the last Saturday of May, Donald Wayne Nafziger of Milverton became the first male graduate of the school. He and 18 female colleagues received their diplomas during exercises on the stage of the Festival Theatre.

Guest speaker that afternoon was Miss Dorothy M. Percy, chief nursing consultant with the federal department of health and welfare. She told the graduates, "It takes courage to be a nurse today, since you must know the 'why' as well as the 'how.' The public knows more about hospitals, disease and medicine than ever before, and so it is more critical. However, I am not sorry for the hard life you have chosen, but rather I envy your strength of mind, body and spirit.

"Premature hardening of the personality can be prevented by frequent applications of curiosity. In addition, don't take yourself too seriously, since the occupational hazard of our times is over-specialization. The real reason you are here this afternoon is because of compassion. Compassion, or love, is the key to the successful treatment of any patient, and although you have much to offer in the way of skill and technique, you must fill the patients' needs for an un-automated nurse."

The program also included three offerings from the newly re-formed nurses-in-training choir, a group of more than 25 voices under the direction of Albert Furtney. A member of that choir, Marjorie Richings of Dorchester, was class valedictorian. She also won the Dr. W. C. Sproat award for proficiency in surgical technique in the operating room and the school cup award as the student chosen by her peers as having the best school spirit and leadership in the school.

By the time SGH graduated its first male, two more were completing their first year in the program. Nafziger went on to also become the first male registered nurse to be made a second lieutenant upon entering the Canadian Forces. In 1966 the hospital's former isolation department was renovated as a residence for male nursing students.

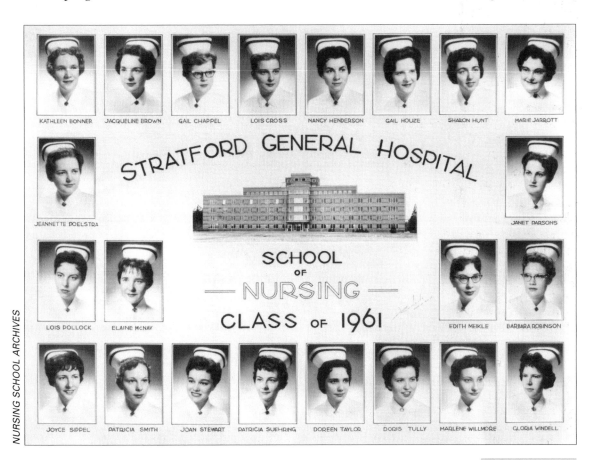

STRATFORD GENERAL HOSPITAL
SCHOOL OF NURSING
CLASS OF 1961

KATHLEEN BONNER · JACQUELINE BROWN · GAIL CHAPPEL · LOIS CROSS · NANCY HENDERSON · GAIL HOUZE · SHARON HUNT · MARIE JARROTT

JEANNETTE POELSTRA · JANET PARSONS

LOIS POLLOCK · ELAINE MCNAY · EDITH MEIKLE · BARBARA ROBINSON

JOYCE SIPPEL · PATRICIA SMITH · JOAN STEWART · PATRICIA SUEHRING · DOREEN TAYLOR · DORIS TULLY · MARLENE WILLMORE · GLORIA WINDELL

In the mid-1960s the Ontario Hospital Services Commission approved a bylaw that called for the establishment of 23 regional schools of nursing throughout the province. In Stratford that meant a new school-residence on the northeast corner of SGH property. The new school also meant a new two-county board, operating independent of but in co-operation with SGH.

The Stratford architectural firm of Kyles, Kyles and Garratt was chosen to design the regional school, and there was a call to use the old residence for graduate nurses coming to Stratford to work. In Canada's centennial year there was also some money available to build a staff residence, which was constructed to the south of the old nurses residence, on the northwest corner of John and Cambria streets. Opened in June 1968, the eight-unit apartment building was called Centennial House. That meant the former nurses residence, the one built in 1929, could be used for a variety of purposes, among them psychiatric services. In 1976 the building was renovated and became the hospital's special services unit.

Late in August 1968, the new Perth-Huron Regional School of Nursing, to the north and east of the hospital, at the corner of St. Vincent Street South and Cambria Street, was accommodating its first 49 students – eight of them from Stratford. Amid the construction noises in a facility not quite finished, 48 females and one male showed up on Sept. 2 for registration and a welcome tea for students and parents. Classes began the next day. The program required students to receive instruction from Conestoga College of Applied Arts and Technology two days a week for 30 weeks. They were bused to the college's Doon campus where they studied English, literature, history, biology, psychology and sociology. As well as in Stratford, the regional school offered clinical training at Clinton Public, Alexandra Marine and General (Goderich), Listowel Memorial,

Seaforth Community, South Huron in Exeter, and St. Mary's Memorial. Each hospital except Stratford (six) and Goderich (three) was allowed two members on the regional board. It was that board that ran the school.

The three-storey school included single accommodation for up to 180 students; laundry facilities on each floor; large bathrooms, designed to serve 30 students each; an auditorium-gymnasium with a hardwood stage and seating for 270 people; an air-conditioned library with a reading room that doubled as a science lab; an outside courtyard with redwood benches, cement walks, gardens and wrought-iron lamps; offices for 21 instructors; a games room; a nursing arts lab that divided into three seminar rooms; a resident supervisor's suite, which was initially occupied by Marjorie Jamison; and a heated outdoor swimming pool, which was donated by SGH.

From the beginning, the Ontario government said it would pay for the land and all the other essentials for the new nursing schools, but not for amenities such as elevators and swimming pools. So the cost of the 99-year lease that SGH put on the land necessary for the new school in Stratford just happened to be equal to the cost of installing an outdoor pool for the students. When the real estate transaction was completed, the hospital donated the money to the school, and the pool was installed. The hospital also attached a condition to the land deal, namely, that if the school stopped training nurses, the property would be returned to SGH for one dollar.

In the fall of 1967, Mary Philpott was appointed principal of the new Perth-Huron regional school, which was completed at a cost of $1,500,000 and opened for business in September 1969. In the first year there were 49 students for the two-year-plus-one program, but accommodation for 180. The

The Perth-Huron Regional School of Nursing, 1971.

third year was for internship, with students rotated through participating hospitals. For that year, students were paid by the hospitals and expected to find their own living accommodation. A native of Grand Falls, Nfld., Philpott had come to Stratford in August 1964 as director of nursing at SGH.

She said adjustment to a new curriculum would be a challenge, but that she was looking forward to the changes. "We have

Mary Philpott, 1968

our own board of trustees, our own budget and have total control of the program," she said. "This is a functional building and will serve outside associations as well, bringing more allied groups together."

A product of a high school residence operated by nuns, and a nursing program at a Catholic hospital, Philpott brought strict rules to the new school. Later, under some pressure from the students, she was forced to relax some of them. Eventually, for instance, residents were allowed to smoke cigarettes in their rooms.

The regional school of nursing was officially opened on Nov. 5, 1969, by Dr. Matthew B. Dymond, the provincial health minister. It was Dymond who in 1965 had announced that provision for nursing education in Ontario needed to be increased. His policy reflected the growing concern over an ongoing shortage of qualified nursing staff, and his target was 5,000 graduates a year. The new Perth-Huron school, he reasoned, was a step towards hitting that target.

In opening it, he was assisted by George O. (Doc) Dickinson, chairman of the school's board of trustees, and Harold Nelson, chairman of the board's education advisory committee. Dickinson was head master at Stratford's teachers college and Nelson was administrator of the hospitals in Hanover and Walkerton.

Dedication of the school was conducted by Rev. James Ferguson, president of the SGH board of directors. Invocation for the day's program was given by Rev. R. W. Tremblay, the school chaplain. Also on hand with greetings and best wishes were John V. Killer, mayor of Stratford; Lawson Cross of

George O. Dickinson, 1971

Listowel, warden of Perth County; and James Hayter of Dashwood, warden of

Huron County. There were some brief remarks as well from contractor Oliver Gaffney of Gaffney Construction, Stratford; architect Brian Garratt of Kyles, Kyles and Garratt, Stratford; and chairman of the building committee Robert W. Watler, Stratford. Watler was general manager of Muirhead Instruments. Guided tours of the new facility followed the opening ceremony, and there were refreshments.

The Stratford General Hospital School of Nursing graduated its 79th – and last – class on Saturday, April 17, 1971, during a ceremony in the Festival Theatre. Guest speaker was Tony van Bridge of the Festival's acting company. "You will have

The last class to graduate from the SGH's school of nursing, 1971. Front row, from left: Marjorie Kent, Sandra Lewis, Vicki Kutcha, Karen McAllister, Valerie Miller and Deborah Hanson. Second row, from left: Muriel Bryant, Anne Ramer, Ellen Quantrell, Carol Ann Roloson, Sandra Hewitt, Theresa Ruth and Evert (Kip) Veenendaal. Third row, from left: Barbara Knapton, Gail Lobsinger, Anna Bydeley, Sheila Paterson [valedictorian] and Karen Crawford. Back, from left: Robert MacLennon, Joan Colquhoun, Ann Cameron, Sharron Chamney, Shela Harkness, Bobbi Ann MacDonald, Joan Chesney and Judy Quipp.

discovered by now that certain parts of your work, which can inspire the uninitiated layman to shed a tear of emotion, can be the sheerest drudgery, demanding an exacting, exhausting and intensely boring attention to detail," said van Bridge, as he noted the parallels between acting and nursing.

NURSING SCHOOL ARCHIVES

Actor Tony van Bridge speaks at the final graduation exercises for the SGH's school of nursing, April 17, 1971. Flanking him on the stage of the Stratford Shakespearean Festival are, from left: Thelma Pelley, director of nursing; Rev. James Ferguson, chair of the SGH board; Gertrud Scheibel, assistant director of nursing education; Rev. Richard Tremblay, school chaplain; and Bob Cameron, SGH's executive director.

"There is nothing funny about playing exacting comedy in my theatre, and similarly I doubt if you have time to think about how wonderfully inspiring it is to fight for a life in yours. As long as the spectator laughs in one, and the patient lives in the other, the point, in each case, is made."

Most of what van Bridge had to say was directed at the 26 graduates (two of them males), but he was also talking to the graduates' friends and relatives and to about 500 of the school's 900 alumnae and alumni – all of whom had gathered to celebrate the end of an era. Many had misty eyes as they watched the renewal of a ceremony that had been a watershed in their lives.

Their 80-year-old alma mater had been replaced by the Perth-Huron Regional School of Nursing, and this was the end of the transition period. "We realize it is not an easy task to close a school of nursing, or to house two separate schools of nursing under the same roof," said 1971 valedictorian Sheila Paterson of Windsor. "We feel that you have successfully accomplished these goals on our behalf. We have completed the last chapter in an unwritten history of this school. With our graduation the book is closed. It is our hope that we have and will uphold the standards and honour of this school." At this ceremony the grads were presented with silver dishes that bore the school crest and the dates 1891-1971. There were more tears when SGH board chairman Rev. James Ferguson asked the assembled to join in the singing of Auld Lang Syne.

By Friday night of that weekend about 225 grads had registered for the farewell reunion, and they spent the evening touring the hospital and residence, and attending homecoming parties. Well into the night they retold well-worn stories – about a patient's false teeth inadvertently being tossed down a laundry chute; about receiving "days off" for sterilizing baby bottles to the point their rubber nipples became useless globs; about feeding interns

The uniform and the pin

Uniforms for nurses trained at Stratford have not always followed the dictates of fashion, but they have changed considerably since about 1897 when a white apron and low-cut narrow bib were worn over a floor-length blue-and-white-checked heavy cotton dress – accented by a tucked bodice, leg o'mutton sleeves, large white collar and white cuffs.

By 1902, sleeves were straight and fitted, and by 1905 cuffs with two rows of hemstitching were added, and the bib was widened and fitted beneath the collar. By 1910 the skirt length had crept above the ankles and its fullness at the hem was five yards. The forerunner to the present cap was adopted in 1915, and by 1939 it was pleated, first with 12 folds and later with 16. By 1940, white shoes and stockings were worn by all students. During the years of the Second World War the checked dress material became unavailable, and it was replaced by a lighter-weight cotton bearing wide blue stripes and narrow white stripes. As a conservation measure, the hem line jumped to slightly below the knee. Not long after the war, the long sleeves were discarded, replaced by short sleeves with detachable pointed cuffs. The bottom of the skirt stayed 13 inches (about 33 cm) from the floor. In the mid-1960s a stitched-on cuff was added, to make laundering easier. Also, the skirt length inched above the knee.

When the first male student was admitted in 1962, his uniform was a white medical jacket with a blue-and-white-striped arm badge, white trousers and white shoes.

In 1894 each graduate was presented with a medal and a diploma. In 1896 that pin was sterling silver, comprising a bar and hanging medal. The bar was crown-shaped with a small cross projecting from the lower edge. Behind the medal was a corded ribbon in St. Luke's blue – the blue of healing. The upper and lower edges of the medal were bordered by an oak leaf enclosing the inscriptions: "Graduate 1896" and "Stratford General Hospital." The graduate's name was engraved on the bar.

By 1902, SGH was using a pin

NURSING SCHOOL ARCHIVES

Student nurses in one of SGH's early operating rooms.

128

designed by lady superintendent Emily Chilman. It featured a large gold letter S superimposed on a red enamel cross. Some winged gold ornamentation joined the cross at six places and on the S was engraved "Stratford General Hospital." By 1906, still in the Chilman era, the pin had become bigger and heavier. The red enamel was pebbled, the gold ornamentation more ornate and the lettering on the S separated by engraved stars. By 1913 the pin had returned to its size of 1902, but it had become more three-dimensional. The gold border around the cross was narrowed, and the red enamel had a striped effect. The overall design had been simplified, and there was less winged ornamentation joining the arms of the cross. The hospital's cost for each pin was $12, and officials opted to replace it with a less expensive bronze shield. But the graduating class was incensed by that proposal and protested loudly enough that the hospital backed down.

By 1915, and for the next 10 years, the pin was much like the 1906 version in weight and size. It was four-dimensional with two levels of ornamentation, including four gold hearts. The engraving was black, and there was a single black line around the S. But in 1926 the graduates changed the design of the pin because they felt the large S made it looked too much like the Singer sewing machine logo. The new pin was unpolished gold, oval-shaped, and centred by an inlaid red enamel cross. It had a polished gold border, the words "Stratford General Hospital – Miseris Succuro" (I help those in distress) and a

The commemorative plate presented to attendees of the nursing school's reunion in 1971. It bears seven versions of the school's coveted pin.

raised gold wreath surrounding the cross.

At least some of the school's alumnae were not impressed by the new design. They convinced the students that the large S on the cross was unique to their school – and had nothing to do with the manufacture and sale of sewing machines. Thus, in 1927, and through 1938, the pin reverted to its basic design. Red enamel was not used on the cross during the Depression, but apart from that it was the one-dimensional pin of old. The cross, unpolished and pebbled in appearance, and the S were slightly depressed, and small hearts of polished gold were attached to the arms of the cross with ornamental handles. The lettering on the unpolished gold of the S was raised.

In 1939, as the Depression gave way to the Second World War, red enamel returned to the cross, and the pin remained unchanged through 1971, the year the school closed.

laxative-laced fudge; about those interns getting even with arm and leg casts; about non-registered males climbing in and out of the windows of the residence; about members of that residence playing semi-nude leapfrog in the corridors; about decorating the hospital with For Sale signs; about falling asleep in the hospital's linen room; about being spooked one dark and icy night when a corpse slid off the cart while it was being transported to the mortuary, which had formally served as the hospital's chicken coop; about a senior class refusing to report to work until some working conditions had been improved; about sneaking back into the residence after curfew.

On Saturday the reunion numbers more than doubled in time for the graduation ceremony – an observance that through the years had been held in a patient's room, on the hospital grounds, on a board member's lawn, at City Hall, in the Majestic Theatre, in the Armouries, at Lakeside Park, in the Collegiate, in the Avon Theatre and, finally, at the Shakespearean Festival Theatre. But whatever the location, the spotlight always fell on the graduates – who sat in their crisp, neatly pressed uniforms, smiling nervously and cradling red roses. That light glistened off their shining pins and illuminated the black velvet band on their caps. In early years, receipt of the cap indicated the acceptance of a probationary or preliminary student into the school of nursing. As of 1953, caps were worn by all students. A blue band for those caps was introduced in 1954, to distinguish students who were in their final year of training. In 1965 a ceremony was initiated to present the blue bands.

The 1971 graduation ceremony was followed by a dinner, pageant and dance, that included spouses, at the Stratford Coliseum. The historical pageant, an updated version, was organized by Charlotte Brown of London – who, as

Charlotte Attwood, had written and directed the pageant when it was first performed, in 1941. On this occasion, however, the author was also the narrator.

As did its predecessor, the 1971 version used rhyming verse and 25 student nurses (among them a male) wearing the uniforms of different periods to recount an interesting story for an appreciative audience. Viola Byrick co-ordinated the pageant. Joan MacDermid looked after casting and costumes, and Frieda Schellenberger played the piano.

On Sunday morning about 200 grads attended a service at Rev. Ferguson's St. Andrew's Presbyterian Church and then wound up the weekend's activities with a luncheon.

Ida (Mrs. Fred) Morrow, a Cambria Street resident, was the oldest grad to register for the homecoming. As Ida C. Bott she was a member of the 1913 class. Maude (Mrs. Irwin R.) Pearce, formerly Maude Blowes of the 1920 class, of Mitchell was the oldest to attend the dinner and dance. They mingled with modern-day counterparts who had a 35-hour workweek and four weeks of annual vacation.

The students of the '70s followed a timetable with a set number of lecture hours and specified time for ward experience – a schedule not subject to the whims of the needs of the hospital. Lecture hours and ward experience were integrated, and the time-honoured apprentice system was all but forgotten. The students of the '70s also had an on-site swimming pool for off-hours relaxation. And they could be married. Seniors were on the honour system as far as curfew was concerned. Those same seniors were also able to take an introductory philosophy course for credit at Waterloo Lutheran University (now Wilfrid Laurier University).

Reunions have been a fairly regular occurrence for some of the graduates of

We were like a big happy family

When it comes to nursing at SGH, few played a more continuous role than Marion McNaught, who came to Stratford from the Seaforth area. Upon her graduation from the Stratford nursing school in 1948, as a double award winner, she went into the operating room as a replacement nurse for someone on leave.

Then she did a stint on wards before returning to the O-R, where she stayed until 1984. She spent her last seven years at SGH in day surgery and endoscopy.

For most of her 43 working years she was a head nurse or acting supervisor. And, she said, much of that time passed quickly. "Admittedly, there were days when I wondered if '91 would ever come, but mostly I looked forward to going to work. It used to be that everybody knew everybody; we were like a big happy family."

She died in July 1999.

SGH's school of nursing. Twelve to 15 members of the class of 1964, for instance, have been getting together about every two years, says Carol Schlemmer. On the occasion of the 30th anniversary of their graduation, 22 of 26 reunited at the Festival Inn, in Stratford. "A lot of us stay in touch," says Schlemmer who, as Carol Stanley of Lucknow, came to Stratford in 1961 to begin her training as a nurse. "We were all 18 or 19 years old, and in those days you didn't travel too far from home," she says, "so it was a big thing to move to Stratford for three years. In the speech on the first day they (school officials) told us and our parents that they were borrowing us for three years. And that was about it. We were dealing with life and death all the time, so we grew up in a hurry. In three years we got to know each other pretty well."

In their first year, Stanley and her classmates were required to live in quarters on the top floor of the old hospital, under the watchful eye of co-resident Martha Racey, the director of nursing education. By that time Racey was severely hampered by arthritis, so the students were required to help her with personal tasks such as baths and getting around. They also had "door duty," which meant watching the entrance and answering the pay telephone.

In their second and third years, the students moved to the residence that had been built in 1929 – which was also home for the director of nursing at SGH. To assist her in keeping an eye on the comings and goings of the residents, house mothers – such as Eileen Langley and Yvonne Wright – were on duty from 3 p.m. to 11 p.m.

"They watched us pretty closely," says Schlemmer. "One night a month we could stay out until midnight. We used to spend a lot of time in the kitchen; that's where the food was. There was also a lounge, but I remember being more in the kitchen." Schlemmer says that upon graduation she and many of her colleagues found work at SGH. She later worked briefly in Calgary before settling permanently in Stratford, where she works in the office of Dr. Edward H. (Ted) Flowers.

Among graduates from the Perth-Huron school on June 29, 1973, was Rose Ann Benninger of Dublin. But, unlike the others honoured on that occasion, she arrived at the ceremony in a wheelchair. She had suffered torn ligaments in a car accident in the previous week. On this day at least, one of the graduating nurses was also a patient.

On Sept. 1, 1973, the Ontario Ministry of Colleges and Universities announced the transfer of all diploma nursing programs from hospitals to community colleges. For the short-lived Perth-Huron school that college was Conestoga, whose main campus was at Doon (Kitchener). In compliance with the agreement made several years earlier, the school offered its land back to SGH. The hospital gladly took it back, along with the building that adorned it. Philpott went back to university, graduated in law, and returned to Newfoundland to practise in St. John's.

The school and the adjoining residence had been financed by a 25-year, low-interest loan from the Canadian Mortgage and Housing Corporation. Because colleges were not in the residence business, the facility at Stratford posed something of a problem. The problem was resolved when SGH agreed to run the residence, and the Ministry of Health agreed to cover the mortgage. It would be SGH's job to determine revenue and expenses, but any profits, it was decided, had to go towards the mortgage. Until that mortgage was paid off, the residence broke even each year.

SGH rented rooms to students individually. It also rented the classrooms and office space to Conestoga at a cost-basis rate that was negotiated annually. The college struck similar deals at five other area hospitals.

At Stratford the marriage survived a rocky start and eventually worked well. In 1974, Stratford students ranked 40 out of 45 among collegians writing the registered nurses examinations. Just 56 per cent of the Stratford students who wrote that year passed the exams. Within five years that percentage rose to 100, where it stayed for three or four years. In 1980 a Stratford student chalked up the highest mark on the exam, and on two occasions the Stratford campus led all Ontario colleges writing the RN exams. The average pass percentage at Stratford was not below 94 in the next dozen years, a period in which there was seldom more than one failure each year.

Bill Jeffrey signed on at Conestoga in 1987 as associate director of health sciences. It was his job to standardize, streamline and consolidate the college's nursing program, which was being delivered, at least in part, in Stratford, Kitchener and Guelph. The program was to be operated out of the college's Doon campus in Kitchener. The consolidation took place, but nursing continued to be offered in Stratford as part of the School of Health Sciences, which Conestoga established in 1989.

In September 1993 the college announced it would be phasing out its Stratford-based nursing program, effective September 1994. "This is really a sign of the times," said Conestoga president John Tibbits. "We know we're here to educate students for jobs – that's our primary mission. This is just an adaptation to the market forces. We are redefining what we're offering in health sciences." Tibbits said the number of positions available in the province for registered nurses fell from 1,473 to 78 between September 1990 and March 1992, and that hospitals surveyed by Conestoga said they had a zero per cent vacancy rate.

The college said it was moving all of its RN program to Doon, but that it also intended to replace its 149 RN seats at Stratford with health sciences programs that better reflected the changing health-care field and offered better prospects for employment. It suggested registered nursing assistant, health-care aide and home support as examples of those programs.

"The hospital is obviously disappointed to see the (RN) course phased out here," said Andrew Williams, SGH's assistant executive director of planning and hospital services. "But it's important that Conestoga College reorient itself and respond to the trends in the industry. We have never thought of them (student nurses) as free labour. They're here to learn. It's unfortunate it has to happen to such a good program, but I think the course they'll introduce will probably be more reflective of what's needed in the community today."

In fact, none of the programs alluded to by Tibbits materialized as Conestoga wound down its RN program in Stratford.

On May 4, 1996, more than 200 friends and relatives gathered at Central United Church for the graduation of the last 24 registered nurses trained in Stratford by Conestoga. Guest speaker Gail Stacey, an instructor with the college and a former nurse at SGH, told the grads to emulate Florence Nightingale's "formidable willpower" and "fantastic compassion for all who suffered."

Valedictorian Elizabeth Bomasuit of Stratford told her classmates to "not be discouraged by the clouds of uncertainty that hang over our profession at this time."

While most at the ceremony were looking ahead, Stratford ophthalmologist John Pyper was in a reflective mood. On hand to present the gold medal for nursing theory and practice to Christine Darling of Stratford, Pyper said, "It's very sad for me that this is the last celebration of this kind."

Conestoga continues to lease part of the former residence, in which it runs employment skills training courses.

Nursing history

The Stratford hospital's school of nursing may be gone, but its memories are preserved in the SGH school of nursing archives, two rooms on the second floor of the old hospital, now known as Avon Crest. The archives, officially opened with a ceremony on Nov. 24, 1993, contain memorabilia and history of the school, as well as surgical instruments and nursing uniforms. There is also a silver tea service which was presented to the school by the family of Sir John C. McLennan, a Stratford man who was a pioneer in the use of radium for the treatment of cancer.

Those on hand for the opening of the archives were nursing school graduates Jean Squire (1946) and Peggy Heinbuch (1951), as well as Thelma Pelley, who was director of the school from 1964 through 1973.

Hospital board chair Chris Thomson told the assembled: "It's important to preserve heritage in these times of rapid change. The archives and the alumnae and alumni are a credit to the hospital and the community as a whole."

The Stratford nursing archives are a low-profile operation, mostly because of a short budget and visitation by appointment only. Its most ardent supporter is Joan MacDermid a former nurse at SGH. "We're a well-kept secret," she says of the collection. But that secret became less secret in May 1999, when the archives were opened to the public during National Nurses Week. The week also featured tours of the hospital for secondary school students and a continuing education day. As well, the Stratford and Area Regional Council for Registered Practical Nurses donated a $700 toddler and infant motor evaluation tool to the pediatric physiotherapy department at SGH.

Nursing administrators at SGH

Lady superintendents
1891-1898	Miss Anna Fennell (later Mrs. Anna Perry)
1898-1908	Miss Emily Chilman (died while superintendent)
1908-1911	Mrs. Anna M. Stabler
1911-1916	Miss Lola Weldon (later Mrs. Bruce Brown)
1916-1919	Miss Elizabeth McArthur (later Mrs. Alex B. Manson)
1919-1924	Miss Alexandra M. Munn

Superintendents of nursing
1924-1926	Miss Aillie Mickle (later Mrs. [Dr.] David Smith)
1926-1943	Miss Zeta M. Hamilton

Directors of nursing
1943-1964	Miss Minerva Snider
1964-1973	Miss Thelma Pelley
1973-1975	Miss Phoebe Stanley
1975-1987	Miss Margaret Price
1987-1992	Doug Pinder

Directors of patient care services
1992-1993	Lynn Strugnell (acting)
1993-1998	Lynn Strugnell

Clinical site leader
1999-	Lynn Strugnell

Chief nursing officer
1999-	Margrét Comack

Directors of nursing education
1923-1939	Miss Bessie Jeffrey (part time)
1939-1939	Mrs. Elizabeth Moulton (part time)
1939-1944	Miss Emma G. Marentette
1944-1945	Miss Christine Murray
1945-1947	Miss D. Duncan
1947-1964	Miss Martha Racey
1964-1965	Eunice [Hockey] Russell (acting)
1965-1967	Miss Mary Philpott
1967-1968	Mrs. Emma [Marentette] Galloway (acting)

Minerva Snider
Director of nursing 1943-1964

NURSING SCHOOL ARCHIVES

Phoebe Stanley, 1974
Director of nursing, P-H regional school

NURSING SCHOOL ARCHIVES

Jean Levy, 1969

| 1968-1969 | Mrs. Jean Levy (later changed to O'Leavey) |
| 1970-1971 | Miss Gertrud Scheibel |

Perth-Huron Regional School of Nursing
Principal

| 1967-1973 | Miss Mary Philpott |

Conestoga College School of Nursing
Chairs

1974	Miss Mary Philpott
1974-1975	Miss Thelma Pelley (acting)
1975-1986	Mrs. Rose Anne Kreps
1989-1994	Mrs. Doris Ryan
1994-	Mrs. Jean Morris, Ms. Lois Gaspar

Co-ordinators

1973-1985	Miss Nelda Yantzie (later Mrs. Nelda Kropf)
1986-1987	Miss Judy Tremblay, Miss Carolyn MacPherson
1987-1989	Miss Judy Tremblay, Mrs. Doris Ryan

Conestoga College School of Health Sciences
Dean

| 1989- | Bill Jeffrey |

Dr. David Smith, 1962.

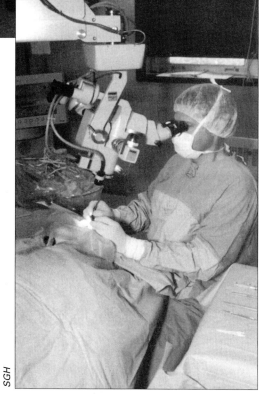

SGH

Eye surgeon Rob Walker, 1996.

Flowers of our civilization

It was Scottish novelist Robert Louis Stevenson (1850-1894) who said the physician "is the flower (such as it is) of our civilization." That quotation apparently caught the fancy of Frederick J. R. Forster, a physician who practised in Stratford for about four decades, beginning in 1906.

In the early 1950s, Forster compiled biographical information about the doctors who worked in Perth County from 1830 through 1954. His introduction to that

Dr. F. J. R. Forster, 1946

THE MIRROR

account includes Stevenson's quotation. Forster's efforts, something of a hobby for him, became a small part of a 940-page document assembled by E. Lillian Morley of Milverton. Morley's intention to produce a history of the county was unrealized.

The Forster compilation provides the basis for the early material presented here. It was his contention that doctors, because they arrived with the pioneers, "doubtless had a moulding influence on the life of the community in the early days and even up to the present time." Forster obtained some of his information from the *1879 Historical Atlas of Perth County*, but gathered most of it with a lot of leg work and perseverance. While he attempted to include all of the doctors, he conceded there may have been some oversights, particularly among those who were in the county for short periods of time and those who were "assistants to the older doctors."

It appears that John I. Flynn, a doctor dispatched by the Canada Company from England, was the first to practise in what was to become Perth County. He set up his office on the Sebastian Fryfogel farm on the main road (Highway 7) about a mile and a quarter (two kilometres) east of Shakespeare. That was in the 1830s. Flynn married Mary Fryfogel, daughter of the earliest settler in the district. He practised medicine until his death in 1872 at the age of 65.

Not long after Flynn's arrival, J. H. Moore became the first physician to locate in Stratford – in the upper floor of a small log shack on Downie Street, near where the Family YMCA of Stratford-Perth is today. In *Floodtides of Fortune*, the City of Stratford history, Adelaide Leitch said cash-less patients of Moore sometimes paid their bills with a nip of whisky or by clearing land the doctor owned.

Others soon followed Moore to Stratford, among them Irish-born John Hyde. He arrived in 1849, after a seven-year stint in Embro, and died in Stratford in 1888. He failed in his bid for a seat on the municipal council but was appointed the village's first coroner, as well as its first medical officer of health. He also became the first surgeon for the county jail, first school superintendent (1856), first chairman of the Mechanics' Institute, and first president of the Perth Mutual Fire Insurance Company (1863). He was a founder of the Congregational Church in Stratford, and in 1872 instigated formation of the community's first medical society, and helped draw up a fee schedule for the members.

Peter R. Shaver, one of the better-known doctors of the era, set up in Stratford in 1854, the year he graduated from McGill University. He built a large practice and served it with a fine team of sorrels. He was also the jail physician and coroner. He died in about 1890.

The 1855 weekly *Herald* contained the business cards of a number of Stratford doctors, including Hyde, Shaver and D. Waugh. Those of James Park and George Gray said, "Advice and operation for the poor is free."

Following are the names of doctors who practised in Stratford for varying lengths of time up to and around the turn of the century, but of whom little seems to be now known: M. J. Hanavan, Edward Paget, J. P. Jackson, Hanley, Harvey, Angus McKinnon, George Smith, Mothersill, T. D. Lucas, William Nichol, D. D. Ellis, M. J. H. Ancrum, J. G. Yeaman, B. C. Hawke, W. G. Walker, J. A. Devlin.

About others there is more information. David Wilson, for instance, is reported to be the first medical officer to "The 28th Perth Battalion of Infantry," which was formed in 1866 and redesignated the "28th Perth Regiment" in 1900. (In 1920 it became, simply, "The Perth Regiment").

Jennie (Jenny) Kidd Gowanlock was born in Kelso, Scotland, on April 21, 1841, and as a six-year-old immigrated to Canada with her parents. She attended elementary and secondary school in Stratford, and in 1860 went to Toronto where she graduated from teachers college at the age of 20. She returned to Stratford and taught until 1865 when she married Toronto publisher Edward Trout. In the first six years of their marriage she suffered from a nervous disorder which was eventually cured. The experience heightened Jenny Trout's interest in the field of medicine.

But interest meant little in an era when women and medical schools were not a happy combination in Canada. She and colleague Emily Howard Stowe were so harassed by professors and male students in their efforts to study medicine in Toronto that Stowe left for a women's medical college in New York, and the 24-year-old Trout enrolled in the Medical College of Pennsylvania in Philadelphia. The latter graduated in 1875, and in the same year she passed the Ontario registration exam. Thus, she became the first Canadian woman licensed to practise medicine in Canada;

Stowe was licensed in 1880. Both women became active promoters of women in medicine. Among her many accomplishments, Trout helped endow the Women's Medical College in Kingston, Ont., in 1883. Illness forced her to retire from medicine in 1882, at the age of 41. Trout and her family moved to California in 1908, where she died 13 years later. About 70 years after her death a factory on the southwest corner of Erie and West Gore streets in Stratford was given new life as a medical centre and the developers elected to name it after Jennie Trout.

Dr. W. N. Robertson, a former Klondiker, became the first Stratford resident to own a bicycle. Known as "Long Robertson the Bicycle Man," he used the two-wheeled conveyance on his rounds, but he also rode it to conventions and competitions. Years later, as a 70-year-old, he bicycled round-trip from Toronto, where he lived, to attend an old boys reunion in Stratford.

Donald M. Fraser, who graduated from McGill in 1869, came to Stratford in 1871. A surgeon with the Grand Trunk Railway, he had a large private practice until his death in 1908.

Another GTR surgeon, James A. Robertson, was born in North Easthope in 1845 and practised first in Tavistock, then Stratford. Eventually he became the MOH for Stratford, a position he held until his death in 1924. The black-iron dogs that now guard the entrance to upper Queen's Park, initially served in the same capacity at the Victorian-style home which Robertson had built in 1899 at 55 Albert Street (beside the old firehall), a house he called The Elms.

For three or four years in the 1870s, Robertson was joined in his practice by a Mohawk named Oronhyatekha, whose father had come north with the legendary chief Joseph Brant. Oronhyatekha married Brant's granddaughter, Irene Hill. Born in 1841 on the Six Nations reserve near Brantford, Oronhyatekha studied medicine in Toronto where, when classmates could not pronounce his name, he was nicknamed "Old Iron Teakettle." He became well known for his treatment of nervous diseases, and of throat and lung problems. He also involved himself in local politics. He left Stratford to work with the Mohawk Indians on the Bay of Quinte and then went on to London, Ont., and Toronto.

Another North Easthope native, Donald Blair Fraser was well-travelled and especially well-educated when he established a practice in Stratford in 1878. For many years he lectured at the University of Western Ontario, and became widely known as a surgical consultant. In the early 1880s, he was the first doctor in Stratford to install a telephone. He died in Stratford in 1933.

Quebec-born John M. Dunsmore set up in Mitchell in 1870, and in 1883 moved to Stratford, where he practised until his death in 1909. For several years he was surgeon for the county jail.

One of the best-known doctors in the county around the turn of the century was James Palmer Rankin, who was born in 1854 in Zorra Township. He studied medicine in Toronto and Edinburgh. He first practised in Tavistock, in 1879, and then went to Toronto. He moved to Stratford in 1891. Rankin was medical officer for the Perth Regiment for more than two decades, as well as a lieutenant-colonel in the Canadian Army Medical Corps. Addicted to politics, he was a Stratford alderman, and twice – in 1908 and 1921 – won the North Perth federal riding for the Liberals. He lost federal elections in 1911 and 1917. Rankin was appointed to the Canadian senate in 1925. He died in 1934.

James Rankin's medical and political careers were paralleled by Joseph Dunsmore Monteith, who was born in 1865. A graduate of Trinity College, he practised in Stratford from 1895 until his death in 1934. He was mayor of the city in 1917-18 and, as a Conservative, he served in the provincial legislature from 1923 through 1934. From 1926 through 1930 he was the Ontario treasurer. He was also the minister of public works and labour. Monteith was an early and longtime president of the Stratford Horticultural Society. He was also a world traveller. His father, Andrew Monteith, had been a member of the first provincial legislature in Ontario, and a brother, John Charles Monteith, had been Stratford mayor in 1893-94.

George Reginald Deacon was born in Bothwell in 1876 but about six years later moved to Stratford when his father, Rev. Daniel Deacon, became rector of St. Paul's Anglican Church. The younger Deacon graduated from McGill with distinction in 1896, and was his class valedictorian. Later that year he returned to Stratford and joined the practice of Donald M. Fraser. When the latter died in 1908, Deacon carried on alone.

It is reported that Deacon was the second city resident (behind Moses Schlotzhauer) – but the first Stratford physician – to own a car. He became district surgeon for the Grand Trunk Railway and practised surgery extensively until illness forced him to retire. He died in 1942. Among the doctors who served with Deacon were Jack Maynard, Emmerson Trow, Percy Barker, William H. K. Crehan, R. Stanley Murray and E. Kirk Lyon. Lyon, who later settled in Leamington, also served a term as president of the Ontario Medical Association.

Daisy M. M. Macklin was born in Stratford, the daughter of one of Stratford's leading dry goods merchants, William Macklin. She graduated from Women's Medical College in Toronto in 1895. After several years in the missionary field in China, Macklin came back to Stratford in 1900. A specialist in the diseases that affect mostly women and children, as well as in electro-therapeutics, she was the first female doctor on staff at Stratford General Hospital. She died in 1925. Two of her

brothers also became doctors.

J. A. Corcoran was among a handful of doctors who practised in Stratford for just a few years around the turn of the century. He served the city from about 1900 to 1904. Stratford-born in 1878, he died in 1939.

In 1903, Lorne Forbes Robertson joined his father, J. A., in a partnership that lasted

THE MIRROR

Dr. Lorne Robertson, 1946

until the latter died in 1924. The junior Robertson, born in 1876, and educated in Toronto, Montreal, England, Scotland and the United States, was prominent in the city's medical, sports and education circles. He was a physician for the Canadian National Railways. He served on the board of education, and became president of the Stratford Hockey Club in 1917 – at about the time Howie Morenz moved to town. Robertson had more than a passing influence on Morenz, a Mitchell kid who was destined to become the world's best hockey player in the first half of this century. At about the time the Montreal Canadiens were wooing Morenz, Stratford was in need of a new arena. It was Robertson's money, energy and influence that became the driving force behind the building in 1924 of what would become the Classic City Arena.

Robertson, who officially retired in 1947, six years before his death, also touched the lives of those who practised medicine with him, a list that includes Norman Bethune and Gordon Murray. As a holiday replacement for the Robertsons, the 27-year-old Bethune first practised in Stratford in 1917. According to Leitch's history of Stratford, Bethune was eccentric and charming. Apparently he accented a light blue suit with a red tie and yellow shoes to take a young lady to a dance. Apparently, too, she was humiliated by the outfit. Bethune stood in for the Robertsons again in 1919, before forging a career as a great surgeon and humanitarian. He served in France and Spain, and later in Mao Tse-tung's China, where he died in 1939, after contracting blood-poisoning during an operation.

Born in Stratford in 1894, Gordon Murray was known as the "blue baby" doctor because of his work with the anticoagulant drug heparin. He practised with the Robertsons in Stratford in 1921-22, after completing a medical training that he interrupted to serve in the First World War. He became a cardiac specialist who developed the first artificial kidney to be used successfully in North America. Murray's distinguished career was recognized in 1967 when he was named a Companion of the Order of Canada, nine years before his death, in Toronto.

Peter Francis Quinlan, who was born in Ellice Township in 1873, taught school in Dublin, Ont., before taking up medicine. He graduated from the University of Toronto in 1903 and then studied in New York before setting up a practice in Dublin. In 1906 he moved that practice to Stratford, where he also served on the board of education and for 20 years was president of the Perth County Liberal Association. He died in Stratford in May 1946.

Like Quinlan, William Thomas Gemmell, who was born in Egmondville in 1875, taught school before studying medicine. Also like Quinlan, he graduated in 1903, but from Trinity College. He practised in Wheatley and Cromarty before settling in Stratford in 1906. For a number of years his practice included all city employees. He served terms as president and secretary-treasurer of the Perth County Medical Association. A raconteur with a keen wit, Gemmell was a popular after-dinner speaker. His hobbies included hunting, fishing, photography and flowers. He died in September 1942.

Frederick Joseph Richardson Forster was born in 1874, a son of Moffitt Forster, a pioneer doctor at Thorndale. An 1897 U of T graduate, the younger Forster was house surgeon at the Hospital for Sick Children in Toronto in 1897-1898 and was in general practice in Acton and Caistorville until 1904. For the next two years he did graduate work in New York, Vienna and London, and in 1906 set up as an ear, eye, nose and throat specialist in Stratford. He was an officer in the Perth Regiment from 1906 through 1915, when he transferred to the army medical corps and was overseas in 1915-16. He was active during the Second World War as a medical examiner for recruits. He also examined Royal Canadian Air Force enlisted personnel during that war.

In 1961, at the age of 86, Forster looked back on his medical life in Stratford and reflected fondly upon his first automobile, a new Ford runabout, which in 1908 cost him $800. It was, he said, the first to be sold by the city's Ford agent of the day, as well as only the third or fourth car in Stratford. He said he could average about 15 miles an hour in the car, and a one-day return trip to Palmerston, where his parents had moved, was considered a major accomplishment. As he told the story of his new car, Forster still held a valid driver's licence.

While at Sick Children's in Toronto, Forster saw his first cases of cleft palate, and when he returned from Europe he sought as much information as possible on the deformity. He made it a personal study. When The Rotary Club of Stratford began its free crippled children's clinics in 1923, Forster, as a Rotarian, volunteered his surgical skills to help those with hare lips and cleft palates.

Active as well in politics, Forster unsuccessfully carried the Liberal colours against Dr. J. D. Monteith in the federal riding of North Perth in 1926. He was treasurer of the Perth County Liberal Association for many years. He was also the founding secretary-treasurer of the Perth County Medical Society when it was organized in 1913. He later became its president. In 1955 he was made a life member of the Ontario Medical Association.

Samuel T. Rutherford, who was born in Millbank in 1864, was another Stratford doctor who took up medicine after first working, for a short time, as a teacher. He set up in Listowel after graduation from the University of Toronto in 1889 but then opted for graduate studies in Europe and the United States. In 1907 he settled in Stratford, where he had an extensive surgical practice until he died in 1930.

George Ford, who first practised in Shakespeare in 1907, died about six years later, soon after he moved his office to Stratford.

Oscar A. Cannon was born in 1882 and graduated from U of T in 1907. In the same year, he joined the Stratford practice of James Rankin. Early in the First World War he joined the army's medical corps and was sent overseas. Upon his return he was stationed in Halifax during the great harbour explosion in December 1917. After the war Cannon practised in Hamilton where he was chief medical officer for the Steel Company of Canada from 1937 through 1942. He retired in 1947 and died in 1951.

Maxwell J. Fraser was born in Stratford in 1886 and graduated from McGill in 1909. After some graduate work in Edinburgh, he set up in Stratford in 1910. During the First World War he was with the medical corps

THE MIRROR

Dr. Maxwell Fraser, 1946

and was also acting medical officer of health for Stratford. As well, he was the MOH for Downie Township. He was surgeon for the county jail in 1930. Illness forced his retirement in 1950.

Ramsay D. Rankin, son of J. P. Rankin, was born in Tavistock in 1888. He graduated from McGill in 1912 and, after a short stint with Dr. Percy L. Tye in Milverton, Rankin joined his father's practice in Stratford. He died in 1921.

Michael Steele was born at Avonbank in 1860. He studied medicine at the University of Toronto. His first practice was in Tavistock but he came to Stratford in 1920. He also maintained an office in Shakespeare. In the late 1920s he moved to Winona but returned to Stratford in 1930 to take over from his brother, James Steele, as registrar for North Perth. As a Conservative, Steele was member of Parliament for South Perth from 1911 through 1921. He died on New Year's Day 1946 in Vienna, Ont., where he had lived for a number of years.

Harold B. Kenner was born in Stratford in 1896. He graduated from Queen's University in 1920. While at Queen's he joined a hospital unit that served in France in 1916-17. In 1922 he returned to Stratford and set up with J. P. Rankin. In 1924 he became the MOH for Stratford, a position

Dr. Harold Kenner, 1946

he held for 42 years, until he retired in 1966. During the Second World War, Kenner joined the army medical corps and became a colonel in charge of the Canadian hospital in England. He died in 1969.

William Henry Killeavy (Bill) Crehan was born in Wallacetown in October 1890. After graduating from Queen's he taught school for six years to earn money so he could study medicine. During the First World War he served as a lieutenant with the Royal Field Artillery in France, where in 1917 he survived a poison gas attack. After the war he enrolled at the University of Toronto to become a doctor. In 1921 he joined George Deacon's Stratford practice for a short time and then opened his own office. He became one the city's most popular doctors and best-known citizens.

Crehan was a member of the city's board of education, president of the Perth County Medical Association, president of the Stratford Scout Association, president of the Stratford Badminton and Social Club, president of the Western Ontario Badminton Association, charter member and president of the Stratford Optimist Club and lieutenant-governor of District 15 of Optimist International, and a director of the tennis club at the Stratford Country Club. While attending a board of education

meeting at city hall in January 1940, Crehan suffered a severe heart attack, from which he never recovered. He died at age 49. The city was so moved that all schools in Stratford were closed the morning of his funeral. The Tudor-style residence that Crehan had built in 1934 remains a (420) William Street landmark.

Born in North Easthope Township, Alexander Fisher (1870-1945) graduated from U of T in 1903. In 1922 he came to Stratford, where he practised for five years before returning to Toronto.

Donald Fraser, son of Donald B. Fraser, was born in Stratford in 1892 and graduated from McGill in 1921. He practised for a short while with his father but then became a medical officer with the provincial government. He died in Toronto in 1951.

Robert Stanley (Stan) Murray was born in Galt (now Cambridge) in June 1888. After graduating in medicine from the University of Western Ontario in 1917, he served

Dr. Stanley Murray, 1946

overseas with the army medical corps. When the First World War ended, Murray set up a practice in Mitchell in 1919. In 1925 he moved to Stratford where he joined George Deacon, and later went on his own. For 25 years he was district medical officer for the Grand Trunk (later Canadian

National) Railway. He was also district representative to the College of Physicians and Surgeons of Ontario, as well as a member of the city's board of education. He served as president of the medical staff of SGH and as president of the Perth County Medical Association. Murray returned to the medical corps in the Second World War and as a major worked at the medical hospital at Crumlin, near London, Ont., and later commanded the military hospital at Ipperwash. He resumed private practice in Stratford in 1946.

Murray was keenly interested in reforestation and for 15 years he planted thousands of trees on 87 acres (34.8 hectares) of property he bought in 1939 near what would later become the Wildwood Conservation Area. Murray died in August 1954. By 1956 the plantation had grown to 175,000 trees on 175 acres (70 hectares) and was sold for $16,000 to the Upper Thames River Conservation Authority. The UTRCA kept 75 acres and gave the rest of the property to the Ministry of Natural Resources for management. Murray had been a charter member of the UTRCA in 1947.

Three years after his death, the UTRCA tract was named the Dr. Murray Forest, and officially opened by his widow Anne and granddaughter Patricia Murray. On Saturday, Oct. 13, 1984, about 50 family members and friends gathered at Wildwood to unveil a plaque in his honour. Among the assembled was Dr. Malcolm Murray of Stone Mountain, Ga., the youngest and lone survivor of three sons of the doctor who created a forest.

George H. Ingham, who was born in Stirling in 1888, is another of the early Stratford doctors who first taught school before taking up medicine. He graduated from the medical school at UWO in 1914 and, after some years in general practice, he did graduate work in New York. As an ear, eye, nose and throat specialist, he came to Stratford in 1924 and joined the practice of

Fred Forster. A number of years later he went on his own. Ingham was a captain with the army medical corps in the First World War and a major with the same corps in the Second World War. He was also on Stratford's board of education from 1936 through 1942.

J. Gordon Grieve, who was born in Mornington Township in 1899, graduated in medicine from U of T in 1922. He set up a

Dr. J. Gordon Grieve, 1946

practice in Stratford two years later. He was with the army medical corps from 1942 through 1945 and served overseas.

T. Russell Nichols was born in Stratford in 1900 and graduated from U of T in 1924. He established a general practice in Stratford in 1925. A year later, when a lab was set up in the basement of SGH, Nichols was appointed to oversee it – something he did for about two decades – until December 1945. He became certified in anesthesia in 1943. Nichols served with the Royal Air Force in 1918 and from 1943 through 1945 he was medical officer with the Perth Regiment.

Fred W. Nelson was born in St. Thomas in 1892 and graduated from UWO in 1917. In 1920 he set up a practice in Sebringville. In 1928 he moved to Stratford and associated with J. D. Monteith. Nelson served more than two years in the First

World War and all of the Second World War and later became the pension medical examiner for the London, Ont., office of the Department of Veterans' Affairs.

E. M. V. Fielding was born in Niagara Falls in 1896 and graduated from U of T in 1926. He immediately went into practice in Stratford with J. D. Monteith, but two years later he returned to his home town. There he became coroner for Niagara Falls and Welland County. Fielding became certified in anesthesia. He also was a member of the Lincoln and Welland Regiment.

Lionel A. (Bud) Macklin was born in Mildmay in 1903. He studied medicine in Toronto where he became house surgeon at the Hospital for Sick Children. He was also lieutenant surgeon with the Royal Canadian

Dr. Bud Macklin, 1946

Sea Cadet Corps. He established a private practice in Stratford in 1931 and specialized in children's diseases. He also headed the pediatrics department at SGH, and served a term as president of the Perth County Medical Association. He was named coroner for Perth in 1950. Away from medicine, Macklin was one of the founders of the Stratford badminton club. He was a board member and president of the YMCA, an ardent supporter of Stratford minor hockey, and a lover of flowers, particularly roses. He died in September 1956.

Wilbur F. Brown was born in St. Marys in 1905, son of Dr. Wilbur F. Brown. Following his father's lead, the younger Brown graduated from U of T in 1931. After some graduate work in Edinburgh, he began practice in Stratford in 1934. In 1939 he joined the medical branch of the Royal Canadian Air Force. He eventually became a wing commander and then senior overseas consultant in internal medicine. After the war he stayed with the RCAF, stationed in Ottawa.

William Macauley Gilmore was born in Blenheim in 1903. He graduated from UWO in 1927 and then earned certification in radiology. He was radiologist at SGH from 1934 until his retirement in 1971 – apart from a stint in Victoria, B.C., in 1950-52. During those two years he was replaced at Stratford by Archibald M. Edington, a 1936 McGill graduate.

James G. McDermott graduated from UWO in 1933 and opened a practice in Stratford in 1937. A surgeon, McDermott was district representative to the Ontario Medical Association. He was also an officer in the army medical corps from 1942 through 1945, and medical officer with the Perth Regiment from 1946 through 1954.

David Gemmell was born in Stratford in 1908, son of Dr. W. T. Gemmell. He graduated from U of T in 1934 and went

Dr. David Gemmell, 1946

into practice in Stratford with his father in 1938.

Born in Sault Ste. Marie in 1905, George M. Bastedo studied medicine at U of T. Certified in general surgery, he practised in Stratford from 1936 to 1946 when he moved to Marathon. In the Second World War he joined the army medical corps and served in France from 1939 through 1945. He retired from the army as a lieutenant-colonel with a distinguished service order.

Kenneth B. Schlotzhauer was born in Stratford in 1908 and graduated from U of T

Dr. William Sproat, 1968

Dr. Ken Schlotzhauer, 1946

in 1932. He established a practice in Stratford in 1935.

Gilbert C. (Gib) Jarrott was born in Kippen in 1908 and studied medicine at UWO, from which he graduated in 1933. A specialist in obstetrics and gynecology, Jarrott was a district rep to the College of Physicians and Surgeons of Ontario. He practised in Seaforth for a number of years before coming to Stratford in 1940.

William C. Sproat also set up in Stratford in 1940. Born in Huron County in 1903, Sproat was a 1926 UWO grad. He interned at Harper Hospital in Detroit and returned to Seaforth in 1927, where he opened a practice. To further his surgical knowledge, Sproat studied in England, Scotland and Austria. He moved to Stratford to take over

the practice of William Henry Killeavy (Bill) Crehan, and also became chief of surgery at SGH.

Evelyn K. McCaul was born in Fort Frances in 1916, daughter of Dr. William Johnston. She graduated from U of T in 1937 and set up a practice in Stratford in 1944. She specialized in the medical problems of women and children.

Hugh H. Thompson was born in Penetanguishene in 1912 and graduated from UWO in 1942. From 1943 through 1946 he was a medical officer with the RCAF. When the Second World War ended he set up a practice in Stratford. He died in 1988.

C. Edward Sylvester was born in Stratford in 1914 and graduated from U of T in 1941. An anesthetist, Sylvester came to Stratford in 1946, where he was appointed physician for the county jail. He also served on the board of education and was its chair in 1955.

John J. Quinlan was born in Stratford in 1919, son of Peter F. Quinlan. Like his dad, John J. studied medicine at U of T and graduated in 1943. He was with the army medical corps during the Second World War, after which he took over the Stratford practice of his father, who died in 1946. He was a member of the board of education from 1947 through 1949. He moved to Brantford in 1949.

Howard C. Hazell was born in Whitby in 1916 and graduated from U of T in 1940. He set up practice in Stratford in 1948 and for a while was medical officer for the Perth Regiment.

John Penistan earned his medical certification in his native England, before he came to Canada in 1949 to become head of pathology at SGH. He held that position until he died of cancer in June 1973.

Toronto-born in 1923, Angus M. (Gus) Wilson graduated from U of T In 1947. He practised in Stratford from 1950 until his retirement in 1994. His son, Douglas M., has been a dentist in Stratford since 1979.

Norvel W. (Pinky) Scratch was born in Saskatchewan in 1915 and studied medicine

Dr. Pinky Scratch, 1968

at UWO, from which he graduated in 1943. He served with the army medical corps from 1943 through 1946. A specialist in internal medicine, Scratch practised in Stratford from 1950 through 1986.

Bruce A. Campbell graduated from UWO in 1947 and specialized in surgery. For six years he served as a surgeon lieutenant with the Royal Canadian Navy. He came to Stratford in 1951, where he practised until 1970, when he moved to New Liskeard. He died in 1993.

Peter Colyer Roberts was born in Folkestone, England, but came to Canada with his parents when he was just a year old. He served with the RCAF medical corps during the Second World War, and when it ended he enrolled in medicine at the University of Toronto. He graduated in 1950 and practised in Wallaceburg and Blenheim before settling in Stratford in 1954. He served as medical officer for the Perth Regiment and for many years was team doctor for the Stratford junior B hockey club. He died in March 1995.

John E. Pyper and Ian Lindsay also came

Dr. John Pyper, 1968

to Stratford in 1954. Pyper was born in Northern Ireland in 1920 and studied medicine in Ireland and England. On behalf of interests in Stratford, he was interviewed in Belfast in October 1953 by John Penistan, who had been the first of what Pyper now calls the British invasion of medical immigrants to descend upon Stratford, Canada, after the Second World War. Pyper says he became the second of those immigrants when he arrived in January 1954 "with $15 in my pocket." A specialist in ophthalmology, Pyper first associated with George Ingham. Beginning in 1957, he practised on his own. Pyper and SGH board chair Len Webster founded the annual medical staff-SGH board dinner in the mid-1960s. For a number of years Pyper also lectured on eye diseases at the nursing school. A Rotarian since 1954, he helped establish the annual Rotary-minor hockey tournament in the early '70s. Two of his children followed his lead and became doctors, though neither is practising in Stratford. Pyper retired in 1997.

Lindsay was born in Edinburgh in 1923 and studied in Scotland and England to become a surgeon. He also served with the reserves of the Royal Canadian Army Medical Corps. He arrived in Stratford in October 1954. Lindsay the Scot and Pyper the Irishman found they shared an interest in British sports, particularly rugby. They also shared an apartment at Front and Ballantyne streets for about six months, until Lindsay's wife, Mollie, and their three children emigrated in the spring of 1955. When nurse Olive Mooney emigrated from Ireland in July 1955 and immediately became Mrs. John Pyper, Lindsay was best man at the wedding. While in Stratford, Lindsay was a board member with the Stratford Festival and served a term as president. He left the city in September 1984. He died suddenly in Toronto in April 1992.

Douglas J. Allan also arrived in Canada in 1954. Margaret D. Allan, also a physician,

Dr. Doug Allan, 1968

followed a year later. They settled in Stratford in 1957.

Pyper says the wave of British doctors to Stratford no doubt contributed to the city's makeover in the 1950s. "It must have been quite a culture shock back then," he says, "knowing Stratford as I now know it. First of all there were all those British actors and directors coming here for the Festival, and then these doctor types."

John B. Moore was born in London, Ont.,

Dr. John Moore, 1968

in 1919 and studied medicine at UWO, from which he graduated in 1943. During the Second World War he was a surgeon lieutenant in the Royal Canadian Navy. He first practised in Mitchell, in association with Kenneth W. McLandress, and was coroner for Perth and Huron counties. In 1963 he moved to Stratford and established his own practice. He retired in 1986.

Another Brit, Archibald Jeffrey (Jeff) Macdonald, a native of Bristol, England, came to Canada in 1955 and became a resident physician at St. Joseph's Hospital in London, where he specialized in medicine and pediatrics. He also spent six months at the children's hospital in London, before he moved to Stratford and took over a practice established by Bud Macklin in the York Apartments on Lakeside Drive. Eventually he teamed with Lloyd Schulthies and Ranald McWilliam in the medical clinic on Cambria Street.

In the late 1960s, Macdonald combined his training in medicine with his love of acting. Sandwiched between the *Edge of Night* and *Lassie*, CTV ran a half-hour show called *Doctor's Diary*, featuring Dr. A. J. Macdonald. In the shows, Macdonald counselled fictional patients about a variety of real-life illnesses. After a year of running off to Montreal two or three times a month to tape 10 shows in two days, Macdonald decided he would "last longer as a physician" and opted for full-time medicine. For 21 years, ending in December 1993, Macdonald was Perth County coroner. He also served on the board of education, which he chaired for two years. He was president of the Stratford Art Association and chair of Gallery Stratford. He retired from active medical practice March 31, 1994, at age 70.

Scores of other medical doctors and dentists who have practised in Perth County over the past 114 years have used the services of SGH. Some of them have worked at the hospital. Most, of them, it is hoped, are listed here:

Terrence R. Aitken
Robert Annis
Jane E. Anwan
Chris Arciszewski
Karl Jason Bandy
Charles L. Bateman
Margaret Barnett
L. R. Barron
R. Paul Bartlett
Peter Bartlett
A. Ralph Beharry
N. Bennett
William L. Bigelow
T. S. (Tim) Bilkey
Robert N. (Bob) Bissonnette
Kirsten Blaine
Sean Blaine
Christine Bloch
Kenneth W. Bown
Paul L. Brady
Richard Branson
Peter Brooks
A. Brookway
Bernard Bukala
M. G. Peter Cameron
Bradley Card
Malcolm Carlson
Roddy T. Caulfield
Joseph Chin
A. Chlebus
J. Chiu

Dennis K. Chong
S. Y. Chung
Sanford T. Clare
David Clark
Luis Cleto
J. Clifford
M. Clin
Charles Clinton-Thomas
Janice Coates
Ron Collins
James Comtois
Michael F. Conlon
John S. Connors
B. Corbett
Vince A. Corrigan
Morris G. Coxon
Dora Cruz
Norman Cruz
Melita Cull
L. Curry
J. Marie Dale
A. R. Dar
Donald S. Davis
Robert W. Davis
William J. Davis
Thomas W. Dean
James A. Devlin
Paul Dickens
Michael Dietrich
Mark Diotallevi
David Drake

Thomas Drake
Donald F. Duffin
John Duggan
T. Duggan
J. M. Dunsmore
P. C. Duval
Joseph Ennett
Yale Erenberg

Dr. Norman Cruz, emergency

Glenn W. Evans
L. I. Fawcett
T. B. Feick
S. Feroze-Din
M. Fiala
David P. Fitzgerald
G. M. P. Fleming

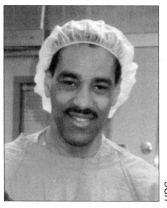
Dr. Andrew Hussey, urologist

Edward H. (Ted) Flowers
Paul J. Foxcroft
Donald R. Fuller
James M. Gall
Charles (Chuck) Gatfield
W. Gawman
N. Gervais
H. Giang
Edward S. Gibson
Michael Gillett
Arnold H. Goldberg
Randal J. Gonser
M. Greenbert
Gregory Haase
Stephen Hall
Gregg Hancock
James M. Hardwick
G. B. Ha'Eri
Joseph C. Hackney
Steven F. Hall
Joyce Harris
Brian Hasegawa
D. S. Heath
R. Heath
Ken Heaton
Anand Hegde
N. Ronald Heitbohmer
Harry A. Hersh
Robert Hill
Cheryl Hillyer
James Hiscock
Susan Hiscock

Peter K. Hodes
Kenneth R. Hook
George Horner
Johnson T. S. Hua
Craig Hudson
Andrew A. Hussey
Edward Barry Isaac
J. Jackney
N. Jakiwychyk
John C. Jenkins
Frederick A. S. Jensen
Fred Jewson
Peter S. Johnston
Andre Joyal
Tibor Kalos
Alnoor Kara
Kim Karry
Denise Keene
Heather Keizer
Stirling Keizer
James R. Kelly
Greg Kenyon
Carmelita Kintanar
Erle J. Kirby
T. Crosby Kirkpatrick
Miriam Klassen
Harvey D. Kohn
Barry Kramer
Larry Lacey
K. G. Lambert
M. Lamba
Grace Langford
Sergio Lappano
Per Larsen
Russell Latuskie
David E. Leaney
Barbara Lee
Stanley F. Leete
R. Lehman
Eric M. Lenczner
Michael Leser
Albert K. Leung
L. Levin
P. B. Lindsay
R. Lohmann
Elgin M. Loney
J. Robert Lorimer

A. MacDonald
D. A. G. MacEachen
J. D. MacIntyre
John MacIntyre
Angus Maciver
J. R. MacKenzie
Janis A. MacNaughton
L. Mak
Edward Malkus
James J. Mallett
Miriam Mann
Steven M. Marchuk
A. Bruce Marshall

Dr. Janis MacNaughton,
internist

M. Marshall
B. Martin
Robert G. Martin
Biju Mathew
Barbara Matthews
G. Mayer
James N. McArthur
A. McKenzie
Philip McCabe
Marcie McCune
T. Mitchell
J. R. McCready
James M. McDermott
D. McGhee
Andrew J. McKenzie
Andrew W. McKenzie

James Ross McKenzie
A. R. McLean
Stuart R. McNeill
Patrick J. McQuade
Ranald S. McWilliam
J. M. Melville
Cecil H. Mickelson
Donald Miettenen
Stephen J. C. Miller
T. Mitchell
Laurel E. Moore
Peter G. Morehan
A. G. Morris
Charles T. B. Moyo
Donald J. Munn
William D. Munn
Donald C. Munro
William D. Myers
B. Neable
D'Arcy R. Nethercott
Fred Netherton
K. Neufeld
William R. Nichols
Michael Northcott
Richard Northcott
Rosemary Northcott
Brendan O'Connor
Keith F. Oliveira
Charles Omole
Julia O'Reilly
Richard Ough
M. J. Ostime
David W. Parratt
G. Wayne Parsons
T. D. Patterson
William L. Payne
James E. Peterson
J. M. Phinn
J. P. Pillar
John J. Pook
Ralph Pototschnik
Vincent P. Quinlan
Arif Qureshi
J. Radwan
G. H. Ramsay
Jay Rao
Victor Rausch

Hans F. Reichenfeld
Kenneth Rodney
William G. Rombough
Hugh A. Rose
R. K. W. Row
Arthur Robert Rowe
R. A. Roy
John Rutherford
Peter A. Rutherford
Andrew J. Rynne
L. Schonberger
B. Showalter
Elfriede K. Schuh
Otto W. Schuh
Lloyd G. (Pete) Schulthies
Ruth Schwarz
F. G. Ellis Scott
Frank Scott
Michael Shannon
John H. B. Sheppard
David S. Smith
Sharyn Smith
A. Kent Sorsdahl
S. John Spiers
Philip Squires
Martin W. Stapleton
Liora Steele
Terrence A. Summers
B. Surti
Heather A. Sylvester
Gordon Sylvester
C. David Tamblyn
Susan E. Tamblyn
L. Chris Tebbutt
Shamim Tejpar
David M. Thomas
Eric Thomas
Douglas J. Thompson
W. Grant Thompson
Melvin K. Tidman
Peter Tinits
William G. Tobin
Donna A. Tomlinson
R. Bruce Tomlinson
Nicholas J. Tower
James D. Town
Murray Treloar

Michael Troster
Ian Turnbull
John Underwood
Arthur A. vanWalraven
Eugene A. Varga
John Vetters
Robin C. Waite

Dr. A. Kent Sorsdahl, surgeon

John R. (Rob) Walker
W. G. Walker
Tim Wallace
R. Wan
Kenneth M. Ward
Tom Warnock
Rex Warren
M. Weber
Paul T. Weir
Evelyn C. Westen
David Westman
Wayne W. Weston
Martin Wheeler
M. Whitaker
Nancy Whitmore
R. J. Whittome
James A. Wickwire
Mark Wilkinson
David Williams
Doug Wilson
S. Wilts
M. Wolnik
K. Van Woolnough
David C. Young

These are some of the early area doctors who used the facilities of SGH.

Atwood
Cowan, Hamilton, Rice, Douglas, Langwill, Murray, Croft, Donald A. Kidd, Charles McMane, Richard T. Kidd, C. E. Connors, D. R. Hunter

Hibbert Township
A. V. Michell, Martin Stapleton, King, Daniel Cremin, Tole, H. R. Simpkins, Victor Trainor, D. E. Sturgis, Stewart McGregor, Keith McGregor, Hume Rae, Issac Aylesworth (came here from Mitchell), Alexander McTavish, A. D. Naismith, W. H. P. Tufford, Hutchison, David Hodgson, William Mair

Dr. Percy Tye, 1946

THE MIRROR

Kirkton
John Stubbs, Alex Kirk, Valentine Hutcheson, Irving, John J. Thompson, Alex K. Ferguson, C. A. Campbell

Listowel
John Nichol, Dingman, J. Philip, Albert H. Nichol, Roy Nichol, J. D. Dillabaugh (came here from Milverton), L. W. Thompson, James Moore, Harry J. Livingstone, W. C. Pratt (came here from Millbank), Campbell, J. E. Sawdon, Andrew G. Shiel, Moore, Henry Hart, James G. Kirk, C. D. Kilpatrick

Millbank
James Johnston, S. G. Rutherford, T. A. Seager, Christie, C. A. Crich, McComb, W. A. Pratt, Shaw, Jones, E. S. Sellers, J. H. Finn

Milverton
J. D. Dillabough, Samuel Richardson, Richard E. Preston, William Parke, P. C. Park, Catermole, William Egbert, A. D. Naismith (came here from Staffa), Frederick Parker, R. H. McComb, Percy L. Tye, H. R. Nicklin. L. Angus, McKittrick, S. McTavish, W. Cameron, Sloan, R. M. Aldis, Ruth E. Alison, P. R. Beacock

Mitchell
Rev. Issac Aylesworth, R. Hornibrook, George Hodge, Jonathon Day, Edwin George (came here from Shakespeare), Richard W. Hurlburt, A. Dalton Smith, William J. M. Armstrong, J. W. Atkinson, A. Mc.D. Murray, L. W. Mair, Wilbert Hall, R. Bruce Gilrie, William R. Aberhart, William Elvey Pridham, Kenneth W. McLandress

Monkton
Alexander Felstead McKenzie, John Proudfoot, Harry L. Bower, Thomas Douglas

St. Marys
Isaac H. Thayer, Nelles, James Coleman, Daniel Wilson, James J. Hall, David H. Harrison, Hugh Matheson, Thomas Sparks, Casey F. Smith, Andrew Alexander Knox, Arthur E. Fraleigh, J. Russell Stanley, Thomas J. McInnes, John G. Jose, John Sinkins, Robert H. Latimer, J. Edgar Williams, Elizabeth McMaster, J. Dwight Smith, Martin H. Humphrys, Frederick George Pim

Sebringville
G. Schmidt, John J. Paul, C. H. Dwyer, Alexander Sinclair

Shakespeare

Edwin George Wood, R. Whiteman, William Pugh, George Ford, Thompson, C. Trow, M. Steele

Tavistock

Preiss, Adams, J. Ross, James Skirving, Michael Steele, Otto G. Niemier, Fred J. Cawthorpe, Charles R. McTavish, Harold M. Taylor, John K. Fisher, Bruce Halliday, R. L. Matthes, W. Davis

1968 NURSING SCHOOL YEARBOOK

Dr. Elvey Pridham, 1968

THE MIRROR

Dr. Edgar Williams, 1946

THE MIRROR

Dr. Robert Latimer, 1946

THE MIRROR

Dr. Harold Taylor, 1946

THE MIRROR

Dr. John Jose, 1946

THE MIRROR

Dr. John Fisher, 1946

153

These doctors, who served at SGH, are listed on a memorial plaque
hanging near the switchboard in the hospital.

John G. Jose	1902-1952	William C. Sproat	1903-1976
Lorne F. Robertson	1876-1952	Harold M. Taylor	1902-1976
R. Stanley Murray	1888-1954	Gilbert C. Jarrott	1908-1977
Lionel A. Macklin	1903-1956	Robert H. Latimer	1895-1980
J. Gordon Grieve	1899-1957	David Gemmell	1908-1982
T. Russell Nichols	1900-1959	George H. Ingham	1888-1985
Kenneth W. McLandress	1908-1966	William M. Gilmore	1903-1986
David Smith	1873-1967	R. Lorimer	1932-1986
Frederick J. R. Forster	1874-1967	Hugh H. Thompson	1912-1988
John K. Fisher	1907-1968	Lloyd G. Schulthies	1917-1989
Harold B. Kenner	1896-1969	Howard C. Hazell	1916-1990
Ranald S. McWilliam	1922-1969	Ian Lindsay	1932-1992
Percy L. Tye	1883-1969	Robert N. Bissonnette	1927-1993
John L. Penistan	1915-1973	Elfreida K. Schuh	1925-1993
K. W. Hampton	1917-1974	Fred Jensen	1924-1994
James G. McDermott	1908-1974	Peter C. Roberts	1918-1995
C. Edward Sylvester	1914-1975	W. Elvey Pridham	1905-1996
Kenneth B. Schlotzhauer	1908-1975	Melvin K. Tidman	1933-1997
Martin H. Humphrys	1924-1976	Arthur R. Rowe	1917-1999
Alexander Sinclair	1903-1976		

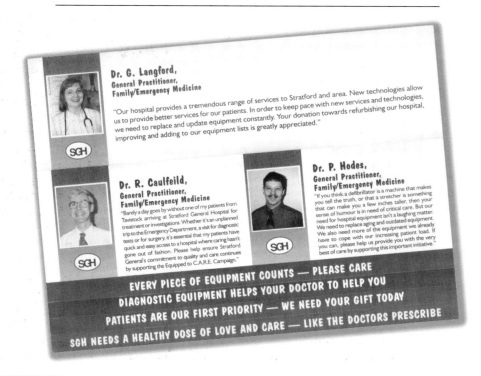

Dr. Dave

In a medical career that spanned five decades, David Smith became one of the best-known, best-loved doctors to practise in Stratford. He was born in West Zorra Township, on Feb. 7, 1873, and taught school before taking up medicine at the University of Toronto, from which he graduated in 1902. He went into practice in Stratford in 1905 with J. D. Monteith, but in a short time set up his own office. To one and all he became known as, simply, Dr. Dave.

During the First World War, Smith was in charge of the military hospital and medical corps training depot in London, Ont. In 1918 he went overseas with the 1st Tank Battalion.

When he returned he became a charter member of the Rotary Club of Stratford, which formed in May 1922. His interest in crippled children led to his becoming founding secretary of the Ontario Society for Crippled Children, also in 1922. The next year, he became president of the Stratford club and was a catalyst in the establishment of annual Rotary-sponsored clinics for crippled children at SGH. Soon there were similar clinics in Huron County.

In November 1957, Smith and the two other living founding members were honoured by the OSCC at a meeting and luncheon in Windsor which celebrated the society's 35th anniversary.

From 1923 through 1944 Smith was a member of the Dominion Medical Council. He also married Aillie Mickle, who had been superintendent of nursing at SGH from 1924 through 1926. An ardent Liberal, Smith ran, unsuccessfully, against David M. Wright for the North Perth federal seat in 1930.

He died Feb. 15, 1966, at the age of 93.

One of the many affected by the humanity of Dr. Smith was Bob Salter, who took up medicine and later became a professor at the University of Toronto and senior orthopedic surgeon at the Hospital for Sick Children in Toronto. The following tribute to Dr. Smith first appeared in a history of the Stratford Rotary Club, which was published in 1992. It is reprinted here with permission of Dr. Salter and the Rotary Club.

By Dr. Robert B. Salter

On Dec. 15, 1924, the day I was born in Stratford, Ont., I met my first and most memorable mentor, Dr. David Smith, when, as a family doctor, he performed an emergency caesarean section to deliver my fraternal twin brother and me.

Years later, I was to learn the circumstances that led up to this dramatic delivery. Our mother had given birth to our older brother without difficulty years earlier. It was assumed that her second pregnancy would also produce a single baby, but after a very prolonged labour, during which our mother became progressively weaker, Dr. Smith, who was still anticipating a single baby, realized that the labour was completely obstructed. Consequently, he performed the emergency caesarean section to save our mother's life as well as that of her baby. At the operation, Dr. Smith was relieved to find a viable baby (my twin brother) but, as he related to me when I was old enough to understand, he was astonished to find a second baby (me). Our chins had become locked (one baby facing downward and the other facing upward) – an extremely rare complication of twin pregnancies and one that renders a normal delivery completely impossible.

Thus, had Dr. Smith not intervened surgically when he did, our mother, my twin brother and I all would have died. And so on that December day in 1924, I met my mentor rather than my maker, under remarkably exciting circumstances.

Earlier in 1924, the year that Dr. David Smith saved the lives of my mother and her twin sons, he had been one of the founders of the Ontario Society for Crippled Children, a fact that was to assume considerable significance in my own professional life three decades later. This is but one manifestation of his public spiritedness and his devotion to those less fortunate than himself.

At that time – and for many years thereafter – Stratford was primarily a railway and industrial town with a population of 20,000. My father was treasurer of a furniture manufacturing company, and my mother was a dedicated parent and homemaker. We lived modestly and, of necessity, frugally, especially during the Great Depression that began in 1929.

Even as a young child growing up in Stratford, I was well aware of Dr. David Smith's reputation as a warm, compassionate and caring family doctor, who was both respected and loved by his patients and their families.

During those early years of my life, Dr. Smith made numerous house calls for members of our family, and I came to think of him as a role model, one whose character I would like to emulate.

When I was only seven years old, I developed a serious ear infection that spread to the mastoid bone of the skull (mastoiditis). Dr. Smith immediately

Dr. David Smith, 1946

THE MIRROR

recognized the seriousness of such an infection – in the pre-antibiotic era, and arranged for one of his colleagues, an eye, ear, nose and throat specialist, Dr. George Ingham, to perform the necessary surgery. Throughout my convalescence from that illness, Dr. Smith came to see me almost daily, and my admiration and respect for him grew progressively deeper.

In September 1933, when my twin brother and I were nine years old, he became ill with rheumatic fever, a potentially serious disease that, in those days, was treated by at least nine months of absolute bedrest. I was very concerned that my brother was going to miss an entire year of school and, consequently, I requested of Dr. Smith to teach him each evening. Dr.

Smith advised me to wait until he was better, which I did. In fact, at the end of the following summer holidays, during which I had taught my brother, he was able to pass the necessary examinations and thereby avoid falling a year behind me in school.

It was during that academic year of my brother's pitiful illness that I resolved to become a doctor "just like Dr. David Smith," whom I had come to know well as a result of his many visits to our home. When I told Dr. Smith of my plans to study medicine, he seemed genuinely pleased and, in a sense, "adopted" me almost as a son. He and his wife had married late in life and had no children.

When Dr. Smith was going to teach first aid to a group of nurses on Saturday mornings at the Stratford General Hospital, he would ask me to be his "demonstration patient," on whom he could apply a wide variety of splints and bandages as well as perform artificial respiration. I, of course, was thrilled to be asked by my medical hero to serve in that capacity.

In 1936, at the age of 12, I moved with my family to Toronto, but I kept in touch with Dr. Smith from time to time. He was delighted when I entered medical school at the University of Toronto and especially when I graduated in 1947. Throughout my undergraduate years in medical school, I held before me the image of my mentor, Dr. David Smith, as an outstanding model of what an exemplary medical doctor should be, with particular respect to compassion and caring for patients.

On the completion of a junior internship in 1948, I married Robina McGee, a science writer and novelist. Together we set out for northern Newfoundland to serve for two years with the Grenfell Medical Mission at St. Anthony. During the second year with the mission our first son was born and, out of a feeling of gratitude, admiration and affection for Dr. David Smith, we named him David. When I wrote to Dr. Smith to inform him of this, he, with his typical thoughtfulness, wrote us a wonderful letter and sent to our newborn son a silver cup inscribed "David Salter."

After our two years in Newfoundland, my wife and I returned to Toronto, where I undertook four years of postgraduate training in orthopedic surgery and an additional year of such training in London, England, on a scholarship. I then joined the surgical staff of the Hospital for Sick Children and the Faculty of Medicine at the University of Toronto. In addition, I became an orthopedic consultant to the Ontario Society for Crippled Children of which, as I mentioned earlier, Dr. Smith had been a founder 31 years earlier.

Some years later, when Dr. Smith was being honoured by the Ontario Society for Crippled Children at its annual meeting in Toronto, I was given the privilege of paying a warm tribute to him and of not only recounting my relationship with him since my birth, but also of expressing my indebtedness to him as my most memorable mentor.

It was always a special privilege for my wife and me to visit Dr. Smith in Stratford during his retirement years. He had been a teacher before he studied medicine, and in his later years he kept his mind active by restudying both Latin and Greek as well as the classics – a manifestation of his enduring scholarship.

When this great Canadian family doctor died at the age of 93, his charming widow – who was much younger and with whom my wife and I kept in contact – gave me his gold pocket watch because she knew that he had wanted me to have it as a memento of our long and memorable friendship.

I shall always be most grateful to Dr. Smith. The only way I can ever repay such indebtedness is to be a mentor to others, something I have tried to do over the last 35 years as an academic, orthopedic surgeon, scientist, teacher and administrator.

By the hand of a visionary

Whittington W. (Bob) Hughes says Dr. John L. Penistan was a man ahead of his time. And, after more than three decades in the lab at Stratford General Hospital – serving under five directors of pathology – Hughes has some credibility.

Penistan, a highly qualified pathologist, emigrated from England to take over the SGH lab on March 30, 1949. A native of Loughton, Essex, he had studied medicine at London Hospital, London, England, and been on the staff there. He had also been the regional pathologist for North Wales and had served in the Royal Army Medical Corps in Accra, West Africa. In Stratford he followed in the footsteps of doctors T. Russell Nichols, Stephen J. C. Miller, L. G. Fischer and J. J. Quinlan, in running a department that had been established in 1925. He would, however, become the lab's longest-serving director. His tenure was cut short by cancer on June 28, 1973.

Hughes, who also emigrated from England, joined the SGH lab in March 1957. He too was well-qualified, and near the end of the following year he was named chief technologist, a role he played through to his retirement in September 1990. He was an influential part of the lab for 33 years.

With no qualification or hesitation, Hughes says, "John Penistan was a man years and years before his time. He was a visionary. I look at my 17 years with him as a privilege."

Hughes credits Penistan with making the Stratford lab a leader among hospitals its size. For instance, he says, Stratford was doing blood exchanges in babies as early as 1957. He pushed for the addition of new testing equipment and procedures well before they were adopted by many Ontario hospitals. "It was an exciting time then," says Hughes. "We had some great people on staff. I used to get up in the morning and look forward to going to work."

As early as the late 1950s, Penistan was talking about a regional laboratory service – something that was formalized in 1970. A first in Ontario, the regional service, which expanded over the years, remains in place and serves hospitals in Perth, Huron, Wellington, Grey and Bruce counties."

About four years after he'd arrived in Stratford, Penistan summarized his impressions in an article he wrote for The London (England) Hospital Gazette. About his new home, he said, "Stratford itself has a population approaching 20,000; it is a compact community although, despite the Canadian's contempt for `class distinction,' is by no means without its social strata. These depend a little upon family, a little upon professional status, but chiefly I fear upon wealth. However, education 100 per cent socialized since its inception, mixes the groups up again to some extent and the schools turn out a standard product each generation. Nor, incidentally, do the few private schools in Ontario appear to be significantly successful in turning out potential leaders in the tradition of the public schools.

"There is no lack of community activity; churches are multitudinous and full, service clubs abound and carry out a wide variety of voluntary tasks. Cultural societies – dramatic, musical and literary – are active, all perhaps a little self-consciously trying to raise standards and educate the public in the attractions of their particular wares. If it is all a little naive, the atmosphere, after the disillusion and cynicism of post-war England, is wholly admirable and tremendously exciting."

Then Penistan turned to the matter of medicine: "It follows that the medical profession works under conditions very different from those at home, whether today

Members of the laboratory staff in September 1971. Front row, from left: John Howard, Brian Worsley, Dick Ferguson, Dr. Robin Waite, Dr. John Penistan, Dr. Keith Oliveira, John Partridge, Bob Hughes and Mike Collins. Second row, from left: Syed Raza, Vi Pallister, Kay Connelly, Phyllis Hammer, Ginny Duench, Hilda Gorman, Ruby Dorse, Shirley Hutchison, Sue Dorse, Avis Baumbach, Linda Givens, Thea Shean, Barbara Hamilton and Phil Simms. Back row, from left: Lois Thibeault, Pat Kennett, Barbara Ann Steinacker, Bev Jackman, Rosemary Kent, Joan Bull, Kian Goh. Gail Pye, Karen Hoddle, Elizabeth Gill, Linda Shaw, Judy Hyde, Boon Goh, Julius Karadi and Arlene Davidson. Absent when the photo was taken were Nancy Marchant, Rena Balmain, Freddy Paris and Barb Dykeman.

under the NHS (National Health Service), or before the war. The basic fact, which conditions all others, is that everyone pays his way – or is classified `indigent.' Consequently, the voluntary system scarcely exists, at least outside the two great cities of Toronto and Montreal. The life of the consultant as it was before the days of the NHS, so largely spent, at least in teaching centres, in the service of the common man (*not* the indigent) is incomprehensible to the Canadian doctor; not necessarily because he is without admiration for such service, but because he cannot visualize such a state of affairs. Nor can he understand how a British doctor can look after the 2,000 or more patients on his list. Here we have only about 1,200 patients for each doctor in practice and the town is not thought to be over-doctored. If the Stratford doctor, on the basis of such figures, feels that his British counterpart cannot do a good job, who can blame him? And he both thinks so and says so in the knowledge that the level of general practice is very high here, as indeed it is. How many UK GPs do routine urinalysis and hemoglobins in their surgeries today? Here almost everyone does, and does them competently. And then cases are referred to hospital when necessary, where the GP may do his own surgery – he has not yet been turned into a glorified office boy!

"The hospital side of the picture restores the balance to some extent. The building itself is new and magnificent considering the size of the community, with the most lavish laboratory accommodation I have ever seen. It is well administered, has an adequate nursing staff (supplemented by private nurses hired by patients) derived mainly from its own training school and provides properly equipped and staffed radiological and pathological services. Once in the hospital, the patient generally continues to be looked after by his family doctor, for most endeavour to specialize, usually in surgery which is highly profitable. Major surgery it is true, tends to be referred to the three or four most experienced men, all of whom are Certified Specialists by the RCPSC (Royal College of Physicians and Surgeons of Canada). Here we have two anaesthetists, one obstetrician and an internist. But the crux of the matter is that with one exception, who sees only surgical cases, patients have direct access to all the specialists. Thus, a practitioner who refers a case may find himself penalized in that the next time that patient is ill he may well go direct to the consultant!

"By and large the staff play fair with each other and the tendency is definitely in the right direction. We are in a phase of transience which hospitals at home were passing through 10 to 20 years ago; that it occurs so much later here results from the absence of the voluntary system and the wide geographical scatter of the population. Small centres have had to be self-contained and the rural GP at least has had to be a jack-of-all-trades. What is more, the thing is not without its merits; for the retention of the GP in hospital practice bolsters the standard of general practice. It is to be hoped that Canada, admirably situated as she is to profit by others' mistakes, will solve the problem of securing first-class specialist services in hospitals without destroying the good general practitioner.

"As might be expected in a booming economy, the cost of all this is high. According to income tax returns, doctors vie with lawyers and engineers as the wealthiest profession. In the civil services and universities, $6,000 – $8,000 is good pay, but (though it is difficult to get at the facts) general practitioners mostly do better than

this and many a surgeon nets $20,000 and more. All of this comes out of the patient of course. An `office' call costs him $2 or $3, a house call a dollar or so more – plus drugs, and a dollar for an injection, etc. Fee for appendectomy is $100 minimum, plus $15 or so each for the assistant surgeon and anaesthetist. Hospitalization will cost him at least $6 a day for the cheapest bed in a four-bed room. To cover himself against all this – for to the worker earning perhaps $50 (about $357 in 2002 dollars) a week, sickness is financially crippling – the wise citizen joins one or other of the several `pre-paid medical care' and hospitalization plans. These are admirably run and do a very good job on the whole. At present it costs a worker between one and two weeks' pay in the year to cover himself and his family reasonably well.

"It is difficult to see how much further we can go on this basis and, in point of fact, an NHS, on a contributory basis, is very much on the political tapis. All parties and official medicine have paid lip service to it; the federal government has all the facts and figures required at its finger tips; and an election is looming. The only ray of hope is that no party dare face the expense of a scheme like the NHS. How far the threat of some form of health service should deter any intending immigrants to Canada is very debatable. At the least it is highly improbable that anything comparable to the NHS will be introduced so long as prosperity remains high, and if it will anywhere in the world, it will do so here."

Near the end of his piece, Penistan encouraged his countrymen to venture out and take part in "an experience we would not have missed for worlds." He did qualify the invitation, however, by saying, "But on no account do as we did and burn all the boats, shake off the bailiffs, and land up at the tail-end of winter inadequately housed and working in a basement passage with leaking pipes overhead and rain flooding in

From left, doctors Gus Wilson, Dave Williams and Vince Quinlan enjoy a moment with colleague Robin Waite (right) during an informal reception on the occasion of the latter's pending retirement from SGH in February 1996. Waite, associate pathologist, had been with the hospital for almost 33 years.

under foot. There is no guarantee that things will always pan out ultimately, or for everybody!"

By the time Penistan arrived in Canada the new hospital was well underway. He and his colleagues were not in the damp basement of the original hospital for much longer. In the new building they settled into quarters on the fifth floor of the north and south wings. The mortuary and autopsy area were where the basement cafeteria and stores are now located. On the sixth floor there were cages with guinea pigs and rabbits, and later frogs. The guinea pigs were used in testing mostly for tuberculosis but also for different toxins of diphtheria. The rabbits were used for pregnancy tests. Later, they were replaced in that role by frogs. By the mid-1960s, all testing was performed with chemicals and the animals were phased out. What was formerly the animal room is now the autopsy room.

When Hughes arrived at the lab in 1957

there were two pathologists, two clerical workers, three lab assistants and about 10 technologists. The pathologists also covered Woodstock General Hospital on a part-time basis. The lab's director, John Penistan, was also the regional pathologist and as such worked for the attorney general's department as a forensic pathologist.

Because it was designated an associate laboratory of the public health service, the Stratford facility regularly tested blood sugars, water, milk, throat swabs and sputum, looking for the likes of diabetes, diphtheria and tuberculosis. It remained a public health lab until 1971 when the regional lab service was introduced and a lab was built near Palmerston.

Up to 1960 the hospital maintained its own blood bank. Each Monday night, donors would make their donations at the lab. Those in need of the blood received it free of charge (except for the cost of the materials needed to transfuse it). But they

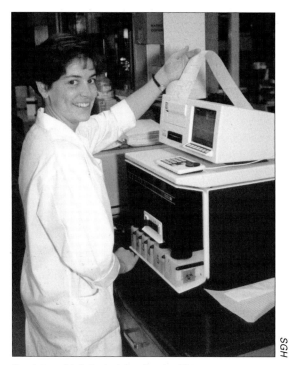

Registered lab technician Louisa Vermast.

Penistan was a gentleman who cared deeply about his profession and about those with whom he worked. In 1964 Penistan was president of the Ontario Association of Pathologists.

In a era when department directors were less encumbered by government directives and restrictions, Penistan was a man whose vision earned the Stratford lab more than passing distinction, says Waite. He says something new and progressive was always being introduced. For example, in 1964 Stratford was the first hospital lab in Ontario to do phenyl ketonuria tests (PKUs) on newborns to detect metabolic deficiencies. And, regularly, there was the addition of newer and more efficient instruments, many which could accommodate multiple tests. As well, Waite points to added interest and activity in the cytology department, an area in which Penistan took special interest. Coincidentally, cytology services were introduced by Mary MacDonald the year Waite arrived at SGH. MacDonald continues to run that area of the lab.

An increased workload forced Stratford, in 1964, to affiliate its lab teaching program with Chedoke-McMaster Hospital in Hamilton. Since then, lab technology students have done their practical training in Stratford, their classroom work in Hamilton.

Penistan became nationally known in 1959 as the pathologist in the case of Steven Truscott, a 14-year-old Clinton-area teen who was convicted in adult court in Goderich of the murder of 12-year-old Lynne Harper. Both teens were children in RCAF families and lived in quarters next to the Clinton air station, a facility for teaching telecommunications.

The Truscott case stirred a lot of controversy and reflection. When a 1966 book by Isabel LeBourdais proclaimed Truscott's innocence, national interest in the case was so rekindled that Parliament

were asked to replace it on a two-to-one ratio. A patient receiving two litres (pints, in those days) of blood, for instance, would be required to round up enough friends and family to donate twice that amount back to the hospital. The practice was discontinued when the Canadian Red Cross began to supply the hospital.

In 1958 or 1959, the lab diagnosed haemophilia in an area patient, something that Hughes says, as a laboratory and hospital "was a big feather in our cap." Around that time, Roy Uttley went from Stratford to Goderich, to found a lab in the hospital there.

Dr. Robin Waite joined the lab as a pathologist in September 1963, and was there for more than three decades. He echoes Hughes' sentiments of Penistan. "Best pathologist I've ever seen," says Waite, "but he was a man who didn't suffer fools kindly." Still, he says, beneath what many saw as a gruff and aloof exterior,

Technical director of the lab, John Howard (left), and associate pathologist Dr. John Vetters, September 1998. John Penistan brought the English-born Howard to SGH in April 1968 from Nova Scotia. Howard's stay lasted 30 years, until his retirement in March 1998. Vetters was the director of laboratory services at SGH from August 1994 to July 1997.

referred the matter to the Supreme Court of Canada for review. LeBourdais said there were inconsistencies in the evidence and what she believed to be questionable medical testimony. As well, she said, the emotions surrounding the case precluded the possibility of a fair trial. Wrote LeBourdais: "Every single statement relating Steven to the girl's death, or to the scene in the bush was conjecture. The sole basis for this build-up of conjecture was the report of the autopsy findings given by Dr. Penistan at the preliminary hearing and by

him and Dr. Brooks (Dr. David Hall Brooks, medical officer at the Clinton RCAF base) at the trial." The high court upheld the conviction, and Truscott served 10 years of a life sentence before his parole.

In 1966, Penistan, in the draft of an article for a scientific journal, said that after "agonizing reappraisal," he had concluded that Harper could have died a full day after her disappearance.

When Penistan died in 1973, less than six months after being diagnosed with cancer, Waite became acting director of the Stratford lab, a role he played until Dr. Michael Dietrich was appointed director in April 1974. Dietrich stayed for about a year and then returned to Windsor. Waite again stepped in, until Dr. George Horner took over the lab near the end of August in 1975.

Horner was big on the lab being accredited by the College of American Pathologists, and he directed his staff to work to that end. It required meticulous record-keeping and near-flawless procedures and practices, says Hughes. When Stratford was granted the CAP accreditation in the late 1970s it was one of the few labs in Canada so designated. It retained the distinction into the 1980s but was eventually dropped. Near the end of the '70s, Stratford technologist Kurt Davis introduced a computer system that was used in the lab until it was replaced by a hospital-wide system called Meditech.

Horner left Stratford for Fort McMurray, Alta., and then moved on to Newfoundland. Dr. Murray Treloar became lab director on July 1, 1981, and when he moved to Oshawa, he was succeeded on July 1, 1984, by Dr. Larry Lacey, who directed the lab until July 1994. He was followed by Dr. John M. Vetters, who stepped down as director in July 1997 but remains in the lab as an associate pathologist. Since July 1997 the laboratory at SGH has been under the direction of Dr. Malcolm Carlson.

Mission statement

The Hospital Auxiliary Association
of the Stratford General Hospital
functions without purpose of gains for its members,
and any profits or any benefits to the organization
are used in promoting its objectives.
We offer our services and conduct fund-raising activities
to help purchase equipment and other special needs,
and assist the hospital and staff wherever possible.
We are a liaison between the hospital and the community
and promote teens in the health care field.

A $2-million auxiliary

Stratford's first general hospital was less than a year old when women interested in hospital work began to talk up the idea of an auxiliary. That's hardly surprising, in that it had been a group of women that had helped to kick-start the hospital idea in the first place. Several women, some of them married to prominent men in the community who were pushing for a hospital, had headed groups of volunteers that canvassed the various Stratford wards to seek funds for the bold new venture.

On June 1, 1892, at a meeting in City Hall, 48 of those women became charter members of the Women's Hospital Aid. Affiliated groups were also formed in Listowel, St. Marys and Mitchell, but they didn't last long.

In short, the purpose of the WHA was to raise money for the purchase of necessities for the hospital, such as linens and china. And for about 110 years, it has been a purpose well served.

At the ceremony to honour the first nursing school graduates, the WHA donated to the hospital a portrait of Thomas Ballantyne, the past board chairman and a man who had a driving interest in the construction and operation of the new hospital. The portrait was hung in the main lobby of the hospital. It was Ballantyne who in 1903 built and donated the first nurses residence, in honour of his late wife, who had been a nurse. The WHA raised funds to furnish that building and from then on tried to serve both the hospital and the residence.

To that end it encouraged formation of the Junior Hospital Aid, which was organized in 1909 primarily to sustain the needs of the nurses residence. Mostly, the JHA membership comprised daughters or daughters-in-law of WHA members. Over the years they provided the likes of magazines, window shades, lockers, linoleum, curtains, bedspreads and rugs. They also varnished floors and painted the interior and exterior of the residence. They repaired the chimney and stairs. They raised funds by holding dances, cabarets and bazaars, and by having movie nights (and matinees) at the Classic and Allen theatres. They put on little theatre productions and bridge parties. They also canvassed for canned fruit and pickles for the hospital. The first president of the JHA was Eva Boles.

By 1903 the auxiliaries' efforts were gaining mention in the annual reports prepared by the hospital's board of trustees: "The Women's Hospital Aid continues to supply materials, furniture and furnishings of many kinds for the hospital and nurses residence, in the furnishing and equipping of which they have been most generous. The liberality of these ladies and the contributors to their funds is most highly appreciated by all connected with the hospital. To the Women's Hospital Aid and to the Junior Aid, we have again to express thanks for their loyal support and continued interest in the well-being of the hospital."

A year later, the 1904 report included: "The efforts of the Women's Hospital Aid have increased rather than diminished during the year . . . They are indefatigable in the systematic collection of small monthly amounts from many willing contributors, and are constantly devising plans for augmenting their gifts in other respects, after consulting with the lady superintendent as to the most pressing needs."

In the first five years of this century the auxiliary donated more than $1,000 (more than $31,500 in 2002 dollars) to the hospital for linens and other household items.

In 1905 it provided money to expand the hospital's laundry facilities. The next year it committed $1,000 to help cover the cost of an elevator when the new wing was built.

Beginning in 1908, the auxiliary prepared and presented its own annual report, complete with executive and membership lists, and the names of ward representatives. To further improve fund-raising efforts, the city was divided into districts, and members were assigned to canvass on a house-by-

house basis. Each district had a ward captain, and the aim of each was to bump up the level of the WHA's mite collections. A mite box was a small box which held systematic collections of small monthly donations from the auxiliary's membership.

In 1909 the WHA had 49 members, who were encouraged to attend 10 regular meetings and three special events that year. One of the events was a winter ball, which was a fixture in the city for a number of years. By 1913 a summer ball, in the Waterloo Street ice rink, was added to the social calendar.

In addition to its regular contribution of linens, the WHA also provided an operating table, a sterilizer, dressing gowns and privacy screens.

When the United Hospital Aid Association of Western Ontario was formed in 1910, the Stratford WHA became one of its charter affiliates. At least two members of the Stratford group, Bessie (Mrs. Thomas) Ballantyne and Edith (Mrs. Joseph N.) Orr, became life members of the UHAAWO. Others served on the advisory board.

In October 1913 the UHAAWO's annual convention was hosted by the Stratford WHA, and the proceedings included a tour of the hospital by lady superintendent Lola Weldon and her assistant.

During the First World War, the work of both auxiliaries was affected because members became involved in the efforts of the Red Cross. In serving both the hospital and the Red Cross, the auxiliary membership jumped to 55. The WHA also held a June concert in 1915.

In 1918, president Edith Orr offered this challenge to her membership: "This year we rejoice in the triumph of the allies in the great cause. But let us not think that with the coming of peace, war work is ended, for unfortunately there is the ever-constant war that must be waged against disease. We, the women of the hospital aid, must recognize as perhaps we have never done before our help to the need of the sick and the suffering."

That year the last of the WHA's regular meetings was cancelled because of the worldwide flu epidemic. The outbreak prevented the WHA from holding some of its social events, though there was one ball, jointly sponsored by the JHA, and two euchre parties in private homes. By now the WHA was also buying Christmas presents for all ward patients at the hospital. In spite of the setbacks, the auxiliary was able to help with the installation of an elevator, provide some equipment for the laundry and give the hospital $800.

In 1920 the members held their first rose day, in May, preceded by a talent tea in February. There were other teas, as well as a bazaar in November. In 1921 the WHA bought a sewing machine for the hospital, and members used it to mend linen and to make pillowcases and sheets.

In December 1921 the group bestowed its first life membership upon Edith Orr in recognition of long and valued service. Her name was enrolled among the WHA's charter members.

In 1922, membership in the auxiliary jumped to 76, an increase of five over the previous year. Also in 1922, her colleagues made Bessie Ballantyne a life member of the WHA.

In 1925 the WHA began to give gifts and copies of *Handy References for Nurses* to graduating nurses. At members' homes, it also held farewell teas for the graduates. In 1926 the first St. Patrick's Day tea was held – another fund-raiser.

Eventually there was a provincial body that united hospital auxiliaries, and in 1931 the Ontario Women's Hospital Aid Association held its first annual convention in Stratford. That was the year the WHA began to observe Florence Nightingale Day with an annual bazaar.

In 1932 members departed from their usual custom of buying linens for the hospital, and instead purchased two specialized lamps for the operating room. Also in 1932, the JHA amalgamated with the WHA.

In its first half-century of service, the WHA raised funds to build a drive shed-stable, set up a travelling library (actually, a bookcase on wheels) and a Samaritan cupboard, improve the heating plant and help install an elevator, and a food conveyor. It supplied furnishings for the operating room, the isolation hospital, the first laundry, ward rooms, and for patients' and matrons' rooms. It bought linens, blankets, china, Goetch-frame beds, roll-curtain systems to surround those beds, aero-flush bed-pan washers, sterilizers and a sewing machine.

The Samaritan cupboard was established by the WHA as a repository for gifts and toys, which could be given to children at SGH at the discretion of the nursing supervisor. During the Depression, auxiliary members replaced the toys with items of clothing, which were more urgently needed.

In their first 50 years, the women of the WHA raised more than $50,000. Perhaps their most significant capital contribution in that time was the renovation, refurnishing and equipping of the third floor of the new wing at SGH as a children's ward, suitable for 14 patients. That was in 1934, during the presidency of Edith McLeod, who became the first WHA member to sit on the hospital board. It was Mary Johnston who convened the children's ward project, which WHA members at the time felt would be a lasting monument to their efforts.

Another driving force was Sophie Turnbull, who wanted to furnish a room in memory of her husband Kenneth, who had been active on the hospital board. For this undertaking the WHA sought and received the support of a number of community groups, including the Independent Order of Foresters, the Lions Club, the Alumnae Association of Stratford General Hospital,

Presidents of the auxiliary

Mrs. T. E. P. Trew

Mrs. D. Deacon

Mrs. J. P. Woods

Mrs. Joseph Rankin

Ethel (Mrs. Robert T.) Harding

Mrs. (Dr.) Donald M. Fraser

Sarah (Mrs. McKee) Wilson

Mrs. John Forbes

Susan (Mrs. George G.) McPherson

Mary (Mrs. [Dr.] James P.) Rankin

Edith (Mrs. Joseph N.) Orr

Jennie (Mrs. Alfred) Hahn

Maude (Mrs. Thomas) Holliday

Edythe (Mrs. [Dr.] Charles L.) Grant

1932-1936	Edith (Mrs. Alexander C.) McLeod
1937-1938	Mary (Mrs. Leonard M.) Johnston
1939-1941	Sophie (Mrs. Kenneth C.) Turnbull
1942-1943	Hilda Shea
1944-1946	Isabel (Mrs. Harold J.) Malone
1947-1949	Mary Wardlow
1950-1951	Helen (Mrs. [Dr.] Albert L.) Baker
1952	Winnifred (Mrs. Edmund K.) Kneitl
1953-1955	Violet (Mrs. Charles E.) Martin
1956-1958	Grace (Mrs. Howard C.) Knechtel
1959-1960	Marianne (Mrs. William A.) Johnston
1961-1962	Lillian (Mrs. Walter V.) Whatmouth
1963-1964	Gladys (Mrs. Peter) Crerar
1965-1966	Ida (Mrs. Wilfred G.) Carr
1967-1968	Elizabeth (Mrs. Harry G.) Livingstone
1969-1970	Catherine (Mrs. [Dr.] Peter C.) Roberts
1971	Vivian (Mrs. William H.) Jarvis
1972-1973	Joan (Mrs. Clifford R.) Taylor
1974-1975	Mary (Mrs. John J. C.) Johnston
1976-1977	Barbara (Mrs. William G.) Lyon
1978-1979	Catherine (Mrs. Victor D.) Clarke
1980-1981	Norah (Mrs. [Dr.] Ernest C.) Huggins
1982	Dorothy (Mrs. George W.) Hayes
1983	Norah (Mrs. [Dr.] Ernest C.) Huggins

1984-1985	Dorothy (Mrs. John) Worden [now Bechtel]
1986-1987	Barbara (Mrs. George F.) Culliton
1988-1989	Shirley (Mrs. William A.) Russell
1990-1991	Mary (Mrs. Robert J.) McTavish
1992-1993	Betty (Mrs. E. Burt) Reid
1994-1996	Anita (Mrs. Gordon) Billo
1996-1999	Mary (Mrs. James) MacPherson
1999-2001	Hazel (Mrs. William) Wivell
2001-2002	Patricia Million
2002-	Pauline Jones

Life members of the auxiliary

Edith Orr *

Bessie (Mrs. Thomas) Ballantyne *

Edith McLeod *

Sophie Turnbull *

Mrs. K. Buckingham *

Helen Baker *

Minerva Snider (later Mrs. Fred Snyder) *

Ida Carr *

Catherine Roberts *

Elizabeth Livingstone *

Mary Johnston

Joan Taylor

Norah Huggins *

Barbara Culliton

Zena (Mrs. David) Thomas

Anita Billo *

Mary Rose Cannan

Phyllis Dawson

Mary McTavish *

Barbara Barrett

Dorothy (Worden) Bechtel

Dorothy Landers

Shirley Russell

* also life members of the Ontario Hospital Auxiliary Association

the women's institutes of North and South Perth, and the Rotary Club of Stratford. Amid much appreciation from the medical and nursing staffs, and from the board of trustees, the new children's ward was officially opened in 1935.

Also in 1935, for its contribution to the cancer society, the Stratford WHA was presented with a picture of King Edward and Queen Mary by Lady Besborough, the wife of Canada's Governor General. And Edith McLeod received a life membership from the Ontario Hospital Aid Association. In 1936 her Stratford association's rose day brought in $125.

In 1937, when the renovated and expanded X-ray facilities were opened by the lieutenant-governor, the WHA held a luncheon for his wife, at the request of the Perth Medical Association.

About that time, the auxiliary also introduced something it called sunshine baskets, an assortment of home-made goodies and other edibles that were sold as a fund-raiser.

As well, the same auxiliary delivered fruit baskets to ward patients each month.

During the years of the Second World War, the St. Patrick's Day tea was suspended and, instead, auxiliary members campaigned for donations. Also during the war, contribution tags replaced roses during the rose day fund-raisers.

But war or not, the WHA continued to buy items for the hospital: a dozen more Goetch-frame beds, more roll curtains, bedpan sterilizers, 12 sets of stainless steel bedside equipment, two specially constructed bassinets, an automatic toaster, kitchen utensils, and a resuscitator for the nursery.

When the hospital's waiting room was enlarged and renovated in 1941, the WHA covered the cost of adding new furniture.

After the war, the auxiliary stepped up its fund-raisers, fuelled perhaps by the talk of a new hospital and all the equipment it

would need. There was Valentine's Day bridge in February, a daffodil tea in April and a penny sale in late September or early October. While some of the proceeds, specifically those from the penny sale, were earmarked for the new building, members continued to buy and donate items for the old one. They also continued their support of the student nurses and their training, with furnishings and books. The group's first penny sale, at City Hall in 1947, netted $547.

Initially, and for several decades, auxiliary members held their meetings in the boardroom at City Hall, but by the late 1940s they were using a room in the nurses residence.

In 1949 the WHA was given a gift shop and display area in the foyer of the new hospital. Profit from the first year of operation totalled $181. In 1950 the WHA introduced a gift package – a silver spoon and a bank account containing $25 – for the first-born baby each year at SGH. As part of the hospital's expansion in 1960, a new gift shop was built, and it served until the mammoth makeover in the 1980s.

Also in 1950, the women changed the name of their organization from Women's Hospital Aid to Women's Hospital Auxiliary and revised their constitution. Their members numbered 108, and they were averaging about 25 of them at each meeting. Their capital donations that year included a kitchen stove for the nurses residence and a food mixer for the hospital. The next year they financed a new kitchen and other housekeeping items in the nurses residence, and some instruments for the nursing staff on the surgical floor. They also bought weigh scales for patients and 60 waste-paper baskets, and they founded a pre-training bursary available to anyone coming to the nursing school.

The new hospital might have spurred an immediate increase in the WHA's membership, but by 1955 it was down to 45.

In 1956 it more than doubled, up to 96, but in the late '50s it was tough slogging for a number of the group's special events. In 1958 a Valentine's Day bridge party was poorly attended and a performance of *My Fur Lady* made no money. Rose day and the penny sale continued to be well received and were significant sources of funds for the WHA.

In 1958 the auxiliary committed to helping at all the Red Cross blood donor clinics in the city, which at that time numbered six a year. Eventually, it became a monthly commitment. The first clinic was in May 1959. Until then, blood had been donated directly to the hospital during weekly sessions in the lab.

Also in 1959, the members re-evaluated their committees and their responsibilities and, it appears, breathed new life into their organization. They established a $1,000 trust fund for a new gift shop in the hospital, which they got during the expansion of SGH in 1960.

That was the year, with membership up to 129, that the WHA celebrated its 50th anniversary as a charter member of the provincial body that linked hospital auxiliaries. The members held a Mad Hatter's tea in March, and they donated birthday presents to the `sunshine box' at the old hospital, then called Avon Crest. They also printed a newsletter.   In helping at the old and new facilities, Stratford's was the only auxiliary in the province serving two hospitals. To better do that, in 1960 the WHA expanded and moved its gift shop to the first floor in the south wing of the new hospital. It also hosted the regional conference at the Stratford County Club.

In 1961 the auxiliary put another $1,000 in bonds, this time for buying hospital equipment. It also bought a 24-bottle warmer for the nursery at the hospital and plastic card holders for patient beds at Avon Crest.

By 1963, WHA members numbered 150, and many of them took part in something called `joy sessions,' in which they made items to be sold in the gift shop, which was quickly become the auxiliary's main fund-raiser. The next year they opened a new coffee bar in the hospital and set up a similar outlet in Avon Crest.

In 1965 they bought a television set for Avon Crest patients and expanded their regular services to include a gift cart, and reading sessions for children in the pediatric ward. The gift cart carried magazines and cigarettes, which generated money for the booth established by the Canadian National Institute for the Blind, and, though its offerings changed somewhat, the cart rolled through the wards until 1991.

In 1966, in an effort to attract male members, the Women's Hospital Auxiliary dropped 'Women's' and added 'Association' to its name. By then the organization had 170 members, each paying a $1 annual membership fee.

In 1967, their 75th year of operation, they established a beauty shop and supplied a hair dryer and tuck shop for Avon Crest, where they also refurbished the men's lounge.

In 1968 the auxiliary bought a TV for the pediatric ward and started bingos for patients in Avon Crest. For those same patients, the auxiliary began to furnish supplies for the weekly craft classes. It also bought two heated lowerators and a cardiac console for the intensive care unit.

There was another name change in 1969 – to the Hospital Auxiliary Association of Stratford General Hospital – but the workload remained much the same, and the money directed to SGH totalled $3,655.

In 1970, weekly visits to patients in the rehabilitation and extended care unit were added to the list of auxiliary duties. On occasion, auxiliary members would entertain the patients; often they would give them fruit and candies. That was the year the name Avon Crest was dropped, and the old hospital became the Rehabilitation and Extended Care Unit. And baby items went on sale for the first time in the gift shop.

By 1971 the HAA was a registered charitable organization. That was the year it started its annual Christmas boutique in the hospital lobby – an excellent money-maker.

Because Conestoga College had taken control of the nurses residence, the auxiliary switched its annual bursary to a deserving teen entering the field of health care.

By this time the members' monthly duties at RECU included: Week 1 – slides of trips; Week 2 – fruit to patients; Week 3 – bingo; and Week 4 – a birthday party for the month.

The library cart service was reintroduced by the HAA in the fall of 1972, and at about the same time, cigarettes were dropped from the sale items on the gift cart. And the members were collecting redeemable grocery tapes from Dominion Stores.

In 1972 the auxiliary celebrated the hospital's 80th anniversary with a luncheon at the Stratford Country Club. Guest speaker was Pauline McGibbon, who in 1974 became Ontario's lieutenant-governor.

In 1973 the auxiliary pledged $15,950 over two years for the purchase of a mammography machine. It was in that year that reports of the HAA's meetings began to appear in the *Stratford Beacon Herald*.

In 1974 the CNIB booth was closed and magazine sales were moved to the gift shop.

In 1975 the hospital invited the HAA members to an appreciation tea. By then the auxiliary was rounding up in excess of $10,000 each year with its regular and special fund-raising events. Seldom did the members have to look far for a wish list to help disperse the money.

In 1976 HAA members Shirley Russell and Phyllis Dawson started the volunteen program and initially approved 27 girls to take part. The teenage volunteers, because of their red-and-white-striped uniforms, became known as "candy stripers."

In 1977 the auxiliary put up the money to refurbish three lounges in the RECU, and formed a telephone committee to remind blood donors of clinic dates. A craft group was started in place of the joy sessions. In the same year, the city presented the HAA with a plaque in honour of the group's 85th year of service to the community. As well, for individual dedication, Catherine Roberts and Elizabeth Livingstone were given lifetime memberships by the provincial auxiliary association.

In 1978 the auxiliary began giving bursaries to two volunteens as well as to one nursing student. It also gave the hospital more than $35,600.

In 1979 the members began offering a babysitting service at the blood donor clinics.

In April 1980 Stratford hosted the Ontario auxiliary association annual conference for Region 2 at the Victorian Inn. Guest speaker at the luncheon was Dama Bell, a local force in the founding of the Stratford Shakespearean Festival in the 1950s. To the auxiliary members she spoke about costume design at the Festival.

In May 1980 the HAA organized a banquet at the hospital to honour nine volunteens who had logged 50 or more hours of service. The young people were presented with pins.

With the help of funds from their annual Easter egg sale, spring tea, penny sale and Christmas boutique, auxiliary members were able to give the hospital a cheque for $19,771 in 1980. Most of the money was spent on equipment for the physiotherapy and pediatric departments.

In 1981 new HAA members were installed by Canon Michael Griffin of St. James' Anglican Church during a candlelight service. That was the year the spring tea had to be moved to the Knights of Columbus Hall because of its growth in popularity. It was also the year the auxiliary donated about $40,000, a new high, to the hospital. Half the money was for electrocardiographic monitoring equipment for the intensive care unit, as well as for other equipment in the operating room, emergency department and RECU.

To celebrate the 90th anniversary of their organization, auxiliary members held a special luncheon at the Victorian Inn on Oct. 14, 1982. Guest speaker was newspaper columnist Helen Barker, who highlighted many of the HAA's activities through the years. The HAA donation to SGH in 1982 was $21,452. The next year it was $23,974 – the last time it would be less than $37,500. By then the annual fee for each active member was $3, for each non-active member $10. In 1984 'non-active' was changed to 'sustaining' on the membership rolls.

Also in 1984, the auxiliary was recognized by the Red Cross for 25 years of work with the society's blood donor clinics.

It was clear after a visit by Rev. Jim Williams and Jeff Preston that the auxiliary's fund-raising abilities would be challenged as never before. The men urged members to be as generous as possible with their personal donations to the hospital's massive expansion and renovation program. They also sought a long-term commitment from the HAA as a body, whose immediate response was a drive for new volunteers.

In 1985 the auxiliary pledged $250,000 to the building program over five years. The members, as individuals, went on the hook for an additional $100,000. They then added a fashion show and a microwave cookbook to their roster of fund-raising events, and many helped with the hospital's initial city-wide canvass for funds.

In 1986 the auxiliary upped the ante for its Penny Sale. But with 25 chances for 50 cents, members still figured it was a bargain without equal. For their April tea they were buoyed by the unexpected support of a woman from Seaforth. Kay O'Rourke made a $400 quilt, and her family sold about

$1,000 worth of raffle tickets on it. At their spring tea, HAA members sold even more tickets. The next year they held their first giant garage sale. By now there was serious talk of SGH acquiring a CT scanner, which meant the big-time fund-raising had only just begun. Also by now, the HAA was annually donating $50,000 to the hospital, in keeping with the pledges it made in 1985.

In 1988, renovations to the coffee and gift shops gave the auxiliary a display case window in the hospital lobby, which helped attract customers and increase sales. Cost to the HAA for those renovations was $15,000.

SGH

HAA members Mary Johnson (left) and Pat Moore prepare for the April 1988 sod-turning ceremony.

In the world of penny sales a microwave oven is considered a big-ticket item. And that is what the HAA raffled off in 1989 to raise $822. Also in 1989, the auxiliary was encouraged by new member Joan Pye to introduce the Smiley doll program to SGH, specifically to the children who go to the hospital as patients. The program was initiated in Arizona and was found to promote faster recovery from surgery and shorter hospital stays, as well as the use of fewer drugs.

"Children don't understand what's going on when they come to the hospital and we want to make their stay as happy an experience as possible," said Doris Macklin, head nurse in the pediatric ward at SGH. "The smaller children relate their feelings through play and they can deal with their fears better by having a doll to use to understand what they're going through."

HAA members made the Smiley dolls, which were donated to any child, mostly from ages 2-10, who wanted one. "We've committed to making the Smiley doll program our ongoing project, and we'll do our best to continue providing dolls for the hospital," said 1989 auxiliary president Shirley Russell. The program was discontinued in 1995, mostly because the average length of hospital stay for children was significantly reduced.

The auxiliary donated the final instalment of its $250,000 pledge in 1989 and followed that up with a further $56,750 in 1990. The $100,000 members commitment was also surpassed. Also in 1989, HAA volunteers Anita Billo and Betty Byatt were runners-up for the city's citizen-of-the-year award.

In 1991 the auxiliary donated $63,000 for the purchase of two laparoscopes, and a further $50,000 as the first instalment towards new gift and coffee shops, which were planned as part of the hospital's new lobby. That was the year the beauty salon was moved to the continuing care and rehabilitation unit on the first floor in the new building.

In the following year the HAA gave the hospital the remainder of the money needed to build the new shops, about $50,000. On Oct. 5 the auxiliary opened an information desk in the hospital lobby. It also adopted the Hospital Equipment Lottery Project for People (HELPP), which was endorsed and supported by the Ontario Medical Association, by the Hospital Auxiliaries

SGH

Information Desk

Auxiliary member Bob Dawson working the information desk in the main lobby of the hospital.

Association of Ontario, and by the SGH's board of directors. The lottery has become an efficient fund-raiser for the HAA.

The auxiliary was 100 years old in 1992 and its celebrations included a float in the city's Victoria Day parade and a donation to the hospital in excess of $75,600. At a centennial luncheon, Barbara Culliton was made a life member of the local organization, and each member with 25 or more years of service was given a certificate of appreciation.

The HAA's new gift and coffee shops were officially open on June 9, 1992. The coffee shop has become the organization's biggest fund-raiser.

On the following day, the hospital's therapeutic children's playground was dedicated. McDonald's Restaurants donated $25,000 for equipment and the auxiliary chipped in another $17,000 for fencing and other necessities.

In the fall of 1993 the auxiliary members pledged $100,000 over two years to the CT scanner fund. SGH responded by dedicating the main CT scanner room in honour of the auxiliary.

On April 15, 1993, the auxiliary used $10,000 of its lottery proceeds to help launch the CT scanner fund. To that fund it pledged $200,000.

It was in 1993 that Norah Huggins, who twice served as auxiliary president and had been made a local life member, was proclaimed Stratford's citizen of the year.

Also in 1993, HAA members heard a proposal by those promoting a therapeutic humour service at the hospital. The program, called the Giggles and Get Well Service (GAGS), was officially launched in April 1995. It includes a mobile lending library, videos and a clown service, all designed to bring laughter to hospital patients. The auxiliary agreed to have one of its members on the GAGS committee.

In January 1994 four HAA members donned hard hats and used a sledge hammer to help break through a wall in the hospital's emergency department. That was the ceremonial start of remodelling the X-ray department and the construction of an addition to house the much sought-after scanner. The CT suite waiting area was later dedicated to the HAA.

Zena (Mrs. David) Thomas was named a life member of the local auxiliary in 1994, the year in which the HAA produced a cookbook which contains recipes from members and hospital staff. It went on sale in the gift shop.

In the spring of 1995 the auxiliary donated a further $8,895 of its lottery proceeds to SGH. The money was to be used for the purchase of specialized equipment for the pediatric rehabilitation outpatients program, to help children with head injuries, those who have suffered strokes, and those with developmental delays, and cerebral palsy and motor control problems.

On April 13 the members agreed to

pledge $55,000 a year for each of the next four years for the purchase of a new mammography machine. More immediate were their purchases of two critical care stretcher beds for the intensive care unit ($8,500 each), two infusion pumps ($2,500 each) and two pulse oximeters ($3,000 each). That fall they gave the hospital their first instalment towards the new mammography machine.

By 1995 the auxiliary's grocery-tape program, which was started in 1990 with only Sobey's participating, had resulted in more than $2,600. A and P, Zehrs and Lori-Jo brought the number of food stores in the program to four.

In June 1995, after its 103rd year of operation, the HAA reported an active membership of 234 – a total that included nine men, and 45 sustaining members. By then they had an office, and storage room for their lottery equipment. In the previous fiscal year those members had logged 16,698 volunteer hours, in addition to those related to fund-raising events. And, with equipment purchases, donations and honoured CT scanner pledge, their contributions to SGH in 1994-95 totalled $92,495.

It was in 1995 that the auxiliary held the first of what became an annual Mennonite quilt raffle. Through 1999 that project netted more than $22,500.

At their annual meeting in 1995, HAA members paid tribute to Dorothy Landers, who retired in 1996 after working for 27 years in the hospital's coffee shop.

The auxiliary's library cart and reading material for hospital waiting rooms were given a boost when Big V Drug Stores

SGH

A past president of the hospital's auxiliary, Dorothy Worden (now Bechtel), tends to SGH's main entrance gardens, 1997. It was in September 1995 that officials dedicated the garden in honour of Dorothy and in memory of her first husband, John D. Worden, "for their contribution in beautifying our hospital."

agreed to donate nine new magazines a month for two years. The Little Folks Toy House donated four bags of toys and games, which members were able to distribute among three waiting rooms in the hospital. For the pediatrics department, the auxiliary furnished more crayons, colouring books and storybooks.

SGH

Auxiliary members, from left, Marg Haynes, Betty Byatt, Pauline Jones and Pat Million at their Valentine's Day bake sale in 1998. On this day they raised more than $400 for the Equipped to CARE fund.

Of the 17,192 hours logged by the HAA volunteers in 1995-96, fewer were in support of the hospital's beauty salon, whose operation was reduced to Tuesdays and Thursdays (9 a.m. to 4 p.m.) because patient stays were shorter. The salon was closed in 2002.

The auxiliary's lottery business was up this year, which resulted in a donation of $13,900 for the purchase of a stretcher for the intensive care unit and an electric medi-lift.

By now the HAA was absorbing the costs of its postal and photocopying expenses, a savings for the hospital. And members were helping cancer, epilepsy and multiple sclerosis agencies with the sale of flowers. They were also assisting in the rehab and geriatric day hospital programs, and holding birthday parties, musicals and bingos for continuing care patients.

In May 1996 the auxiliary's spring luncheon and raffle netted about $5,600. The bridge and euchre luncheon in November brought in close to $1,000, and the Christmas boutique and raffle about $5,000.

The redemption of grocery tapes resulted in another $1,231.

It was in 1996 that another auxiliary member, Rosemarie Anthony, was named Stratford's citizen of the year.

In the 1996-97 fiscal year the HAA volunteer hours reached 17,367. Since the mid-1970s the auxiliary had been cultivating successors with its support of the teen volunteer program at SGH. Annually, it honoured those teens with an awards dinner, sometimes in the form of a pizza party, and gave bursaries to those who volunteered the most.

On June 4, 1997, the guest speaker for the dinner was a graduate of the first class of volunteers, Kim (Russell) Wright. A special guest on that occasion was the first teen volunteer convenor Phyllis Dawson.

In June 1998 the spotlight was on 16 teens. The three singled out for having logged the most hours were Pam Montgomery (300 plus hours), Angie Lee (292 hours) and Suzanne Appleton (112 hours). Among other things, the teens helped patients with leisure activities and served on the information desk. In 1999, Montgomery led the teens again, with another 300-plus hours.

No one had to convince Pat Hopwood that volunteers were essential to SGH. In a newspaper column that year, the director of volunteer services wrote: "From hospital and foundation volunteer board members who guide our organization to auxiliary members, patient services volunteers, and all those who make our patients feel special – all volunteers have a tremendous impact on our hospital and the community. Volunteers are the backbone, the heart and soul of our health care system."

Before the end of their 1997-98 fiscal year – ahead of schedule – the auxiliary members had fulfilled their pledge of $220,000 for the hospital's new mammography suite. At the same time, they had bought a number of items on SGH's Equipped to CARE wish list.

In their almost-18,000 volunteer hours, the 228 active members had continued to help in the beauty salon, with the blood donor clinic, in the coffee shop, in the gift shop, on the information desk, with the cancer society's sale of daffodils, with the library cart and with the GAGS program.

Their fund-raisers that year included the spring luncheon and raffle ($8,000), a summer book sale ($360), the fall bridge and euchre luncheon ($800), the Christmas boutique and raffle ($4,350), a Valentine's Day bake sale ($450), and grocery tapes ($1,000).

In September 1998 the HAA was recognized by the Canadian Red Cross for having helped with blood donor clinics for more than four decades.

It was a pledge of more than $150,000 from the auxiliary that made possible the opening of a bone mineral densitometry unit in December 1998. About 400 of those dollars came in from Pharma Plus Drug Mart customers during a month-long campaign early in 2000. "We're pleased," said auxiliary president Pat Million. "That's $400 we didn't have. I hope we can have more of those community partnerships in the future."

The auxiliary donated a further $4,474 in 1999 to complete a pledge for the purchase of two bassinets. It was in 1999 that the annual fee for active members went to $5.

In 1999-2000, retirement reduced the auxiliary's roll by 15, but with 18 recruits,

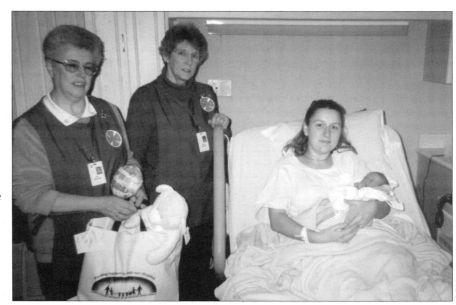

Linda Saville and her daughter Spencer Pauline, the first girl born at SGH in 2000. Making a presentation to them on behalf of the hospital auxiliary are Pauline Jones (left) and Nancy Snedden.

the members numbered 271, 16 of whom were males. Collectively, they topped the 19,000 mark in volunteer hours.

Some of those events in 2000 were the Easter luncheon and bake sale at the Knights of Columbus Community Centre, the Mother's Day bake sale and raffle at the hospital, the fun calendar in July, a project for Elections Canada in October, the Thanksgiving bake sale and the Christmas boutique raffle and food basket draw.

In March the HAA's music night lineup at St. Andrew's Presbyterian Church was anchored by the Stratford Male Choir, and the Amazing Grace Jazz Choir directed by Gail Selkirk.

It was also in March that the auxiliary fulfilled its pledge for the densitometry machine – in just two years rather than the expected three. With another $25,000 the members bought stretcher beds and a ventilator humidifier, and with $12,000 a portable transfer monitor. Then it went on the hook for a further $10,000 over two years for the purchase of operating room equipment.

The HAA's ongoing money-makers in 2000 included the grocery tape program and the penny collection.

As a millennium project, past president, Mary McPherson compiled a 23-page history of the auxiliary, and it went on sale in the hospital gift shop for $5 a copy.

At their annual meeting in 2000, guest speaker Bonnie Adamson spoke to the members about "where we are at."

Those members' list of events in 2001 included a Valentine's Day bake sale and teddy bear draw, another evening of music at St. Andrew's Church in March, a spring luncheon in April, and an exhibition hockey game that pitted the Revs on Ice against an Area Dawks (as in doctors) team. The game, played in the Tavistock Arena in November, ended in a 5-5 tie and raised $1,575 for the hospital. The Dawks' lineup included Eric Thomas, Ralph Pototschnik, Gregg

Hancock, Paul Weir and Mark Wilkinson – pucksters better known in other roles at SGH.

There was also a pre-Christmas silent auction of 30 donated teddy bears, which

AUXILIARY MEMBERS "GET AN UP CLOSE LOOK" AT HOW THEIR GENEROSITY COUNTS.

Members of the Hospital Auxiliary Association were invited to a special demonstration of the Cardiac Exercise Stress System and the BiPap machine funded through their most recent $50,000 gift to the Equipped to CARE campaign. Cardiorespiratory staff, Anne Forsyth and Neil Dartch and Clinical Leader, Kathie Cuerden personally thanked the members for their gift and explained the difference these essential pieces of equipment have made to patient care.

The Auxiliary's and our community's ongoing commitment towards the purchase of essential medical equipment benefits countless individuals each and every day. We can never say thank you enough!

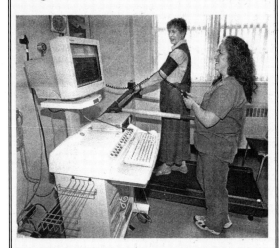

Auxiliary member Nancy Sneddon helps demonstrate the Cardiac Exercise Stress System with Cardiorespiratory staff member, Anne Forsyth.

SGH

From the June-July 2002 issue of *Generally Speaking*, the SGH newsletter.

Auxiliary member Judy Gee in the hospital gift shop.

the contributions of the HAA with a volunteer tea. On hand to help pour tea were several past presidents of the auxiliary, among them Cae Roberts, Dorothy (Worden) Bechtel, Barb Culliton, Shirley Russell, Betty Reid, Anita Billo, Mary McPherson and Hazel Wivell. Another past president, Mary McTavish, was guest speaker.

The HAA's volunteer hours for 2000-2001 totalled 18,154.

In 2001-2002 the auxiliary membership stood at 270 adults and 14 teen volunteers. Their scheduled hours – many of which were logged in support of the blood donor clinics, coffee shops, GAGS, gifts shops, HELPP lottery, information desk and library cart – exceeded 21,000.

Their equipment purchases for the hospital exceeded $130,000 and included $54,000 for an immunohistorchemical slide stainer and $50,000 for a bi-pap machine and a new cardiac stress test system.

The fund-raisers in 2002 included the traditional Valentine bake sale, the spring luncheon and the Mother's Day bake sale. The HAA members were also back at St. Andrew's Church in April 2002, for what they called a musical collage. It featured Earl Clark and the Stratford Male Choir, and Suzanne and David Strahan and the Perth County youth choirs. Among the individual performers were soprano Rachel Mallon, baritone Michael Ewert, soloist Laura Elligsen and harpist Roseanna Vito. Proceeds from the night amounted to about $3,000.

At its annual meeting in June 2002, the auxiliary's donation total to SGH for 2001-2002 was reported as $132,000. While the HAA's volunteers have been called faithful and friendly, by any instrument of monetary measure they should also be called productive. In their first 50 years as an organization, they donated more than $50,000 to the hospital. Since then they have run that total to more than $2 million.

raised more than $2,000.

In 2001 the HAA gave the hospital $12,000 towards the purchase of a $20,000 microscope, and the members pledged the remaining $8,000 for 2002.

During the schools' March break in 2001, another seven teens were trained, which brought that volunteer corps to 10. In addition to delivering fresh water to surgical and rehab patients, the teens, under the supervision of staff nurses, were helping to feed patients. In July those teens were honoured with a pizza party in the palliative care dining room. Each was given a gift package and certificate of recognition. SGH site administrator Andrew Williams was on hand to thank the volunteers, as were other hospital officials and members of the auxiliary – in this the International Year of the Volunteer.

On Oct. 10, 2001, president Pat Million and vice-president Pauline Jones recognized

A firm foundation

It's been around for close to two decades now. It's registered as Ontario Corporation 560081. It operates as the Stratford General Hospital Foundation. And its purpose is to "receive and maintain a fund and other property and to apply from time to time all or part thereof and the income there from for the benefit of or to enhance or improve the services or patient care provided by or the facilities of Stratford General Hospital, Stratford."

By the time the foundation was created in 1983, the hospital had kicked off its For Your Health campaign, a five-year drive to raise $6 million in public funds. That money was to be matched by the provincial government for the hospital's biggest expansion-renovation project to date, one that would result in replacement of SGH's rehabilitation and chronic care unit. It was a project that would grow even bigger, and within a few years the hospital was going after $17 million in local money.

To avoid confusion with that well-publicized and successful campaign, the foundation remained mostly in the background for a number of years, developing a marketing plan and putting in place the means to solicit and recognize donations. There are no entries in the foundation's minutes book between Feb. 1, 1984, and Feb. 27, 1986.

In the late 1980s the rumblings about a computerized axial tomography scanner (CAT or CT scanner) for SGH, were more than rumblings, and the foundation was preparing to play a big role in its acquisition.

In 1992 the foundation hired Andrea Weiner as its first director of development and Marion Burr as its secretary. It established offices for them on the main floor of the original hospital, by then renamed Avon Crest. One of the first tasks of the new hires was to help streamline and direct fund-raising initiatives.

In November 1992 the hospital received Ministry of Health approval for a CT scanner, and the foundation officially launched its Scanning for Your Health

Ken Hall and Colleen Misener, foundation and hospital board members in the 1980s.

campaign. Within two years, the goal of $2.5 million had been realized. Actually, the tally was $2.8 million.

In September 1995 a donor wall was unveiled in the waiting room of the medical imaging department. On it are listed the more than 500 donors who gave from $500 to $100,000 to the CAT scan fund.

In November 1995 the foundation was into another campaign, this one called Equipped to CARE and with a goal of $5 million over five years. The money was for the purchase of about 150 pieces of surgical, medical and diagnostic equipment.

While rounding up money is serious business, those obliged to do that took a little time out to laugh at the foundation's annual meeting in May 1997. Their guest speaker was Sister Mary Christelle Macaluso of Omaha, Neb., who inducted the gathering of 70 or so into the Order of Fun Nuns. Using cartoons and assorted props, she urged her listeners to lighten up, to laugh more, and make others laugh more. She advised them to practise laughing instead of bitching. "We need to go to the funny-bone pharmacy," she said. "People that laugh together are less likely to kill each other."

A year later, those attending the foundation's annual meeting received another dose of humour, this time from journalist, cartoonist and motivator Ben Wicks. But with the laughs came the message: caring into the millennium. "We (in Canada) are incredibly fortunate," said Wicks. "But despite our good fortune, there are those who need us." He encouraged the assembled to continue caring.

In the spring of 1999 the foundation hired Linda M. Jones as its executive director, after accepting the resignation of Andrea Page (née Weiner). Jones's stay ended on Dec. 31, 2000.

In April 2001, Page returned to the foundation and has been its executive director since.

In May 2002 the SGH foundation was recognized for its abilities to raise money. At the Canadian annual meeting of the international Association for Healthcare Philanthropy, it received two Showcase Awards, one in the direct mail category, the other in the publication category.

Also in May 2000, guest speaker at the foundation's annual meeting was Bill Brady, a former radio and television personality from London. He is also the co-founder of Transplant International and a past chairman of the board of University Hospital and London Health Association.

In June 2002 the guest speaker was Stephen Lewis, former leader of the New Democratic Party in Ontario and Canada's ambassador to the United Nations from 1984 through 1988. In 2001 he was appointed the UN's special envoy for HIV-AIDS in Africa, and at the foundation's annual meeting he talked mostly about how the western world has been slow in its response to the pandemics that are ravaging the Dark Continent.

By then the foundation had announced the most ambitious campaign in its short history. For a redevelopment project that included reconfiguring and enlarging the emergency department, the operating rooms, the recovery room, the intensive care unit, the maternal-child unit and the psychiatry unit, the foundation was going after least $10 million in local funds. It was hoping for the same amount from the Ministry of Health.

Stratford General Hospital Foundation Monitor

fall 2002

volume 4; issue 8

WE CAN NEVER SAY THANK YOU ENOUGH!!

The year 2002 was a year of celebration at Stratford General Hospital Foundation with the completion of our five-year, $5-million Equipped to C.A.R.E. Campaign and the unveiling of the donor recognition system in appreciation of more than 5,500 donors responsible for our success.

Several celebrations were held during the spring to mark the Campaign's success—including an "Over the Top" announcement in March where staff, physicians, volunteers and media were told the exciting news that the Equipped to C.A.R.E. had reached goal.

As part of the celebration, individuals and groups within the hospital who played key roles in the campaign were awarded gold medals—in the spirit of the just-completed winter Olympics. Chris Thomson, Foundation Board Chairman, awarded six gold medals in true Olympic fashion.

"Together we have gone for gold, with spirit and dedication. Together as a team, anything we strive for is attainable," said Andrea Page, Stratford General Hospital Executive Director.

However the true celebration for the general public and generous donors was even grander and culminated in a special donor recognition system unveiling ceremony in the Hospital's main lobby on May 7th.

Hospital and Foundation Board members, along with local dignitaries, were on hand to salute the generosity of our donors. Board Chairman, Chris Thomson thanked each of the donors whose gifts—more than 24,200 in total over five years—brought the Campaign to the $5.1 million mark in cash and pledges.

Two members of the Hospital Auxiliary Association, Anna Walkom and Robert Dawson pulled the cord to unveil the recognition system to enthusiastic applause. Donors who attended the unveiling soon crowded around, locating their names and those of friends on the system—some posing to snap a few photos to remember the occasion. Employee Campaign Council member, Anne Reintjes, also unveiled a plaque listing all employees who gave during the campaign.

A unique cube shape design ensured sufficient room to inscribe 350 names of donors on the system. Brook Recognition Systems, the designers of the system, partnered with the Foundation, agreeing to donate $10,000 towards the project in exchange for use of the system as a "showcase" unit for Ontario. This ensured quality workmanship, unique design work and affordability for the Foundation.

Prior to the recognition system unveiling, a number of donors also took the opportunity to make additional donations and pledges—some $49,000 worth—ensuring they were recognized at an appropriate level.

"Throughout our campaign donor recognition and thanks has been a key to our success," said Ms. Page. "As we set our sights on the next campaign for Critical Care Redevelopment, we'll continue to thank and recognize our generous and enthusiastic donors."

As part of the event, a mini health fair showcased many of the pieces of equipment purchased over the last five years. Displays included an Endoscopy suite, a Maternity birthing room, and mock Operating Room. Equipment that couldn't be brought to the display was photographed and listed.

"It was a chance for our donors to actually see some of the equipment their generosity has purchased," explained Ms. Page.

People Caring for People

A Publication for the Supporters of Stratford General Hospital

Stratford General Hospital Foundation

Year	Chair	Vice-Chair	Secretary-Treasurer	Board Members
1983	Maurice P. Dean	Jeff Preston	Robert J. Cameron	Dr. Douglas Thompson, Robert J. McTavish, Colleen Misener, Dr. F. G. Ellis Scott, J. Duncan Gould, James J. Morris, Bessie Wilhelm, Rev. Jim Williams
1984	Maurice P. Dean	Jeff Preston	Robert J. Cameron	Stuart Cheney, Sandra L. Graff, Dr. Philip McCabe, Robert McTavish, James J. Morris, Boris J. Sibold, Dr. Douglas Thompson, Rev. Jim Williams, Ellard Lange
1985	Jeff Preston	Rev. Jim Williams	Robert J. Cameron	Maurice D. Beacock until June, Dr Douglas Thompson, Sandra Graff, Ellard Lange, Dr. Philip McCabe, Robert J. McTavish, James C. Preston, Boris J. Sibold
1986	Jeff Preston until July 30, then Dr. Douglas Thompson	Jeff Preston from July 30	Robert J. Cameron	John Callan, Dr. Douglas Thompson, Philip McCabe, Robert J. McTavish, Colleen Misener, James C. Preston, Sandra Graff, Ellard Lange, Boris J. Sibold, Kenneth Hall
1987	Dr. Douglas Thompson	Jeff Preston	Robert J. Cameron	Dr. Philip McCabe, Robert J. McTavish, Kenneth Hall, Ellard Lange, John Callan, Colleen Misener, James C. Preston, Boris J. Sibold, Sandra Graff
1988	Dr. Douglas Thompson	Jeff Preston	Robert J. Cameron	Colleen Misener, Dr. Art vanWalraven, John Callan, Robert Mountain, Kenneth Hall, Robert J. McTavish, Boris J. Sibold
1989	Dr. Douglas Thompson	Sandra L. Graff	Robert J. Cameron	Kenneth Hall, Dr. Steve Marchuk, Jim McMillan, Colleen Misener, Robert Mountain, Boris J. Sibold, Gordon Steed
1990	Sandra L. Graff	Robert Mountain	W. Terry E. Fadelle	John Callan, Mary McTavish, Colleen Misener, Jeff Preston, Gordon Steed, Chris W. C. Thomson, Margaret Wade, Dr. Steve Marchuk

1991	Sandra Graff until Nov. 26, then Robert Mountain	Robert Mountain until Nov. 26, then Colleen Misener	Bernie D. Schmidt	Mary McTavish, Colleen Misener, Dr John Moore, Jeff Preston, John Callan, Chris W. C. Thomson, Boris J. Sibold, Dr. Steve Marchuk
1992	Robert Mountain	Colleen Misener	Bernie D. Schmidt	Karlene Hussey, Dr. Steve Marchuk, Mary McTavish, Jeff Preston, Frank Romano, Chris W. C. Thomson, Gordon Steed, John Callan, Dr. John Moore
1992-3	Robert Mountain	Colleen Misener	Bernie D. Schmidt	John Callan, Dr. Steve Marchuk, Jeff Preston, Betty Reid, Frank Romano, George Schroeder, Chris W. C. Thomson, Dr. K. Van Woolnough
1993-4	Robert Mountain then Frank Romano	Frank Romano	Bernie D. Schmidt	Chris W. C. Thomson, Barbara Culliton, Karlene Hussey, Dr. Ralph Potoschnik, Mary MacPherson, Dianne Hiller, David Rae, George Schroeder, Dr. K. Van Woolnough
1995	Colleen Misener	Dr. K. Van Woolnough	Bernie D. Schmidt	L. Ray Waller, Mary MacPherson, Glenn Blackburn, Chris C. W. Thomson, Barbara Culliton, Dave Rae, Dianne Hiller, Vic Hayter, Dr. Ralph Pototschnik
1996	Colleen Misener	Dianne Hiller	Bernie D. Schmidt	L. Ray Waller, Barbara Culliton, Mary MacPherson, Glenn Blackburn, Dave Rae, Dr. Ralph Pototschnik, John Lawson, Dr. Chris Tebbutt, Bill Preston
1997	Dianne Hiller	John Lawson	Bernie D. Schmidt	L. Ray Waller, Hazel Wivell, Barbara Culliton, Dave Rae, Glenn Blackburn, Bill Preston, Dr. Ralph Pototschnik
1998	Dianne Hiller	John Lawson	Bernie D. Schmidt	L. Ray Waller, Dr. Nancy Whitmore, Barbara Culliton, Diana Henry, Dorothy Taylor, Terry Gillis, Bill Preston, Hazel Wivell, Glenn Blackburn, Anne Lake
1999	John Lawson	Barbara Culliton	Dianne. Hiller treasurer Linda Jones secretary	Terry Gillis, Diana Henry, Pat Million, Bill Preston, Dorothy Taylor, Chris C. W. Thomson, L. Ray Waller, Jim McMillan, Pat Young, Dr. Nancy Whitmore

2000	John Lawson	Dorothy Taylor	Dianne. Hiller treasurer Linda Jones secretary	Bill Preston, Chris C. W. Thomson, Barbara Culliton, Jim Burns, L. Ray Waller, Diana Henry, Jim McMillan, Andrew Williams, Pat Million, Pat Young, Jim Brisson
2001	Chris W. C. Thomson	Bill Preston	Dianne Hiller treasurer Linda Jones secretary	Dorothy Taylor, Pauline Jones, Jim McMillan, Jim Burns, L. Ray Waller, Diana Henry, Scott Tolton, Pat Young, Barbara Culliton, Dr. Miriam Mann, Andrew Williams
2002	Chris W. C. Thomson	Bill Preston	Dianne Hiller treasurer Andrea Page secretary	Dorothy Taylor, Pauline Jones, Jim McMillan, L. Ray Waller, Diana Henry, Scott Tolton, Dianne Hiller, Dr. Miriam. Mann, Jim Burns, Barbara Culliton, Pat Young, Andrew Williams
2002-3	Bill Preston	L. Ray Waller	Jim Burns treasurer Andrea Page secretary	Chris W. C. Thomson, Dorothy Taylor, Pauline Jones, Jim McMillan, Diana Henry, Scott Tolton, Dianne Hiller, Dr. Miriam Mann, Paul Roulston, George Skowby, Jeff Skubowius, Andrew Williams, Rick Orr

SGH mission statement

Stratford General Hospital is a regional health centre serving communities primarily within Perth and Huron counties. Service is also provided to communities within Oxford, Bruce and Wellington counties.

Within an environment committed to health promotion and disease prevention, we provide selected outpatient and inpatient programs in medical, surgical, maternal/child, long-term care, rehabilitation and mental health services. Supporting these services are specialized diagnostic and therapeutic programs.

The scope of these programs is guided by community input and needs, as well as available resources. The ongoing development of these programs is built on our commitment to continuous quality improvement, and the professionalism of our staff.

Board strength

There have been some remarkable stretches of commitment among those who chose to serve on the board of Stratford General Hospital.

Rolph Trow logged 28 years, six as chair. The longest-serving secretary-treasurer has been Isabelle McGillawee, with 21 straight years. Andrew Jeffrey held that position for 17 consecutive terms.

Harry Griffith was a SGH director for 13 years. His brother Ewart added 24 terms, four as vice-chair, to bring the Griffith total to 37 years.

Another family, the Prestons, have chalked up 51 terms on the boards of the hospital and its foundation. William, beginning in 1906, was a SGH trustee for 19 years, four as chair. His grandson Jeff spent a decade on the foundation board, of which he was chair for two years.

Jeff's son Jim was on the hospital board for 11 years, two as chair, and on the foundation board for three terms. Jim's brother Bill, current chair of the foundation, has been with that board for eight years.

But in this arena of community service, the title for longevity belongs to Harry Strudley, who was on the SGH board from 1914 to 1952. For 13 of those 39 years, he was the chair. And for six he was joined by his son Donald, a hospital trustee for 22 years, seven as chair. That brought the family contribution to 61 years.

"Ladies and gentleman, you have just heard a modest man. All members of the building committee have worked hard and faithfully, but their leader at all times has been Mr. Strudley."

A reference to Donald B. Strudley by Dr. David Smith at the official opening of the new SGH, July 22, 1950

Stratford General Hospital

Year	Chair	Secretary-Treasurer	Board Members
1891	John Hossie		
1892	William Davidson		John Hossie, John Brown, John Idington, James O'Loane, Edward T. Dufton, John McIntyre, Charles J. Macgregor
1893	William Davidson	William Buckingham honorary secretary	John C. Monteith, George V. Poole, John Hossie, Charles J. Macgregor, John Idington, James O'Loane, John Brown, Edward T. Dufton, John McIntyre
1894	William Davidson		John Idington, John Hossie, James O'Loane, John McIntyre, Charles J. Macgregor, John Brown, Edward T. Dufton, John C. Monteith, John A. Hacking
1895	John Hossie		William Davidson, Thomas Coveney, Charles J. Macgregor, James O'Loane, John Idington, John Brown, John McIntyre, Edward T. Dufton, John C. Monteith
1896	John Hossie	Thomas Ballantyne honorary treasurer	William Davidson, Thomas Ryan, John Idington, James O'Loane, Edward T. Dufton, John McIntyre, John C. Monteith
1897	John Hossie		John O'Donoghue, Nelson Monteith, Edward T. Dufton, John Brown, John Idington, James O'Loane, Charles J. Macgregor, John McIntyre, William Davidson
1898	John Hossie		John O'Donoghue, James Torrance, John Brown, William Davidson, John Idington, Edward T. Dufton, James O'Loane, Charles J. Macgregor, John McIntyre
1899	John Hossie		William Davidson, James O'Loane, John McIntyre, Charles J. Macgregor, John Idington, James Hodd, Thomas E. Hay
1900	John Hossie		John Brown, William Davidson, Edward T. Dufton, John Idington, Charles J. Macgregor, John McIntyre, James O'Loane, James Hodd, W. F. Sanderson
1901	John Hossie		Thomas Ballantyne, John Brown, William Davidson, William Buckingham, Edward T. Dufton, John Idington, Charles J. Macgregor, James Hodd, James Dickson
1902	John Hossie		James Stamp, Charles H. Merryfield, Thomas Ballantyne, John Brown, William Buckingham, William Davidson, Edward T. Dufton, John Idington, Charles J. Macgregor, John McIntyre, James O'Loane

1903	Thomas Ballantyne		John Brown, William Buckingham, William Davidson, Edward T. Dufton, John Hossie, John Idington, John McIntyre, James O'Loane, William Hepburn, Robert T. Kemp
1904	Thomas Ballantyne		John Brown, William Buckingham, William Davidson, Edward T. Dufton, John Hossie, John Idington, John McIntyre, John McMillan, James O'Loane, William Hepburn, Robert Berry
1905	Thomas Ballantyne		John Brown, William Buckingham, William Davidson, Edward T. Dufton, John Hossie, John McIntyre, John McMillan, James O'Loane, William Maynard, William J. Ferguson, James Donaldson
1906	Thomas Ballantyne		John Brown, William Preston, William Davidson, Edward T. Dufton, Charles Packert, John McMillan, James O'Loane, William Maynard, W. J. Ferguson, Robert Armstrong
1907	Thomas Ballantyne		John Brown, William Preston, William Davidson, Edward T. Dufton, J. J. Mason, John McMillan, James O'Loane, William Maynard, Robert S. Robertson, William Gordon, John A. Hacking
1908	William Preston	Andrew J. Jeffrey	Conrad Hasenpflug, William Smith Dingman, William Davidson, James O'Loane, John McMillan, John Brown, Edward T. Dufton, William Preston, J. J. Mason, Samuel R. Hesson, Thomas Ballantyne, Robert S. Robertson
1909	William Preston	Andrew J. Jeffrey	David Bonis, William Smith Dingman, William Davidson, James O'Loane, John McMillan, John Brown, Edward T. Dufton, William Preston, J. J. Mason, Samuel R. Hesson, Thomas Ballantyne, Robert S. Robertson
1910	William Preston	Andrew J. Jeffrey	Luther F. W. Turner, William Smith Dingman, William Davidson, James O'Loane, John McMillan, Edward T. Dufton, J. J. Mason, Samuel R. Hesson, Thomas Ballantyne, Robert S. Robertson, Thomas Magwood
1911	William Preston	Andrew J. Jeffrey	John Rudolph, John Brown, William Davidson, James O'Loane, John McMillan, Thomas Magwood, Edward T. Dufton, J. J. Mason, Samuel R. Hesson, Thomas Ballantyne, Robert S. Robertson
1912	James O'Loane	Andrew J. Jeffrey	John McLaren, John Brown, William Davidson, James O'Loane, John McMillan, Thomas Magwood, James Dickson, William Preston, J. J. Mason, Samuel R. Hesson, Thomas Ballantyne, Robert S. Robertson

1913	James O'Loane	Andrew J. Jeffrey	James Hill, Chalmers W. Greenwood, William Davidson, Clement McIlhargey, John McMillan, Thomas Magwood, James Dickson, William Preston, John C. Monteith, Samuel R. Hesson, Robert S. Robertson
1914	Thomas Ballantyne	Andrew J. Jeffrey	Samuel E. Smith, John Stevenson, William Davidson, Clement McIlhargey, Thomas Magwood, James Dickson, William Preston, Harold W. Strudley, Jeremiah Augustus Dugan, Alex Faill, Robert S. Robertson
1915	Alex Faill	Andrew J. Jeffrey	William Scott, Elijah Kitchen Barnsdale, William Davidson, Clement McIlhargey, Thomas Magwood, James Dickson, William Preston, Harold W. Strudley, Thomas E. Henry, Thomas Ballantyne, George G. McPherson
1916	Alex Faill	Andrew J. Jeffrey	M. F. Irvine, Elijah Kitchen Barnsdale, William Davidson, Clement McIlhargey, Thomas Magwood, James Dickson, William Preston, Harold W. Strudley, Thomas E. Henry, Thomas Ballantyne, George G. McPherson
1917	Alex Faill	Andrew J. Jeffrey	Oliver Harris, Dr. Joseph D. Monteith, William Davidson, Clement McIlhargey, Thomas Magwood, James Dickson, William Preston, Harold W. Strudley, Thomas E. Henry, Thomas Ballantyne, George G. McPherson
1918	Alex Faill	Andrew J. Jeffrey	Robert Armstrong, Dr. Joseph D. Monteith, William Davidson, Clement McIlhargey, John Whyte, James Dickson, William Preston, Harold W. Strudley, Alexander C. McLeod, Thomas Ballantyne, George G. McPherson
1919	Alex Faill	Andrew J. Jeffrey	Samuel E. Smith, John Stevenson, William Davidson, Clement McIlhargey, John Whyte, James Dickson, William Preston, Harold W. Strudley, Alexander C. McLeod, Thomas Ballantyne, George G. McPherson
1920	Alex Faill	Andrew J. Jeffrey	John McCallum, John Stevenson, William Davidson, Clement McIlhargey, John Whyte, John A. Makins, Kenneth C. Turnbull, Harry Lyman Griffith, William Preston, Harold W. Strudley, Alexander C. McLeod, Thomas Ballantyne, George G. McPherson
1921	Alex Faill	Andrew J. Jeffrey	Werner Krug, William H. Gregory, Clement McIlhargey, John A. Makins, Kenneth C. Turnbull, Harry Lyman Griffith, William Preston, Harold W. Strudley, Alexander C. McLeod, Thomas Ballantyne, George G. McPherson
1922	Alex Faill	Andrew J. Jeffrey	Albert A. Colquhoun, William H. Gregory, Clement McIlhargey, John A. Makins, Kenneth C. Turnbull, Harry Lyman Griffith, William Preston, Harold W. Strudley, Alexander C. McLeod, Thomas Ballantyne, George G. McPherson

1923	Alex Faill	Andrew J. Jeffrey	Thomas Boyes, Tom Brown, Clement McIlhargey, John A. Makins, Kenneth C. Turnbull, Harry Lyman Griffith, William Preston, Harold W. Strudley, Alexander C. McLeod, Thomas Ballantyne, George G. McPherson
1924	Alex Faill	Andrew J. Jeffrey	Michael Hagarty, Tom Brown, James P. King, John A. Makins, Kenneth C. Turnbull, Harry Lyman Griffith, William Preston, Harold W. Strudley, Alexander C. McLeod, George G. McPherson, David McKenzie Wright
1925	Alex Faill	Mae McIntosh	John A. Makins, Kenneth C. Turnbull, Harry Lyman Griffith, Harold W. Strudley, Alexander C. McLeod, Arthur Mutton, George G. McPherson, David McKenzie Wright, James P. King, Duncan M. Scott, Duncan Ferguson, Tom Brown
1926	John A. Makins	Mae McIntosh	Alex Faill, Kenneth C. Turnbull, Harry Lyman Griffith, Harold W. Strudley, Alexander C. McLeod, Herbert A. Beggs, George G. McPherson, David McKenzie Wright, James P. King, Duncan M. Scott, Duncan Ferguson, David R. Marshall
1927	John A. Makins	Mae McIntosh	George G. McPherson, Kenneth C. Turnbull, Harry Lyman Griffith, Harold W. Strudley, Alexander C. McLeod, Dr. Percival Lawrence Tye, David McKenzie Wright, Duncan M. Scott, Duncan Ferguson, David R. Marshall, Dr. George Reginald Deacon, Robert Hoggarth
1928	John A. Makins	Mae McIntosh	George G. McPherson, Kenneth C. Turnbull, Harry Lyman Griffith, Harold W. Strudley, Alexander C. McLeod, John Moody Kincaid, David McKenzie Wright, Duncan Ferguson, George Archibald McFadgen, John A. Andrew, Dr. George Reginald Deacon
1929	John A. Makins	Isabelle McGillawee	George G. McPherson, Kenneth C. Turnbull, Harry Lyman Griffith, Harold W. Strudley, Alexander C. McLeod, George Keith, David McKenzie Wright, Joseph C. S. Heideman, Duncan Ferguson, John A. Andrew, Dr. George Reginald Deacon, Robert Hoggarth
1930	John A. Makins	Isabelle McGillawee	George G. McPherson, Kenneth C. Turnbull, Harry Lyman Griffith, Harold W. Strudley, Alexander C. McLeod, Aaron Ringler, David McKenzie Wright, Joseph C. S. Heideman, Duncan Ferguson, Charles E. Moore, Dr. George Reginald Deacon, Robert Hoggarth
1931	John A. Makins	Isabelle McGillawee	George G. McPherson, Kenneth C. Turnbull, Harry Lyman Griffith, Harold W. Strudley, Alexander C. McLeod, W. Angus Dickson, David McKenzie Wright, Jessie M. Robertson, Duncan Ferguson, Charles E. Moore, Dr. George Reginald Deacon, Robert Hoggarth

1932	John A. Makins	Isabelle McGillawee	George G. McPherson, Kenneth C. Turnbull, Harry Lyman Griffith, Harold W. Strudley, Alexander C. McLeod, David McKenzie Wright, Jessie M. Robertson, Duncan Ferguson, Mayor George I. Graff, Dr. George Reginald Deacon, Conrad Schmidt
1933	John A. Makins	Isabelle McGillawee	George G. McPherson, Kenneth C. Turnbull, Rolph M. Trow, Harold W. Strudley, Alexander C. McLeod, David McKenzie Wright, Jessie M. Robertson, James L. Killoran, George I. Graff, Dr. George Reginald Deacon, Robert Hoggarth, William F. Dalling
1934	John A. Makins	Isabelle McGillawee	George G. McPherson, William John Anderson, Rolph M. Trow, Harold W. Strudley, Alexander C. McLeod, David McKenzie Wright, Jessie Webb, James L. Killoran, Oliver J. Kerr, Dr. George Reginald Deacon, Robert Hoggarth, David M. Arbogast
1935	Robert Hoggarth	Isabelle McGillawee	John A. Makins, George G. McPherson, William J. Anderson, Dr. George Reginald Deacon, Rolph M. Trow, Harold W. Strudley, Alexander C. McLeod, David McKenzie Wright, George McKellar, James L. Killoran, Oliver J. Kerr, William W. Roger, Edith McLeod
1936	Robert Hoggarth	Isabelle McGillawee	John A. Makins, George G. McPherson, William J. Anderson, Rolph M. Trow, Harold W. Strudley, Alexander C. McLeod, David McKenzie Wright, Duncan M. Scott, James L. Killoran, William H. Gregory, Dr. George Reginald Deacon, William S. Donaldson, Edith McLeod
1937	Robert Hoggarth	Isabelle McGillawee	George G. McPherson, William J. Anderson, Rolph M. Trow, Harold W. Strudley, Alexander C. McLeod, David McKenzie Wright, Duncan M. Scott, James L. Killoran, Thomas E. Henry, Dr. George Reginald Deacon, Gerrance H. Jose, Mary Johnston
1938	Robert Hoggarth	Isabelle McGillawee	John A. Makins, George G. McPherson, William John Anderson, J. Archibald C. Kay, Rolph M. Trow, Harold W. Strudley, Alexander C. McLeod, Dr. George Reginald Deacon, Joseph C. Heideman, James L. Killoran, Thomas E. Henry, George Ronnenberg, Mary Johnston
1939	Harold W. Strudley	Isabelle McGillawee	John A. Makins, George G. McPherson, William J. Anderson, J.Archibald C. Kay, Rolph M. Trow, Alexander C. McLeod, Sophie Turnbull, Dr. George Reginald Deacon, James L. Killoran, Thomas E. Henry, Robert Hoggarth, Walter Hayter, William H. Good

1940	Harold W. Strudley	Isabelle McGillawee	John A. Makins, George G. McPherson, William John Anderson, J. Archibald C. Kay, Rolph M. Trow, Alexander C. McLeod, Sophie Turnbull, Albert J. Bradshaw, James L. Killoran, Dr. George Reginald Deacon, Robert Hoggarth, Joseph C. Heideman, Thomas E. Henry
1941	Harold W. Strudley	Isabelle McGillawee	George G. McPherson, John A. Makins, Dr. William Charles Sproat, Rolph M. Trow, Alexander C. McLeod, J.Archibald C. Kay, James L. Killoran, Henry St. George Lee, Robert Hoggarth, Thomas E. Henry, Donald McCallum, Dr. Harold Brown Kenner, William John Anderson, Sophie Turnbull
1942	Harold W. Strudley	Isabelle McGillawee	George G. McPherson, John A. Makins, William John Anderson, Rolph M.Trow, Alexander C. McLeod, J. Archibald C. Kay, James L. Killoran, Henry St. George Lee, Robert Hoggarth, Thomas E. Henry, William J. Kay, William Charles Sproat, Hilda Shea, Walter Hayter
1943	Harold W. Strudley	Isabelle McGillawee	George G. McPherson, William John Anderson, J. Archibald C. Kay, James L. Killoran, Henry St. George Lee, Alexander C. McLeod, James Morgan Riddell, Rolph M. Trow, Robert Hoggarth, Alfred Denstedt, Dr. Lionel Alfred Macklin, Hilda Shea, Fred Bryant, Thomas E. Henry, Ewart Trayte Griffith
1944	Harold W. Strudley	Isabelle McGillawee	William John Anderson, Dr. Joseph Angus Boyd, Ewart Trayte Griffith, Robert Hoggarth, J. Archibald C. Kay, Henry St. George Lee, Alexander C. McLeod, James Morgan Riddell, Rolph M. Trow, Isobel Malone, J. Waldo Monteith, Dr. Lionel Alfred Macklin, Theodore Parker, Fred Bryant
1945	Harold W. Strudley	Isabelle McGillawee	William John Anderson, Dr. Joseph Angus Boyd, Ewart Trayte Griffith, Robert Hoggarth, J. Archibald C. Kay, Henry St. George Lee, Alexander C. McLeod, James Morgan Riddell, Rolph M. Trow, Isobel Malone, J. Waldo Monteith, Dr. Lionel Alfred Macklin, James Neilson Corry, Joseph C. Heideman
1946	Harold W. Strudley	Isabelle McGillawee	William John Anderson, Joseph Angus Boyd, Ewart Trayte Griffith, J. Archibald C. Kay, Henry St. George Lee, Alexander C. McLeod, James Morgan Riddell, Rolph M. Trow, Isobel Malone, J. Maurice King, Dr. Robert Stanley Murray, William Alexander Tuer, Joseph C. Heideman

Year	Chair	Vice-chair	Secretary-Treasurer	Board Members
1947	Harold W. Strudley	Rolph M. Trow	Isabelle McGillawee	William John Anderson, Dr. Joseph Angus Boyd, Roy Butson, Ewart Trayte Griffith, William Graham, J. Archibald C. Kay, Mary Wardlaw, Henry St. George Lee, Douglas E. Marks, Alexander C. McLeod, James Morgan Riddell, Joseph H. Rodgers, Donald Bell Strudley, Leslie Whittemore, Alex Anderson, J. Maurice King, Joseph C. Heideman, Dr. James G. McDermott
1948	Harold W. Strudley	Rolph M. Trow	Isabelle McGillawee	William John Anderson, Dr. Joseph A. Boyd, Roy Butson, W. Graham, Ewart Trayte Griffith, J. Archibald C. Kay, Henry St. George Lee, Douglas E. Marks, Alexander C. McLeod, James Morgan Riddell, Joseph H. Rodgers, Dr. David Smith, Donald Bell Strudley, Leslie Whittemore, Martin Mogk, Mary Wardlaw, Thomas E. Henry, Joseph C. Heideman, Dr. W. Mac Gilmore
1949	Harold W. Strudley	Rolph M. Trow	Isabelle McGillawee	William John Anderson, Dr. Joseph A. Boyd, Roy Butson, Walter H. Dorland, Andrew K. Fisher, Ewart Trayte Griffith, Henry St. George Lee, Douglas E. Marks, James L. Millar, Helen Baker, Dr. David Smith, Donald Bell Strudley, Dr. C. Edward Sylvester, Thomas E. Henry, Joseph H. Rodgers, Winnifred Mulford, John J. Vosper, Leslie Whittemore
1950	Harold W. Strudley	Rolph M. Trow	Jack L. Bateman secretary John F. Ward treasurer	William John Anderson, Dr. Joseph A. Boyd, Roy Butson, Walter H. Dorland, Andrew K. Fisher, Ewart Trayte Griffith, Henry St. George Lee, Douglas E. Marks, James L. Millar, Joseph H. Rodgers, Dr. David Smith, Donald Bell Strudley, Helen Baker, Dr. Howard C. Hazel, Thomas E. Henry, Winnifred Mulford, John J. Vosper, Leslie Whittemore
1951	Harold W. Strudley	Rolph M. Trow	Jack L. Bateman secretary John F. Ward treasurer	William John Anderson, Dr. Joseph A. Boyd, Roy Butson, Walter H. Dorland, Andrew K. Fisher, Ewart Trayte Griffith, Henry St. George Lee, Douglas E. Marks, James L. Millar, Joseph H. Rodgers,

				Dr. David Smith, Donald Bell Strudley, Helen Baker, Dr. Hugh H. Thompson, A. David Simpson, Joseph C. Heideman, William Oliver Gaffney, Leslie Whittemore
1952	Rolph M. Trow	Donald B. Strudley	Jack L. Bateman secretary John F. Ward treasurer	Ewart Trayte Griffith, James Morgan Riddell, Henry St. George Lee, Dr. David Smith, Harold W. Strudley, Roy Butson, Harold Cosens, Walter H. Dorland, Joseph C. Heideman, Winnifred H. Kneitl, Joseph H. Rodgers, Dr. Norval W. Scratch, Leslie Whittemore
1953	Rolph M. Trow	Donald B. Strudley	Jack L.Bateman secretary John F. Ward treasurer	Hans Buscher, Ewart Trayte Griffith, Henry St. George Lee, James Morgan Riddell, Dr. David Smith, Frank Allen, Violet Martyn, Roy Butson, Andrew K. Fisher, Dr. Harold Brown Kenner, Alexander C. McKenzie, Joseph H. Rodgers, Leslie Whittemore
1954	Rolph M. Trow	Donald B. Strudley,	Jack L. Bateman secretary Stanley H. Wilkins treasurer	Hans Buscher, Ewart Trayte Griffith, Henry St. George Lee, James Morgan Riddell, Dr. David Smith, Roy Butson, Andrew K. Fisher, Dr. George. H. Ingham, Alex C. McKenzie, Violet Martyn, Joseph H. Rodgers, John A. Stephen, Leslie Whittemore
1955	Rolph M. Trow	Donald B. Strudley	Jack. L. Bateman secretary Stanley H. Wilkins treasurer	Hans Buscher, Willoet Kelterborn, Violet Martyn, Dr. David Smith, Ewart Trayte Griffith, Henry St. George Lee, James Morgan Riddell, Roy Butson, Winnifred Mulford, Joseph H. Rodgers, Dr. David Gemmell, Alex C. McKenzie, Leslie Whittemore
1956	Rolph M. Trow	Donald B. Strudley	Jack L. Bateman secretary Stanley H. Wilkins treasurer	Hans Buscher, Ewart Trayte Griffith, Henry St. George Lee, James Morgan Riddell, Dr. David Smith, Roy Butson, Dr. David Gemmell, William C. Jack, Grace Knechtel, John F. Warriner, Joseph H. Rodgers
1957	Rolph M. Trow	Donald B. Strudley,	Jack L. Bateman secretary Stanley H. Wilkins treasurer	Hans Buscher, Ewart Trayte Griffith, Henry St. George Lee, James Morgan Riddell, Dr. David Smith, Roy Butson, Dr. David Gemmell, Fred Ratz, Grace Knechtel, John F. Warriner, Joseph H. Rodgers, Leslie Whittemore

1958	Donald B. Strudley	Ewart T. Griffith	Jack L. Bateman secretary William F.J. Swindall treasurer	Hans Buscher, Stuart S. Cheney, James Johnson, Sydney R. Skelton, Rolph M. Trow, Leonard C. Webster, Arthur W. Blowes, Earl Boyes, Roy Butson, Grace Knechtel, Dr. James G. McDermott, Joseph H. Rodgers, Arthur G. Skidmore, Dr. C. Edward Sylvester, John F. Warriner, Leslie Whittemore, Henry St. George Lee, James Morgan Riddell
1959	Donald B. Strudley	Ewart T. Griffith	Jack L. Bateman secretary William F.J. Swindall treasurer	Rolph M. Trow, Winnifred Kneitl, Marionne Johnston, Dr. Harold M. Taylor, Sydney R. Skelton, Leonard C. Webster, T. Campbell, Roy Butson, Thompson, Stuart S. Cheney, Joseph H. Rodgers, Hans Buscher, John F. Warriner, Alex C. McKenzie
1960	Donald B. Strudley	Ewart T. Griffith	Jack L. Bateman secretary William F.J. Swindall treasurer	Alex C. McKenzie, Rolph M. Trow, Sydney R. Skelton, Joseph H. Rodgers, Leonard C. Webster, Hans Buscher, Stuart S. Cheney, Walter Mogk, Anne Rhodes, Dr. W. Mac Gilmore, Roy Butson, Fred Cox, Marionne Johnston
1961	Donald B. Strudley	Ewart T. Griffith	Jack L. Bateman	Hans Buscher, Rev. James Ferguson, Marionne Johnston, Sydney R. Skelton, Leonard C. Webster, Arthur W. Blowes, Roy Butson, William George Dixon, Howard Lowe, Arthur G. Skidmore, John F. Warriner, Dr. William Charles Sproat, Dr. Bruce A. Campbell, Lillian Whatmough, Dolores Whiteman
1962	Donald B. Strudley	Leonard C. Webster	Jack L. Bateman	Hans Busher, Ewart Trayte Griffith, Marionne Johnston, Rev. James Ferguson, Sydney R. Skelton, Arthur W. Blowes, Roy Butson, Dr. Bruce A. Campbell, William George Dixon, Walter C. Gerth, Arthur G. Skidmore, Dr. William Charles Sproat, John F. Warriner, Lilliam Whatmough, Dolores Whiteman
1963	Donald B. Strudley	Leonard C. Webster	Jack L. Bateman	Hans Buscher, Rev. James Ferguson, Ewart Trayte Griffith, Marionne Johnston , Sydney R. Skelton, Arthur W. Blowes, Dr. Bruce A. Campbell, Gladys Crerar, Winnifred Kneitl, Willard Mohr, Dr. John E. Pyper, Dr. Cecil R. Quinlan,

			Arthur G. Skidmore, John F. Warriner, Dolores Whiteman
1964	Donald B. Strudley	Leonard C. Webster	Jack L. Bateman	Hans Buscher, Rev. James Ferguson, Ewart Trayte Griffith, Marionne Johnston, Sydney R. Skelton, Arthur W. Blowes, Dr. Bruce A. Campbell, Gladys Crerar, Winnifred Kneitl, David White, Dr. John E. Pyper, Dr. Cecil R. Quinlan, Arthur G. Skidmore, John F. Warriner, Dolores Whiteman
1965	Leonard C. Webster	Rev. James Ferguson	Jack L. Bateman	Hans Buscher, Oliver J. Gaffney, Ewart Trayte Griffith, Boris J. Sibold, Donald Bell Strudley, Rudolph Bauer, Arthur W. Blowes, Ida Carr, Peter W. Case, A. McTavish, Dr. John E. Pyper, Dr. Cecil R. Quinlan, Dr. Lloyd G. Schulthies, John F. Warriner, Dolores Whiteman
1966	Leonard C. Webster	Rev. James Ferguson	Jack L. Bateman	Hans Buscher, Oliver J. Gaffney, Ewart Trayte Griffith, Boris J. Sibold, Donald Bell Strudley, Arthur W. Blowes, Ida Carr, Peter W. Case, Arthur McTavish, Dr. John E. Pyper, Dr. Cecil R. Quinlan, Dr. Lloyd G. Schulthies, Dolores Whiteman, Albert E. Carson, Dr. James G. McDermott, James M. Scott
1967	Leonard C. Webster	Rev. James Ferguson	Jack L. Bateman	Hans Buscher, Oliver J. Gaffney, Boris J. Sibold, Dr. James G. McDermott, Donald Bell Strudley, Arthur Blowes, Peter W. Case, Arthur McTavish, James M. Scott, Dr. Lloyd G. Schulthies, Dolores Whiteman, Dr. Ian Lindsay, Elizabeth Livingstone, Wilfred Seebach
1968	Rev. James Ferguson	Boris J. Sibold	Jack L. Bateman then Robert J. Cameron	Hans Buscher, Oliver J. Gaffney, Dr. John E. Pyper, Boris J. Sibold, Donald Bell Strudley, Arthur W. Blowes, Elizabeth Livingstone, Arthur McTavish, Dr. Lloyd G. Schulthies, James M. Scott, Dolores Whiteman, Ellard Lange, John N. Paterson, Dr. Arthur R. Rowe, Dulcie Wyatt
1969	Rev. James Ferguson	Boris J. Sibold	Robert J. Cameron	(partial list) John N. Paterson, Arthur McTavish, Dr. Arthur R. Rowe, Hans Buscher, Oliver J. Gaffney,

				James M. Scott, Andrew A. Park, Dr. Peter C. Roberts, Dulcie Wyatt
1970	Rev. James Ferguson	Boris J. Sibold	Robert J. Cameron	Hans Buscher, Dr. David P. Fitzgerald, Oliver Gaffney, John R. Goodman, Maurice Helperin, Kenneth Jones, Dr. James R. Kelly, Ellard K. Lange, Alastair MacLeod, Ross McPhail, John N. Paterson, Dr. John E. Pyper, Cae Roberts, Dr. Arthur R. Rowe, John D. Strautnicks, Robert W. Watler, Dolores Whiteman, Dr. David Fitzgerald, Andrew A. Park
1971	Rev. James Ferguson	Boris J. Sibold	Robert J. Cameron	E. George Bettger, Hans Buscher, Thomson W. Dickson, Dr. David P. Fitzgerald, Oliver J. Gaffney, Leslie A. Garvie, John R. Goodman, Maurice Helperin, Vivian Jarvis, Kenneth Jones, Dr. James R. Kelly, Ellard K. Lange, Cae Roberts, Alistair MacLeod, Ross McPhail, Dr. James G. McDermott, James McKay, John N. Paterson, Dr. Elisabeth Schuh, Dolores Whiteman, Dulcie Wyatt
1972	Boris J. Sibold	John N. Paterson	Robert J. Cameron	E. George Bettger, Thomson W. Dickson, Edward Doerr, Rev. James Ferguson, Dr. David P. Fitzgerald, Leslie A. Garvie, Alan G. Graff, Vivian Jarvis, Kenneth Jones, Dr. James R. Kelly, Clarence S. King, Ellard K. Lange, Alistair MacLeod, Dr. James G. McDermott, James McKay, Dr. Elisabeth Schuh, Joan Taylor, Dolores Whiteman, Dulcie Wyatt
1973	Boris J. Sibold	John N. Paterson	Robert J. Cameron	Bruce Aitcheson, E. George Bettger, Maurice P. Dean, Edward Doerr, Dr. Donald Fuller, Leslie A. Garvie, Alan G. Graff, Harvey Greenberg, Mary Johnson, Kenneth Jones, Dr. Andre C. Joyal, Clarence S. King, George Kollman, Dr. A. Jeffrey Macdonald, Alistair MacLeod, Colleen Misener, Dr. James G. McDermott, Dr. John B. Moore, Joan Taylor, Dr. Elisabeth Schuh, Bruce Swerdfager, Dolores Whiteman

1974	Boris J. Sibold	Alistair MacLeod	Robert J. Cameron	Bruce Aitcheson, Dr. Douglas J. Allan, E. George Bettger, Maurice P. Dean, Leslie A. Garvie, Alan G. Graff, Harvey Greenberg, Frances Greene, Mary Johnston, Kenneth Jones, Clarence S. King, George Kollman, Dr. A. Jeffrey Macdonald, Colleen Misener, Dr. Elisabeth Schuh, Bruce Swerdfager
1975	Alistair MacLeod	Frances Greene	Robert J. Cameron	Dr. Douglas J. Allan, E. George Bettger, Maurice P. Dean, Arthur Goodwin, Alan G. Graff, Harvey Greenberg, Mary Johnston, Kenneth Jones, Dr. Ian Lindsay, Dr. A. Jeffrey Macdonald, Colleen Misener, Harold Siberry, Boris J. Sibold, Wilfred Tuer, Carl Vock, Dulcie Wyatt
1976	Alistair MacLeod	Frances Greene	Robert J. Cameron	Dr. Douglas J. Allan, E. George Bettger, Maurice P. Dean, Arthur Goodwin, Alan G. Graff, Harvey Greenberg, Kenneth Jones, Barbara A. Lyon, Dr. A. Jeffrey Macdonald, Colleen Misener, Leonard Plaskett, Harold Siberry, Boris J. Sibold, John Sinclair, Wilfred Tuer, Carl Vock, Dr. James A. Wickwire, Rev. James M. Williams, Dulcie Wyatt
1977	Frances Greene	Harold Siberry	Robert J. Cameron	James Burns, Maurice P. Dean, Alan G. Graff, Harvey Greenberg, Ellard K. Lange, Barbara A. Lyon, Alistair MacLeod, Dr. Andrew W. McKenzie, Dr. Patrick J. McQuade, Colleen Misener, Leonard Plaskett, Dr. Elisabeth Schuh, John Sinclair, Wilfred Tuer, Rev. James M. Williams, Dulcie Wyatt
1978-9 term changed (April 1 to March 1)	Frances Greene	Harold Siberry	Robert J. Cameron	James Burns, Cathy Clarke, Maurice P. Dean, J. Duncan Gould, Alan G. Graff, Harvey Greenberg, Mary Johnston, Ellard K. Lange, Dr. A. Jeffrey Macdonald, Colleen Misener, James J. Morris, Leonard Plaskett, Dr. F. G. Ellis Scott, John Sinclair, Wilfred Tuer, Dr. James A. Wickwire, Rev. James M. Williams
1979-0	Harold Siberry	Maurice P. Dean	Robert J. Cameron	James Burns, Cathy Clarke, J. Duncan Gould, Frances Greene,

				Norah Huggins, Mary Johnston, Ellard K. Lange, Dr. Eric Lenczner, Dr. A. Jeffrey Macdonald, Colleen Misener, James J. Morris, Leonard Plaskett, James Preston, Dr. F. G. Ellis Scott, Wilfred Tuer, L. Ray Waller, Dr. James A. Wickwire, Rev. James M. Williams
1980-1	Harold Siberry	Maurice P. Dean	Robert J. Cameron	James Burns, J. Duncan Gould, Frances Greene, Perry Hill, Norah Huggins, Mary Johnston, Ellard K. Lange, Dr. Eric Lenczner, Dr. A. Jeffrey Macdonald, Robert J. McTavish, Colleen Misener, James J. Morris, Leonard Plaskett, James Preston, Dr. F. G. Ellis Scott, Wilfred Tuer, L. Raymond Waller, Dr. James A. Wickwire, Bessie Wilhelm, Rev. James M. Williams
1981-2	Maurice P. Dean	Rev. Jim Williams	Robert J. Cameron	James Burns, John Callan, J. Duncan Gould, Dorothy Hayes, Norah Huggins, Mary Johnston, Dr. Eric Lenczner, Dr. A. Jeffrey Macdonald, Robert J. McTavish, Colleen Misener, James J. Morris, James Preston, Dr. F. G. Ellis Scott, R. Scott, Harold Siberry, Dr. Douglas Thompson, L. Raymond Waller, Bessie Wilhelm, Rev. James M. Williams
1982-3	Maurice P. Dean	Rev. Jim Williams	Robert J. Cameron	James Burns, John Callan, J. Duncan Gould, Dorothy Hayes, Norah Huggins, Dr. Andrew Hussey, Mary Johnston, Dr. Eric Lenczner, Robert J. McTavish, Colleen Misener, James J. Morris, James Preston, Dr. F. G. Ellis Scott, R. Scott, Harold Siberry, Dr. Douglas Thompson, L. Raymond Waller, Bessie Wilhelm
1983-4	Rev. James Williams	James Preston	Robert J. Cameron	John Callan, Maurice P. Dean, Dr. Donald Fuller, J. Duncan Gould, Norah Huggins, Dr. Andrew Hussey, Mary Johnston, Dr. Philip McCabe, Robert J. McTavish, Colleen Misener, James J. Morris, Barb Noel, Ralph A. Pike, William A. Russell, Dr. F. G. Ellis Scott, Dr. Douglas Thompson, L. Raymond Waller, Bessie Wilhelm, Dorothy Worden

1984-5	Rev. James Williams	James Preston	Robert J. Cameron	John Callan, Maurice P. Dean, Dr. Donald Fuller, J. Duncan Gould, Kenneth Hall, Dr. Andrew Hussey, Dr. Philip McCabe, Robert J. McTavish, Colleen Misener, James J. Morris, Barb Noel, Ralph A. Pike, William A. Russell, Dr. C. David Tamblyn, L. Raymond Waller, Bessie Wilhelm, Dorothy Worden
1985-6	James Preston	Robert J. McTavish	Robert J. Cameron	John Callan, Barbara Culliton, Maurice P. Dean, J. Duncan Gould, Kenneth Hall, Dr. Andrew Hussey, Dr. Philip McCabe, Colleen Misener, James J. Morris, Barb Noel, Stanley Picton, Ralph A. Pike, William A. Russell, Dr. C. David Tamblyn, Dr. Art A. vanWalraven, L. Raymond Waller, Bessie Wilhelm, Rev. James M. Williams, Dorothy Worden
1986-7	James Preston	Robert J. McTavish	Robert J. Cameron	John Callan, Barbara Culliton, J. Duncan Gould, Kenneth Hall, Calvin Innes, Dr. Phillip McCabe, W. James McMillan, Colleen Misener, James J. Morris, Barbara Noel, Stanley Picton, Ralph A Pike, William A. Russell, Dr. C. David Tamblyn, Dr. Art A. van Walraven, L. Raymond Waller, Rev. James M. Williams Gordon Steed, Bessie Wilhelm
1987-8	Robert J. McTavish	Colleen Misener	Robert J. Cameron	John Callan, Barb Culliton, Kenneth Hall, Calvin Innes, W. James McMillan, James J. Morris, Barb Noel, Stanley Picton, James Preston, William A. Russell, Art A. vanWalraven, L. Raymond Waller, Dr. Kenneth Ward, Dr. Paul Weir, Bessie Wilhelm, Gordon Steed
1988-9	Robert J. McTavish	Colleen Misener	Robert J. Cameron	John Callan, Kenneth Hall, Calvin Innes, Richard Linley, W. James McMillan, Barb Noel, James Preston, Shirley Russell, William A. Russell, Gordon Steed, Chris W. C. Thomson, Dr. Art A. vanWalraven, L. Raymond Waller, Dr. Kenneth Ward, Dr. Paul Weir, Bessie Wilhelm, Barb Culliton, James J. Morris, Stanley Picton

1989-0	Colleen Misener	Kenneth Hall	Robert J. Cameron	John Callan, Michael Dunn, Calvin Innes, Richard Linley, Dr. Steve Marchuk, W. James McMillan, Robert J. McTavish, David Rae, Shirley Russell, William A. Russell, George Schroeder, Gordon Steed, Chris W. C. Thomson, Dr. Paul Weir, Bessie Wilhelm, Barb Noel, James Preston, Dr. Art A. vanWalraven, L. Raymond Waller
1990-1	Colleen Misener	John Callan	Robert J. Cameron	Helen Anderson, Pat Young, Calvin Innes, Gordon Steed, Robert J. McTavish, Barbara Culliton, John Callan, Michael Dunn, Rick Linley, Dr. Steve Marchuk, Colleen Misener, Dave Rae, Shirley Russell, William Russell, George Schroeder, Chris Thomsom, Dr. Art A. vanWalraven, Dr. Paul Weir
1991-2	John Callan	Chris W. C. Thomson	Bernie D. Schmidt	Helen Anderson, Ron Christie, Barbara Culliton, Michael Dunn, Calvin Innes, Dr. Steven Marchuk, Dr. James N. McArthur, Mary McTavish, Colleen Misener, David Rae, George Schroeder, Gordon Steed, Dr. Art A. vanWalraven, Margaret Wade, L. Raymond Waller, Pat Taylor
1992-3	John Callan	Chris W. C. Thomson	Bernie D. Schmidt	Helen Anderson, Ron Christie, Barbara Culliton, Robert D. Davidson, Michael Dunn, Thomas J. Hogan, Calvin Innes, Dr. Steve Marchuk, Dr. James N. McArthur, Colleen Misener, David Rae, Betty Reid, George Schroeder, Art A. vanWalraven, Margaret Wade, L. Raymond Waller
1993-4	Chris W. C. Thomson	David Rae	Bernie D. Schmidt	Helen Anderson, John Callan, Ron Christie, Barbara Culliton, Robert D. Davidson, Michael Dunn, Thomas J. Hogan, Calvin Innes, Dr. David Parratt, Dr. Ralph Pototschnik, Betty Reid, George Schroeder, Dr. Art A. vanWalraven, Margaret Wade, L. Raymond Waller, Pat Young
1994-5	Chris W. C. Thomson	David Rae	Bernie D. Schmidt	Helen Anderson, Anita Billo, John Callan, Barbara Culliton, Robert D. Davidson, Michael Dunn, Thomas J. Hogan, Calvin Innes, Anne Lake,

				George Schroeder, Dr. Chris Tebbutt, Dr. Art A. vanWalraven, Margaret Wade, L. Raymond Waller, Dr. K. Van Woolnough, Pat Young
1995-6	David Rae	Anne Lake	Bernie D. Schmidt	Helen Anderson, Anita Billo, Barbara Culliton, Robert D. Davidson, Dr. Randy Gonser, Dr. James Hardwick, Calvin Innes, Ruth Lawson, John Lichti, Dr. David Parratt, George Schroeder, Chris W. C. Thomson, Dr. Art A. vanWalraven, Marg Wade, L. Raymond Waller, Pat Young
1996-7	David Rae	Anne Lake	Bernie D. Schmidt	Helen Anderson, Barbara Culliton, Dr. Randy Gonser, Dr. James Hardwick, David Jutzi, Mary MacPherson, Ruth Lawson, John Lichti, Dr. David Parratt, George Schroeder, George Skowby, Chris W. C. Thomson, Margaret Wade, Pat Young
1997-8	Anne Lake	John Lichti	Bernie D. Schmidt	Helen Anderson, Barbara Culliton, Dr. Randy Gonser, Dr. James Hardwick, Dr. Craig Hudson, David Jutzi, Mary MacPherson, Ruth Lawson, Dr. David Parratt, David Rae, George Schroeder, George Skowby, Chris W. C. Thomson, Marg Wade, L. Raymond Waller, Pat Young
1998-9	Anne Lake	John Lichti	Bonnie Adamson	Helen Anderson, Barbara Culliton, Dr. Randy Gonser, Dr. James Hardwick, Paul Howley, Dr. Craig Hudson, David Jutzi, Ruth Lawson, David Rae, George Schroeder, George Skowby, Dr. Eric Thomas, Margaret Wade, L. Raymond Waller, Hazel Wivell, Pat Young
1999-0	John Lichti	Paul Howley	Bonnie Adamson	Helen Anderson, Barbara Culliton, Jo Deslippe, Dr. James Hardwick, Dr. Craig Hudson, David Jutzi, Anne Lake, Ruth Lawson, Lorne Rachlis, George Skowby, Dr. Eric Thomas, Margaret Wade, L. Raymond Waller, Hazel Wivell, Pat Young

2000-1	John Lichti	Paul Howley	Bonnie Adamson	Jo Deslippe, Robert Gulliford, Dr. Craig Hudson, Anne Lake, Ruth Lawson, Dan Mathieson, Michael McKenna, Pat Million, Lorne Rachlis, Sean Raleigh, George Skowby, Dr. Eric Thomas, L. Raymond Waller, Dr. Nancy Whitmore, Pat Young
2001-2	Paul Howley	Jo Deslippe	Bonnie Adamson	Dr. Peter Brooks, Robert Gulliford, Dr. Craig Hudson, Anne Lake, Ruth Lawson, John Lichti, Dan Mathieson, Michael McKenna, Pat Million, Lorne Rachlis, Sean Raleigh, George Skowby, Dr. Eric Thomas, L. Raymond Waller, Pat Young

DOUGLAS SPILLANE

A view of the SGH buildings and grounds from the corner of St. Vincent and West Gore streets, 1971.

Two views of SGH, 2002. Above: Looking west from St. Vincent St. S. At right is the former regional school of nursing. Below: Looking north into the east courtyard.

DEAN ROBINSON

DEAN ROBINSON

About Dean Robinson

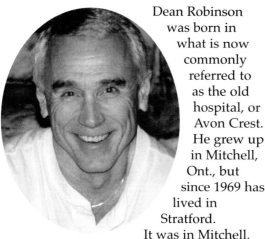

Dean Robinson was born in what is now commonly referred to as the old hospital, or Avon Crest. He grew up in Mitchell, Ont., but since 1969 has lived in Stratford.

It was in Mitchell, as a high school student, that he contributed stories to the *Mitchell Advocate* and became hooked on journalism.

He joined the London Free Press in 1965, and from then through 1982 worked on newspapers and magazines, and at radio and television stations in London, Kitchener and Stratford.

His first of more than 15 books, a biography of hockey legend Howie Morenz, was the outgrowth of a project he completed for his master of arts degree in journalism at the University of Western Ontario. It was published in 1982.

Since then his work has included books on hell driver Lucky Lott, the towns of Mitchell and Seaforth, his high school, the Stratford Agricultural Society, the Stratford YMCA, the Stratford Rotary Club, the Stratford Cullitons, and the history of the railway in Stratford. He has also edited five township histories, and produced the photographs for a book on daytripping in southwestern Ontario.

From 1989 to 2001 he taught journalism at the Doon campus of Conestoga College. His other interests include kayaking, sailing, travel and the Montreal Canadiens.

For more than 20 years, he and his wife Judy have lived within a short walk of SGH.

About Carolynn Bart-Riedstra

Carolynn Bart-Riedstra has been an archivist at the Stratford-Perth Archives since 1986. Born and raised in Stratford, she has a master of arts degree in Canadian history from Wilfrid Laurier University. She has been involved with the Local Architectural Conservation Advisory Committee, Chair of the Heritage Conservation District and the Perth County Branch Ontario Genealogical Society. From 1992 -1996 she was on the building committee of the Ontario Heritage Foundation. She was president of the Archives Association of Ontario from 1996 to 1998.

She has provided research about Stratford for many books and is a regular contributor to the Stratford Beacon Herald. She co-authored the book Stratford: Its heritage and its Festival with her husband Lutzen Riedstra. Her second book, Images of Canada - Stratford, was published in 2002.

She and her husband have a nine-year-old son, Lutzen Jr.